D1593350

Occupational Medicine

Law and the Workplace

Guest Editors:

Jack W. Snyder, MD, JD, PhD
Thomas Jefferson University Hospital
Philadelphia, Pennsylvania

Julia E. Klees, MD, MPH
BASF Corporation
Mount Olive, New Jersey

Volume 11/Number 1
HANLEY & BELFUS, INC.

January–March 1996
Philadelphia

STATE OF THE ART REVIEWS

Publisher: HANLEY & BELFUS, INC.
210 South 13th Street
Philadelphia, PA 19107
(215) 546-4995
Fax (215) 790-9330

OCCUPATIONAL MEDICINE: State of the Art Reviews is included in *Index Medicus, MEDLINE, BioSciences Information Service, Current Contents* and *ISI/BIOMED.*

OCCUPATIONAL MEDICINE: State of the Art Reviews   (ISSN 0885-114X)
January–March 1996   Volume 11, Number 1   (ISBN 1-56053-199-1)

OCCUPATIONAL MEDICINE: State of the Art Reviews is published quarterly by Hanley & Belfus, Inc., 210 South 13th Street, Philadelphia, Pennsylvania 19107. Second-class postage paid at Philadelphia, PA, and at additional mailing offices.

POSTMASTER: Send address changes to OCCUPATIONAL MEDICINE: State of the Art Reviews, Hanley & Belfus, Inc., 210 South 13th Street, Philadelphia, PA 19107.

The 1996 subscription price is $88.00 per year U.S., $98.00 outside U.S. (add $40.00 for air mail).

Occupational Medicine: State of the Art Reviews
Vol. 11, No. 1, January–March 1996

LAW AND THE WORKPLACE
Jack W. Snyder, MD, JD, PhD, and
Julia E. Klees, MD, MPH, Editors

CONTENTS

injured workers. The author concludes that the optimal implementation of managed care and capitation in workers' compensation requires a paradigmatic shift to a community commitment based on a public health imperative to ensure quality medical care.

The role of the occupational physician as plant physician, treating physician, referral physician, and examining physician in determining causation in workers' compensation is outlined. The authors argue that adopting a systematic approach to determining causation, which requires an understanding of legal systems, will lead to more rapid, equitable, and reasonable allocation of compensation.

Because the laws pertaining to licensing, practice, and malpractice vary by state, the author addresses the unique legal challenges of occupational medicine from a general perspective. Of specific interest are issues in occupational medicine that challenge the traditional physician-patient relationship.

This chapter takes the perspective of federal health care providers and identifies issues and principles controlling significant legal vulnerabilities that federal officers and employees may personally face. The importance of physicians knowing the laws and regulations of their jurisdictions is emphasized.

Occupational medicine often requires its practitioners to function as experts in legal proceedings. Issues related to expert testimony summarized in this chapter include the examination of witnesses, the qualification of experts, obligations to truthtelling, grounds for expert opinion, hypothetical questions, degree of certainty, novel scientific testimony, causation, damages, and use of the professional literature in cross-examination.

Seventy-five alphabetized entries describe an array of regulatory agencies, medicolegal terms, governmental programs, and other common entities often encountered in the practice of occupational medicine. Topics run the gauntlet from *administrative law judge* to the *United States Code*.

This chapter provides an overview of the major federal environmental laws and regulations that reach beyond ecological protection to contemplate public, environmental, and occupational health interests. Acts discussed include the Resource Conservation and Recovery Act; Toxic Substances Control Act; Federal Insecticide, Fungicide and Rodenticide Act; Comprehensive Environmental Response, Compensation and Liability Act; Emergency Planning and Community Right to Know Act; Clean Air Act; Clean Water Act; and Safe Drinking Water Act.

CONTRIBUTORS

Michael S. Baram, LLB
Professor and Director, Center for Law and Technology, Boston University School of Law and School of Public Health, Boston, Massachusetts

William B. Bunn III, MD, JD, MPH
Director, Health Worker's Compensation, Disability and Safety, Navistar International, Chicago, Illinois

Karen Taylor Donmoyer, JD
Associate; Vedder, Price, Kaufman & Kammholz, Chicago, Illinois

Jay A. Gold, MD, JD, MPH
Principal Clinical Coordinator, Wisconsin Peer Review Organization; Assistant Clinical Professor, Department of Preventive Medicine and Health Policy Institute, Medical College of Wisconsin; Senior Lecturer, Department of Preventive Medicine, University of Wisconsin, Madison, Wisconsin

Dean M. Hashimoto, MD, JD, MOH
Assistant Professor of Law, Boston College School of Law, Newton; Adjunct Assistant Professor of Occupational Health, Harvard School of Public Health, Cambridge; Staff Physician, Pulmonary Associates, Massachusetts General Hospital, Boston, Massachusetts

Clarion E. Johnson, MD
Senior Clinic Director, Mobil Corporation, Fairfax, Virginia; Assistant Professor of Medicine, Uniformed Services University of the Health Sciences, F. Edward Hébert School of Medicine, Bethesda, Maryland

Debora L. Jones, RN, COHN, MPH
President, The Darien Group, Ltd., Glen Mills, Pennsylvania

Roy S. Kennon, MD, JD, FCLM
Head, Department of Occupational Medicine, Navy Medical Center, San Diego, California

Aria A. Klees, JD
Counsel, Environmental Safety and Health, Unisys Corporation, Blue Bell, Pennsylvania

Julia E. Klees, MD, MPH
Assistant Corporate Medical Director, BASF Corporation, Mount Olive, New Jersey; Adjunct Assistant Professor of Medicine, Division of Environmental Medicine and Toxicology; Department of Medicine, Jefferson Medical College, Philadelphia, Pennsylvania

Carolyn S. Langer, MD, JD, MPH
Instructor in Occupational Medicine, Occupational Health Program, Harvard School of Public Health; Director, Occupational Health and Safety Services, ML Strategies, Inc., Boston, Massachusetts

Susan G. McQuiggan, BSN, RN
Quality Management Coordinator, Department of Quality Management, Thomas Jefferson University, Philadelphia, Pennsylvania

D. Gary Rischitelli, MD, JD, MPH
Clinical Fellow, Division of Occupational Health, The Johns Hopkins University School of Hygiene and Public Health, Baltimore, Maryland

Mark A. Rothstein, JD
Hugh Roy and Lillie Cranz Cullen Distinguished Professor of Law; Director, Health Law and Policy Institute, University of Houston, Houston, Texas

Jack W. Snyder, MD, JD, PhD
Associate Professor, Departments of Emergency Medicine and Laboratory Medicine, Thomas Jefferson University Hospital, Philadelphia, Pennsylvania

Gregg M. Stave, MD, JD, MPH
Associate Director, Occupational Health Services, Glaxo Wellcome Inc., Research Triangle Park; Consulting Associate, Division of Occupational and Environmental Medicine, Duke University Medical Center, Durham, North Carolina

Nina G. Stillman, JD
Partner; Vedder, Price, Kaufman & Kammholz, Chicago, Illinois

Susan Hanley Tilton, MD, JD, MPH
Occupational Health Services, Valley Medical Center, Renton, Washington

PUBLISHED ISSUES
(available from the publisher)

1996 ISSUES

Law and the Workplace
Edited by Jack W. Snyder, MD, JD, PhD
Thomas Jefferson University Hospital
Philadelphia, Pennsylvania
and Julia E. Klees, MD, MPH
BASF Corporation
Mount Olive, New Jersey

Violence in the Workplace
Edited by Robert Harrison, MD, MPH
California Department of Health Services
Berkeley, California

Occupational Epidemiology
Edited by Ki Moon Bang, PhD, MPH
National Institute for Occupational Safety
  and Health
Morgantown, West Virginia

**Impact of Psychiatric Conditions in
the Workplace**
Edited by Ibrahim Farid, MD
United States Postal Service
San Bruno, California
and Carroll Brodsky, MD, PhD
University of California School of Medicine
San Francisco, California

1995 ISSUES

**Effects of the Indoor Environment
on Health**
Edited by James M. Seltzer, MD
University of California School of Medicine
San Diego, California

Construction Safety and Health
Edited by Knut Ringen, DrPH,
Laura Welch, MD, James L. Weeks, ScD, CIH,
and Jane L. Seegal, MS
Washington, DC
and Anders Englund, MD
Solna, Sweden

Occupational Hearing Loss
Edited by Thais C. Morata, PhD,
and Derek E. Dunn, PhD
National Institute for Occupational Safety
  and Health
Cincinnati, Ohio

Firefighters' Safety and Health
Edited by Peter Orris, MD
Cook County Hospital
Chicago, Illinois
and Richard M. Duffy, MSc
International Association of Fire Fighters
Washington, DC
and James Melius, MD, DrPH
Center to Protect Workers' Rights
Washington, DC

1994 ISSUES

Occupational Skin Disease
Edited by James R. Nethercott, MD
University of Maryland
Baltimore, Maryland

Occupational Safety and Health Training
Edited by Michael J. Colligan, PhD
National Institute for Occupational
  Safety and Health
Cincinnati, Ohio

Reproductive Hazards
Edited by Ellen B. Gold, PhD, B. L. Lasley,
PhD, and Marc B. Schenker, MD, MPH
University of California
Davis, California

Tuberculosis in the Workplace
Edited by Steven Markowitz, MD
Mount Sinai School of Medicine
New York, New York

Ordering Information:
Subscriptions for full year and single issues are available from the publishers—
Hanley & Belfus, Inc., 210 South 13th Street, Philadelphia, PA 19107
Telephone (215) 546-7293; (800) 962-1892. Fax (215) 790-9330.

PREFACE

As the 20th century closes, the enormous impact of law on medical practice is undeniable. In this climate, health care professionals increasingly seek guidance on issues involving a remarkably broad span of legal topics. The primary goal of this edition of Occupational Medicine: State of the Art Reviews is to provide health professionals with an authoritative, single-volume source of information on the role of law in the practice of occupational medicine.

The information presented herein offers readers a wide view of the laws of the land in which they practice. The array of topics includes how the Americans with Disabilities Act affects the practice of occupational medicine; ways of making sense of conflicting federal, state, and local rules and regulations; complex issues involving drug testing; and ways to improve one's courtroom performance as an expert witness. Another important issue, the conflicting roles of the occupational physician, is addressed eloquently by several of the authors: Are physicians bound to be loyal to a patient or to the corporation that has paid them to perform the exam? Answers to this and similarly vexing questions await the reader.

JACK W. SNYDER, MD, JD, PhD
JULIA E. KLEES, MD, MPH
GUEST EDITORS

JULIA E. KLEES, MD, MPH
JACK W. SNYDER, MD, JD, PHD

LAW AND THE WORKPLACE: AN INTRODUCTION

From the BASF Corporation
Mt. Olive, New Jersey (JEK)
and
Thomas Jefferson University
Philadelphia, Pennsylvania (JWS)

Reprint requests to:
Julia E. Klees, MD, MPH
BASF Corporation
3000 Continental Drive-North
Mt. Olive, NJ 07828-1234

A UNIQUE RESPONSIBILITY

In the workplace, occupational health professionals are *Between Medicine and Management*[1] in consideration of the individual, the business organization employing the individual, and society. The law serves to represent the interests of society in the workplace as well as in the community at large that surrounds it. Thus, for the occupational health professional, knowledge of the laws and regulations governing occupational and environmental health is essential to meet the socially and politically defined legal obligations to employees, employers, and their neighbors.

Health effects due to workplace exposures or affecting fitness for duty are the expert domain of occupational and environmental medicine practitioners. Occupational health professionals may act as consultants to employers regarding design, evaluation, and implementation of occupational health programs. As environmental health has increased in importance, the role of the occupational health practitioner has expanded to address, in addition to the workplace environment, the nonoccupational, environmental concerns of neighborhoods and communities adjacent to business organizations. Occupational and environmental health professionals are challenged daily by the integration of medical, scientific, managerial, and legal concepts necessary to meet their professional obligation to provide objective assessment, information, and advice.

Because occupational medicine practitioners often provide patient services at the request of an

OCCUPATIONAL MEDICINE: State of the Art Reviews—
Vol. 11, No. 1, January–March 1996. Philadelphia, Hanley & Belfus, Inc.

1

employer, the traditional physician-patient relationship is affected. The usual, privileged nature of the physician-patient relationship may be altered as a third party requests an examination to determine physical and mental fitness for a specific job; a diagnosis is determined not only for the purpose of the patient's needs and treatment but also to address administrative concerns. Besides the patient, the physician, and the business organization, parties including unions, insurers, and regulatory agencies have interest in the outcome of an examination. Recommendations regarding job placement, medical impairment, return-to-work, and medical removal have economic and social implications and require professional judgment in consideration of the applicable federal and state laws and regulations.

The prevention, evaluation, and treatment of injuries and illnesses mediated by the workplace environment is a source of conflict between the needs and desires of individuals and business organizations. As an objective, expert provider of care and advice, the occupational physician may find himself or herself in the midst of an adversarial dispute. Government, through regulation and litigation, seeks to alter behavior and settle disputes by means of due process and delegated authority. Legal process and substance guides the resolution of workplace health conflicts as well as affects the practice of medicine. This volume of Occupational Medicine: State of the Art Reviews highlights the essential elements of legislation, regulation, and litigation that affect the practice of occupational and environmental medicine.

Fitness for Duty

The initial chapters in this volume discuss the legal issues regarding the determination of fitness for duty. The process by which a workforce is selected and maintained requires an understanding of the need for medical confidentiality and the body of law prohibiting employment discrimination. Medical qualification of individuals to perform the essential functions of a job may initiate a sequence of events in which the employer's obligation of reasonable accommodation must be carefully balanced with a defined bona fide occupational qualification. However, because the medical information is confidential, the determination of fitness for duty resides with the examining physician; understanding of the job requirements by the examining physician is essential. The interests of both the employee and employer are balanced so that the goal of equal employment opportunity is met without compromising the function and safety of a business organization.

The American with Disabilities Act is an attempt at a comprehensive solution to discrimination against the disabled. It is a federal mandate to assure equality of opportunity, self-sufficiency, and independence for disabled individuals. The ADA clearly is intended to isolate an employer's consideration of an applicant's nonmedical qualifications from any review of physical or mental medical conditions, impairments, or perception of impairment. The ADA more broadly defines long-term disability than the traditional medical use of the term; it exempts only illegal drug use, sexual preference, and pregnancy from the definition of disability. It limits the medical conditions to be considered in the employment process to conditions that are directly related to job performance and how that determination can be made while maintaining the legal and ethical obligation of medical confidentiality. The physician must understand the right to privacy, the privileged nature of physician-patient communications, and the circumstances by which disclosure of medical information may be made to an employer. Additional layers of complexity emerge when equal employment opportunity goals are considered. These goals emphasize an individual's desire to work, possibly at the expense of their exposure to health hazards; this emphasis may conflict with the occupational safety and health regulatory agenda. The medical screening function is a pivotal role in which the physician becomes a partner to ensure that proper placement is made available to employees in protected employment classes; any exclusion of a protected class member from eligibility for desired employment based on health or safety considerations must be supported by reasonable medical opinion. The occupational medicine practitioner has the role of applying medical standards, in a confidential manner, to produce clinical recommendations regarding fitness for duty. However, it is the responsibility of the employer to act upon the medical recommendations; if restrictions are medically indicated on a job-specific basis, the employer ultimately determines if placement is feasible in a given work environment.

Regulated Medical Practice

The chapters regarding OSHA, biologic hazards, environmental legal concerns, and drug testing attempt to define some of the specific circumstances in which occupational and environmental health services are provided. Occupational and environmental health services often involve special process, certification, or reporting requirements defined by law. Examinations affected by regulatory interests reflect society's demand that employers assume responsibility for health effects induced by the workplace environment. This regulated practice of medicine often reaches beyond usual clinical practice, where information exchange is within the scope of the physician-patient relationship. The legal obligation that these requirements be met is squarely set upon the occupational physician, to provide professionally comparable services that meet the full panoply of state and federal regulations; otherwise, general liability beyond malpractice may ensue.

Medical Adjudication

It is unusual for a physician's relationship with a patient to be uncomplicated by third-party intrusions, financial concerns, and other conflicts of interest. This is particularly true of the workers' compensation system. The medical adjudication role of an occupational physician in the workers' compensation system is fraught with conflict; the physician may serve as a facilitator between employer and employee (as well as insurers and managed care organizations) when their interests diverge. The workers' compensation system attempts to address the conflict between the needs and desires of individuals and business organizations; its framework for the evaluation and treatment of work-related illness and injury uses the social role of the physician as a definer of reality (objective evidence) and provider of judgment of meaning and value (probability of work-relatedness). The broader interests of injury prevention and mitigations are often ignored in state workers' compensation statutes, yet improvement of the health and safety of workplaces is a clear functional role of occupational health practitioners. Focus upon the broader public interest serves the social imperative of the law to protect the community at large.

Liability and Expertise

The complex nature of the multiple roles and tasks of occupational physicians causes the legal risk of practice to vary significantly, depending on the laws and regulations specific to a jurisdiction. Legal issues regarding practice and malpractice affect the specialty because they pertain to the unique regulatory considerations and specter of third-party liability. In addition, the private and public sectors have different issues and principles that control legal vulnerability. Federal health care providers are particularly immersed in rules and regulations, some of which have criminal penalties.

Occupational physicians may be required to function as experts in judicial and administrative proceedings, a role in which they determine causation with a reasonable degree of certainty, within the framework of dispute resolution in which expert testimony may be given. This role has its own conflicts: it unrealistically assumes that the occupational medicine expert can provide objective scientific truth for the resolution of conflict. However, even if conclusive scientific evidence does not exist, the physician should proffer evidence that is scientifically valid and relevant to the issue under consideration.

CONCLUSION

This volume presents a broad perspective on the legal interface between occupational and environmental health services and the individual-business organization relationship that affects the determination of impairment and fitness for duty, confidentiality, regulated medical practice and reporting, physician liability, and the role of the physician in dispute resolution. The law provides regulation to protect society's welfare and process for the resolution of the social conflicts surrounding the workplace. The practice of occupational and environmental medicine requires an understanding of these concerns; awareness is an essential challenge to proficiency in occupational medicine.

REFERENCES
1. Walsh DC: Corporate Physicians: Between Medicine and Management. New Haven, CT, Yale University Press, 1987.

CAROLYN S. LANGER, MD, JD, MPH

TITLE I OF THE AMERICANS WITH DISABILITIES ACT

From Harvard School of Public
    Health
Boston, Massachusetts

Reprint requests to:
Carolyn S. Langer, Director
Occupational Health and
    Safety Services
ML Strategies, Inc.
One Financial Center
Boston, MA 02111

Mary applies to ABC Company for a job that involves heavy labor. The company inquires about previous workers' compensation claims on the job application, and Mary discloses that 5 years ago she received compensation for a back injury. Dr. Smith, the company physician, performs a preplacement physical on Mary and informs the company that it should not hire her due to her previous injury and the likelihood that she will go out on workers' compensation again. On the same day, Tom from the purchasing department presents to Dr. Smith for treatment of his sinusitis. During this visit, Dr. Smith learns that Tom has recently tested positive for HIV and immediately divulges this information to Tom's supervisor. Three days later, ABC Company discharges Tom from his job. Do Tom and Mary have any cause of action?

INTRODUCTION

Americans "with disabilities are a discrete and insular minority who have been faced with restrictions and limitations [in the workplace] ... resulting from stereotypic assumptions not truly indicative of the individual ability ... to participate in, and contribute to, society."[1] Historically, employers have often used medical information about job applicants and current employees to exclude individuals with disabilities, particularly those with hidden disabilities, from the workplace. The enactment of the Americans with Disabilities Act reflects a recognition by Congress that stereotypic assumptions about disabilities and the limitations of individuals with disabilities pose major discriminatory barriers to the workplace. Traditionally, the underlying theory of civil

OCCUPATIONAL MEDICINE: State of the Art Reviews—
Vol. 11, No. 1, January–March 1996. Philadelphia, Hanley & Belfus, Inc.

5

rights law has been to protect against discrimination based on largely immutable characteristics, such as race, national origin, and gender. While individuals with disabilities may experience the types of discrimination that confront these other groups, they also may encounter unique forms of discrimination due to the nature of their disabilities and the effect that their present, past, or perceived conditions have on other persons.

Disabled applicants denied employment often would not know whether their rejection was due to disclosure of a disability or due to nonmedical criteria. One of the primary purposes of the ADA is to isolate an employer's consideration of an applicant's nonmedical qualifications from any consideration of the applicant's medical condition. In this way, individuals know whether, and to what extent, their physical or mental disabilities have affected the hiring decision. With enactment of the ADA, Congress made a commitment to improve access to mainstream society for the disabled and to eliminate discrimination that confronts individuals with disabilities.

Health care professionals are an important interface between the disabled and the work setting. Whether company employees or independent contractors, they interact with workers at every phase of employment: preplacement physicals, periodic examinations, and return-to-work assessments. Moreover, many physicians perform workers' compensation and disability evaluations. Health care providers also are frequently responsible for storing and safeguarding employee medical records. For all these reasons, they need to understand their ethical and legal duties in the employment process. Health care professionals not only play a critical role in protecting patient confidentiality and employment rights but also in educating employers on disability-related health issues.

SCOPE OF THE ADA

The Americans with Disabilities Act was enacted on July 26, 1990. Title I of the ADA prohibits employment discrimination against the disabled.* The ADA became effective for employers with 25 or more employees on July 26, 1992. As of July 26, 1994, the ADA also applied to employers with 15 or more employees. Covered entities who must comply with the ADA include private employers, state and local governments, employment agencies, labor unions, and joint labor-management committees. Federal executive agencies are exempt from the ADA, but these employers must comply with analogous nondiscrimination laws under Section 501 of the Rehabilitation Act of 1973. Other exempt employers include corporations fully owned by the U.S. government, Indian tribes, and certain bona fide, tax-exempt, private membership clubs that are not labor organizations.

The ADA prohibits discrimination against qualified individuals with disabilities in regard to any employment practice or terms, conditions, and privileges of employment. The prohibition covers all aspects of the employment process, such as job application, testing, hiring, assignment, training, promotion, medical examinations, lay-off/recall, termination, compensation, leave, and benefits. Under other laws that prohibit employment discrimination, inclusion within a protected class, such as race, gender, national origin, or age, is often more obvious or objective. By contrast, protection of an individual under the ADA involves a case-by-case analysis to determine if that person meets the act's definitions of "disability" and "qualified individual."

---

* Although the ADA consists of five titles, this chapter only examines Title I. The remaining titles of the ADA are as follows: Title II, Public Service/Public Transportation; Title III, Public Accommodation & Services Operated by Private Entities; Title IV, Telecommunications; and Title V, Miscellaneous Provisions.

Definition of Disability and Impairment

Because the definition of **disability** under the ADA is specifically designed to eliminate particular types of discrimination experienced by people with disabilities, it may differ from the definition of disability found in workers' compensation, social security, disabled veterans, and other laws. The ADA defines disability as (1) a physical or mental impairment that substantially limits one or more major life activities, or (2) a record of such an impairment, or (3) being regarded as having such an impairment. A person must fulfill at least one of these three criteria to be considered disabled under the ADA. The first part of the statutory definition for disability covers individuals who actually have physical or mental impairments that substantially limit one or more major life activities. The remaining parts of the statutory definition of disability cover individuals who may not have an impairment that substantially limits a major life activity, but who nonetheless experience discrimination due to a history of previous disability, misclassification, or mistaken perceptions about their limitations. In addition, the ADA prohibits discrimination against an individual, with or without a disability, who has a relationship or association with another person who has a disability.

The ADA defines a **physical impairment** as any "physiological disorder, or condition, cosmetic disfigurement, or anatomical loss affecting one or more of the following body systems: neurological, musculoskeletal, special sense organs, respiratory (including speech organs), cardiovascular, reproductive, digestive, genito-urinary, hemic and lymphatic, skin and endocrine."[2] The ADA defines a **mental impairment** as any "mental or psychological disorder, such as mental retardation, organic brain syndrome, emotional or mental illness, and specific learning disabilities."[3]

The regulatory definition of impairment does not provide an exhaustive list of specific impairments covered by the act, but rather defines the type of condition that constitutes an impairment. Furthermore, the decision to characterize a condition as an impairment is made without regard to mitigating measures such as medications or prostheses, even if these or other interventions minimize or eliminate the adverse impact of that condition. For example, a non–insulin-dependent diabetic who is well controlled on oral hypoglycemics nonetheless has a physiologic impairment. It is the scope or perceived scope of the condition itself, rather than its origin or capacity for being corrected, that ultimately defines a particular condition as an impairment.

Some aspects of the human condition are not viewed as physiological or mental disorders under the ADA. Therefore, the definition of impairment under the act does not include the following:

1. Physical characteristics, such as left-handedness, eye color, or hair color.
2. Normal deviations in height, weight, or strength. (While obesity or excessive weight per se is not considered an impairment under the ADA, morbid obesity, defined as body weight exceeding twice the norm, is an impairment. In addition, obesity caused by an underlying physiologic disorder may be considered an impairment.)
3. Pregnancy per se, since it is not the result of a physiologic disorder. (By contrast, hypertension and other complications of pregnancy may be considered impairments.)
4. Age (by itself, in the absence of a medical condition).
5. Environmental, cultural, and economic disadvantages, such as a prison record, lack of education, or poverty.
6. Homosexuality and bisexuality.

7. Personality traits, such as poor judgment, quick temper, or irresponsible behavior. An employer may hold all employees (disabled and nondisabled) to the same performance and conduct standards. Therefore, an employer does not have to excuse a worker's misconduct, even when due to psychosis or other disability-related impairment, if the employer does not tolerate similar misconduct from its other employees.

8. A characteristic predisposition to illness or disease because nonmedical factors, such as environmental, economic, or social conditions, may account for the predisposition. However, discrimination based on genetic screening or an employer's perceptions of increased susceptibility to disease falls within the definition of *regarding* the individual as having an impairment that substantially limits a major life activity and, therefore, is prohibited under the ADA.

The ADA specifically excludes the following disorders from the category of protected "disabilities": (1) current illegal drug use and (2) certain sexual and behavioral disorders, including transvestism, transsexualism, pedophilia, and exhibitionism; compulsive gambling, kleptomania, or pyromania; or psychoactive substance use disorders from current illegal use of drugs.

Substance Abuse

Individuals engaging in illegal drug use are not protected by the ADA as disabled persons. Workplace drug testing does not violate the ADA. If the illegal drug use is sufficiently recent to justify an employer's belief that involvement with drugs is an ongoing problem, the employer may discharge or deny employment to such individuals. However, a rehabilitated drug addict not currently using drugs receives the full protection of the ADA.

Both current and rehabilitated alcoholics also qualify as individuals with disabilities and receive protection under the ADA. While alcoholics are entitled to accommodation if otherwise able to perform the essential functions of the job, they may be disciplined, discharged, or denied employment if their use of alcohol impairs job performance or conduct such that they are no longer "qualified."

Substantial Limitations on Major Life Activities

To result in disability, an impairment must substantially limit one or more major life activities. The ADA defines major life activities as "those basic activities that the average person in the general population can perform with little or no difficulty."[4] Examples of major life activities include walking, speaking, breathing, seeing, hearing, learning, caring for oneself, performing manual tasks, and working. In addition, the appendix to the regulations includes sitting, standing, lifting, reaching, thinking, concentrating, reading, and interacting with others. These lists are only representative; other activities could be viewed as major if they have unique or disproportionate impact on the functioning of selected individuals.

An impairment becomes a disability only if it substantially limits one or more major life activities. An individual must be unable to perform or must be significantly restricted in the ability to perform a major life activity compared to an average person in the general population. The conclusion that an impairment substantially limits a major life activity must be reached only with reference to a specific individual and the effect of the impairment on *that* individual's life activities. For example, two individuals with similar back injuries may differ widely in restrictions on their activities. The first may suffer considerable pain and exhibit severe limitations in the ability to walk, sit, drive, lift, or provide self-care. The second individual may be completely symptom-free and exhibit no restrictions in life activities. Only the first individual would have a disability under the ADA. An individualized approach is necessary because the same types of impairments often vary in severity and may restrict different people to different degrees due to a number of factors, including stage of the disease and presence of other aggravating factors or impairments.

In general, the effect of an impairment on the life of the individual, rather than the name or diagnosis of the impairment, determines whether an individual has a disability. However, in some instances, impairments are so severe that courts will often presume that they substantially limit major life activities. For example, HIV infection, blindness, deafness, insulin-dependent diabetes, and manic depressive disorder are often substantially limiting, thereby resulting in disability. The ADA enumerates three criteria for use in determining whether a person's impairment substantially limits a major life activity:

- The nature and severity of the impairment;
- The duration or expected duration of the impairment; and
- The permanent or long-term impact, or expected impact, of the impairment.

Non-chronic impairments that are of short duration and that have little or no long-term impact generally are not disabilities. For example, temporary conditions such as fractures, sprains, concussions, appendicitis, common colds, or influenza typically would not constitute disabilities. There are no established time intervals that define the point at which impairment must be viewed as substantially limiting; however, conditions that last for only a few days or weeks and that have no permanent or long-term effects are typically not substantially limiting impairments. On the other hand, conditions lasting several months or conditions of indefinite and unknowable duration may be substantially limiting. In addition, an impairment that takes significantly longer than normal to heal and that prevents or significantly restricts the performance of a major life activity for an extended period may be a disability. In other instances, a person may sustain an injury that heals but leaves a permanent or long-term residual effect. For example, a fractured ankle may be surgically repaired but leave the worker with a residual limp. Thus, an apparently temporary impairment that leads to long-term, substantial limitations of one or more major life activities may result in a disability. As with all other ADA-related matters, these determinations must be individualized.

A worker need not establish substantial limitations on the ability to work if he or she has already established that an impairment substantially limits another major life activity. Therefore, it is presumed that a blind individual is substantially limited not only in seeing but also in working. A person not substantially limited in any other major life activity has substantial limitations in working when significantly restricted in the ability to perform either a class of jobs or a broad range of jobs in various classes, compared to an average person with similar training, skills, and abilities. An inability to perform a single, particular job for one employer or to perform a very specialized job in a particular field does not constitute a substantial limitation in the major life activity of working. For example, a carpenter who is allergic to a particular type of resin may not be substantially limited in working, but the same individual with a musculoskeletal disorder that precludes reaching and lifting may be significantly restricted in performing the general class of carpentry jobs as well as various manual labor jobs.

The regulation details additional factors that can assist in the determination of whether a person is substantially limited in working. These factors include (1) the geographical area to which the individual has reasonable access; (2) the type of job from which an individual has been disqualified due to the impairment; (3) the number and types of jobs using similar training, knowledge, skill, or abilities from which the individual is disqualified within that geographical area; and/or (4) the number and types of other jobs not involving similar training, knowledge, skill, or abilities in that geographical area from which the individual is also disqualified due to the impairment. Disabled individuals need not identify the exact number and types of jobs using similar or dissimilar skills in a specified geographic area. Rather, they need only present evidence of general employment demographics or recognized occupational classifications that indicate the approximate number of jobs from which they would be excluded.

Job Applicants and Job Descriptions

Employers are not required to hire or retain unqualified individuals to perform a job. Therefore, to fall under the protection of the ADA, a person must not only have a disability, but must also be qualified for the job. A qualified individual with a disability is a person with a disability who satisfies the necessary skill, experience, education, and other job-related requirements of the employment position and who, with or without reasonable accommodation, can perform the essential functions of that position.

The first step, then, is to determine if an individual with a disability is "otherwise qualified," connoting that an individual meets all job prerequisites except those that cannot be met due to disability. Such job prerequisites include education, work experience, training, skills, licenses, certificates, and other job-related qualities, such as good judgment or ability to work with others.

If an individual with a disability meets the necessary job prerequisites, the employer must next apply a two-pronged test by (1) identifying the **essential functions** of the job and (2) determining whether the individual with a disability can perform these functions, **with or without reasonable accommodation**.

Essential functions include tasks that employees in a particular position are actually required to perform. If removal of that function would not fundamentally change the job, the function is probably not essential. The EEOC offers the following factors as proof that a function is essential:

1. The position exists to perform the function.
2. There are a limited number of other employees available to perform the function or among whom the function can be distributed.
3. A function is highly specialized, and the person is being hired for special expertise or ability to perform that function.

For example, a disabled applicant who is wheelchair-bound can type 75 words per minute and answer telephones. Nonetheless, the company refuses to hire the applicant, claiming that the secretary would not be able to make rapid courier runs to surrounding businesses. The company's actions would be discriminatory if the deliveries were not an essential function of the job because, for example, they were only infrequently required and could be assumed by a number of other people in the office.

Employers typically determine the essential functions of a job, relying on the above factors, which are principally nonmedical. However, employers will frequently call upon health care professionals to ascertain if an employee or job applicant is medically qualified to perform these functions. The physician also may play a role in suggesting possible accommodations to enable a worker to perform these essential functions. The ADA does not require an employer to conduct a job analysis or to develop job descriptions. Moreover, if an employer uses written job descriptions, the ADA does not require that such descriptions be limited to or identify the essential functions. Nonetheless, providers who conduct medical examinations or inquiries for an employer should request a current job description to improve the accuracy of their assessments of an individual's functional abilities and limitations in relation to the job. Providers who are not familiar with actual job demands may make incorrect assumptions about the nature of the job or the ability of an individual to perform specific tasks. A job description facilitates focus on the applicant's or employee's abilities and limitations based on the purpose of the job and the importance of actual job functions.

Qualification Standards and Selection Criteria

Under the ADA, qualification standards or selection criteria that screen out or tend to screen out an individual with a disability on the basis of disability must be job-related and consistent with business necessity. Moreover, if a standard that is job-related and consistent with business necessity screens out an individual with a disability, the employer must consider whether the individual could meet the standard with a reasonable accommodation. The employer may establish production standards, including quality, quantity, performance, and attendance standards, as long as they are uniformly applied to all applicants and employees in that job. Employers are not required to lower existing production standards or selection criteria for individuals with disabilities, including those using alcohol or drugs.

To be job-related, a selection criterion must be a legitimate measure or qualification for the specific job to which it is being applied. In other words, it is insufficient for selection criteria to simply measure qualifications for a general class of jobs. For example, the ability to draw blood may not be job-related to a nursing position if, in fact, a person in that particular nursing job never performs phlebotomy due to the use of in-house phlebotomy teams. To be consistent with business necessity, the selection criteria must relate to the essential functions of a job. Thus, a fast food chain could not use an oral exam to screen out a deaf job applicant and refuse to hire the applicant as a short order cook as long as he or she could perform the essential functions of the job (cooking) and the disability would not pose a direct threat to the individual's own or others' health and safety. Moreover, even if a qualification standard or selection criterion is job-related and consistent with business necessity, the employer must consider whether this individual could satisfy the criteria with a reasonable accommodation. For example, the secretary who has difficulty meeting word processing qualification standards due to a history of carpal tunnel syndrome may be able to demonstrate the ability to meet the qualification standards using a computer assistive device.

The employer may impose physical fitness requirements or agility tests as selection criteria provided that these tests are job-related and consistent with business necessity. If these tests screen out individuals with disabilities, the employer must further provide an opportunity for the individual to meet the standards with a reasonable accommodation. For example, an applicant with a disability that prevents reaching above shoulder height applies for a job as a mail room clerk. The individual's inability to meet the physical requirement to lift heavy packages from a 6-foot high shelf could be accommodated by a number of interventions, such as lowering the shelf, providing a step stool, or other assistive devices. In the pre-offer stage, the employer may not require the job applicant to undergo medical screening. Therefore, physical, mental, or agility tests may not encompass medical examinations or diagnoses by a physician. Nonetheless, employers may engage in a very restricted inquiry to ensure safe performance of the test by requiring a note from the applicant's private physician to verify that administration of the physical or agility test will not harm the applicant.

Reasonable Accommodation

Reasonable accommodation is a crucial component of the ADA's mandate to eliminate unnecessary barriers that restrict employment opportunities for otherwise qualified individuals with disabilities. Disabled persons face not only physical barriers that prevent access to worksites, but also mental barriers, such as stereotypes and misconceptions about job performance, absenteeism, costs, or acceptance by coworkers and customers. For these reasons, the ADA requires reasonable accommodation in all major aspects of employment, including the application process; the performance of the essential functions of a job; and the enjoyment of equal benefits and privileges of employment.

Reasonable accommodation is any modification or adjustment to a job, an employment practice, or the work environment that enables an individual with a disability to enjoy an equal employment opportunity. Examples of reasonable accommodation include job restructuring, modified work schedules, creation of accessible work stations, equipment modification, job reassignment, modification of examinations and training materials, and provision of readers or interpreters. This list is not exhaustive and cannot account for all possible accommodations because reasonable accommodation must be individualized. In other words, reasonable accommodation requires consideration of both the specific abilities and functional limitations of the particular individual and the specific functional requirements of a particular job.

Undue Hardship Exception

An employer is not required to provide an accommodation if it will impose an undue hardship on business operations. An accommodation creates an undue hardship when it is unduly costly, extensive, substantial, disruptive, or would fundamentally alter the nature or operation of the business. Factors in determining undue hardship include the nature and cost of the accommodation relative to the size; financial resources; type, location, nature, and structure of the employer's operation; and the impact of the accommodation on the specific facility.

Employers are required to accommodate only known limitations. While the employer must give notice of its obligation to provide accommodations, the applicant or employee must inform an employer that an accommodation is necessary. Employers may request documentation of an individual's functional limitations to support a request for accommodation. Employers need only provide an *effective* accommodation, not necessarily the *best* accommodation. Moreover, an employer is only required to provide accommodations to reduce employment barriers related to a person's disability. An employer is not required to provide personal items or an accommodation that is primarily for personal use, such as eyeglasses, a wheelchair, or a prosthesis. However, the employer might be required to provide an accommodation that is specifically designed to meet job-related rather than personal needs (e.g., special eyeglasses for use with a desktop computer screen). An employer may voluntarily exceed the requirements of the ADA and provide accommodations beyond those it mandates. Conversely, an individual with a disability has the right to refuse an accommodation if he or she has not requested the accommodation and does not believe that it is needed. However, if the individual cannot perform the essential functions of the job without the accommodation, that individual may not be qualified for the job. Finally, if the cost of an accommodation imposes an undue hardship on the employer, the disabled person has the option of providing the accommodation or paying the portion of the cost that would constitute an undue hardship.

Direct Threats to Health and Safety

An employer may disqualify individuals who pose a direct threat to their own or to others' health or safety. To establish that an individual poses a direct threat, the employer must show that there is:

1. A significant risk of substantial harm, i.e., a high probability of substantial harm, not mere speculation unrelated to this individual.

2. A specific risk—considering duration of the risk; and nature, severity, likelihood, and imminence of the potential harm.

3. A current risk, not one that is speculative, remote, or based on future risk.

4. An assessment of risk based on objective medical or factual evidence regarding this particular individual.

Even when a significant risk of substantial harm exists, an employer must still consider reasonable accommodation to eliminate or reduce the risk. When accommodation is not possible, the employer may refuse to hire an applicant or may discharge an employee who poses a direct threat.

Medical Examinations and Inquiries

The ADA's provisions concerning medical examinations and disability-related inquiries serve to protect individuals with disabilities from employment discrimination and to ensure that employers fairly assess an applicant's nonmedical qualifications. The ADA imposes differing obligations on the employer at three stages of the employment process to preclude employment decisions that are not based on factors that are job-related and consistent with business necessity:

Pre-Employment, Pre-Offer. The ADA prohibits medical inquiries and medical examinations prior to extending a conditional job offer to an applicant.

Post-Offer, Pre-Placement. After extending a conditional job offer but before the person starts work, an employer may conduct unrestricted medical inquiries or medical examinations, including inquiries about workers' compensation claims. Although a post-offer inquiry or examination need not be job-related and consistent with business necessity at this stage, any refusal to hire an individual based on the results of such inquiries must be job-related and justified by business necessity. As a practical matter, many employers prefer to limit the scope of their post-offer inquiries to job-related matters in order to demonstrate their lack of knowledge of an individual's disability should the applicant allege discrimination.

The ADA recognizes that employers may need to conduct post-offer medical examinations to determine if applicants possess the physical or mental qualifications necessary to perform certain jobs effectively and safely. The ADA does not require an employer to justify its desire to conduct post-offer medical examinations. The ADA mandates only that such medical inquiries or examinations be conducted as a second step after an individual has met all other job prerequisites. Moreover, any medical inquiry or examination must be uniformly applied to all applicants for a particular job category, not merely to those with known disabilities. A post-offer medical examination is not required for all applicants in all jobs, only to those in the same job category. Thus, an employer may choose to administer a medical examination only to all entering employees in heavy lifting jobs but not to those performing accounting jobs. While the scope of the initial medical examination and inquiry must be uniform among all examinees, follow-up may differ depending on the results of the initial examination.

Post-Employment, Post-Placement. After an employee has started work, any subsequent medical examinations or inquiries required of that employee must be job-related and consistent with business necessity. Exceptions include mandated examinations required by other federal laws, such as the Occupational Safety and Health Act, as well as voluntary participation in employee health programs and health screenings.

Definition of Disability-Related Inquiries

To fully comply with the provisions of the ADA, employers and health care professionals must understand what constitutes a disability-related inquiry or medical examination. Under the ADA, disability-related inquiries are questions that are likely to elicit information about a disability. Examples include questions about specific diseases (such as heart disease or AIDS), alcohol consumption, use of prescription drugs, number of sick days taken in the previous year, and the presence of disabilities or previous workers' compensation claims.

Inquiries about the ability to perform job functions are not disability-related. At the pre-offer stage, therefore, an employer may ask job applicants if they can perform the functions of the job, with or without reasonable accommodation. They may further request that applicants describe or demonstrate how they would perform these functions. Employers also may inquire about the number of days of leave that an employee took the previous year and whether the employee could meet the attendance requirements of this particular job.

Definition of Medical Examination

Medical examinations are procedures or tests that seek information about an individual's physical or mental impairment or physical or psychological health. The following factors may indicate that a particular test is medical:
- The test is administered by a healthcare professional;
- The results of the test are interpreted by a healthcare professional;
- The test is designed or given for a purpose of revealing an impairment or the state of physical or psychological health;
- The test is invasive;
- The test measures physiological or psychological responses (as opposed to performance of a task);
- The test is normally performed in a medical setting; and
- Medical equipment or devices are used for the test.

The following tests normally are not considered medical:
- Physical agility or physical fitness tests that do not include medical monitoring;
- Psychological tests that reveal an individual's skills or tastes, such as personality tests, IQ tests, aptitude tests, and honesty tests; and
- Tests for illegal drug use.

Physicians who conduct employment-related medical examinations have two primary responsibilities vis-à-vis the employer. The first is to advise the employer about an individual's functional abilities and limitations in relation to job functions. The physician should focus on the current ability of the examinee to perform this particular job with or without an accommodation.

The second task is to determine whether the individual meets the employer's health and safety requirements. Here, the physician should gather evidence that the person can perform this job without posing a direct threat to the health and safety or himself or herself or others. To make these two determinations, the physician must have some understanding of the actual demands of the job, preferably in the form of a detailed job description.

Although occupational physicians must render opinions concerning functional abilities and limitations, the employer has the sole responsibility for making all employment decisions. Moreover, it is the responsibility of the employer to determine whether or not a reasonable accommodation is feasible and to select that accommodation. Nonetheless, physicians may suggest possible accommodations, and the employer may permissibly seek this medical advice.

Confidentiality and Medical Records

Employers create medical records and gather medical information on employees from several sources, including OSHA-mandated recordkeeping and medical surveillance, preplacement and periodic medical examinations, return-to-work assessments, workers' compensation claims, and health and life insurance plans. Historically, health care professionals have played a pivotal role in maintaining and safeguarding confidential medical information, often guided by their own codes of ethics or state laws. The ADA recognizes the need to balance the privacy rights of workers with the employer's interest in maintaining a safe and effective workforce. Therefore, the ADA imposes strict limitations on the release and use of information obtained from medical examinations and inquiries in the workplace.

The ADA mandates that employers treat information from medical examinations and inquiries as confidential medical records. The privacy and security of the sources of such information must be assured. Employers or medical professionals acting on their behalf must collect and maintain this information on separate forms and in separate locked medical files, apart from personnel files. Moreover, employers must designate a specific person or persons to have access to the medical file. These confidentiality provisions apply to the records of all job applicants, including those who were hired, those who were not hired, and those who no longer work for the employer.

Under the ADA, the employer may share medical information with those involved in the hiring process who have legitimate need for that information. The ADA permits limited disclosure to the following parties:

- Supervisors and managers who may need to know about required work restrictions and accommodations,
- First aid and safety personnel who may need to be familiar with appropriate emergency treatment or evacuation procedures for persons with disabilities,
- Government agencies investigating compliance with the ADA and other federal and state laws,
- Workers' compensation offices or second injury funds, and
- Insurance companies administering health or life insurance plans.

Example: A job applicant with a history of poorly controlled epilepsy applies for a job in a warehouse. The physician must determine the applicant's fitness for this job by assessing functional abilities and limitations. To assure confidentiality, the physician should merely inform the employer that based on the post-offer medical examination, the applicant is medically qualified to perform the job with the following restrictions: no driving of company vehicles and no working at heights. The physician also may choose to share more specific information with selected managers, supervisors, and first aid personnel so as to educate them about first aid procedures and possible accommodations, if necessary. Even though such limited disclosures are most likely permissible under the ADA, it is often prudent to have the examinee sign a release form specifically granting permission.

The ADA does not preempt other federal laws and regulations that may require disclosure of relevant medical information. However, the ADA would preempt state law that is less stringent with regard to safeguarding confidential medical documents. Where state confidentiality laws are more stringent than the ADA, employers and health care providers should comply with provisions of both the ADA and state law if the state law serves to further protect confidentiality of the medical record. For example, some states require health care providers to obtain a release form from patients before divulging information concerning HIV status to third parties. In these situations, physicians typically must obtain the release form. They should consider, however, the possibility that lesser disclosure such as comments on functional abilities and limitations could also accomplish the intended purpose.

CONCLUSION

"Discrimination denies the disabled the many advantages of employment: prestige, power, self-esteem, economic well-being, social outlets, and access to health insurance and other job benefits."[5] The ADA will ensure that employers consider the nonmedical qualifications of both the disabled and non-disabled to the same extent. As such, the "ADA will have far-reaching consequences in protecting the right of the disabled and more fully integrating them into the workplace. Health professionals can play a critical role in fostering patient autonomy and educating employers while simultaneously promoting a safe and healthful workplace."[5]

REFERENCES

1. 42 USC 12101(a)(7)(Supp. IV 1992).
2. 29 CFR 1630.2(h).
3. 29 CFR 1630.2(h).
4. 29 CFR 1630.2(i).
5. Langer CS: Occupational health law. In American College of Medicine: Legal Medicine. 3rd ed. St. Louis, Mosby, 1995, pp 545–553.

SUSAN HANLEY TILTON, MD, JD, MPH

RIGHT TO PRIVACY AND CONFIDENTIALITY OF MEDICAL RECORDS

From the Valley Medical Center
Renton, Washington

Reprint requests to:
Susan Hanley Tilton, MD, JD, MPH
Occupational Health Services
Valley Medical Center
372 W. Valley Highway North
Suite 116
Auburn, WA 98001

Historically, no privilege existed in the common law for communications between a physician and patient,[1] although English law did seem to recognize a breach of *honor* by a physician if information regarding a patient was disclosed outside the courtroom.[2] Neither the patient nor the physician could refuse to disclose in court a communication by one to the other, because no evidentiary privilege existed, nor did the patient have a privilege that the communication not be disclosed to a third person outside of a court proceeding.[3] This concept has been perpetuated, even today, under federal common law in the United States, but in occupational medicine practice, it is of importance mainly when a federal agency such as OSHA or NIOSH seeks possession of medical records.[4]

Eventually, states developed, either by statute or case law, evidentiary privileges that protected patients from in-court disclosures of private medical information, where their physical status was not an element of a cause of action. Evidentiary rules regarding physician-patient privilege were not necessarily applicable to communications to a third party outside the courtroom and, in some instances, a patient had no recourse against a physician who disclosed confidences without consent.[5] When administrative rules of a medical board or ethical rules prohibited such a release of patient information, their breach could be grounds for revocation of a medical license.[6] Some courts also recognized the possibility of civil action for breach of an implied contract that the examination results would remain confidential. When a physician was hired by someone other than the patient, breach of implied contract might not apply due to absence of a physician-patient contractual relationship.[7]

Some courts, noting that neither common law nor statutes protected the patient's confidentiality, constructed legal rules prohibiting such releases based on a composite of public policy considerations[8] and various legal theories. To support the legal concept of confidentiality of medical records, courts have relied on courtroom testimonial privilege regarding confidential communications;[9] medical practice administrative provisions defining acceptable professional conduct;[10] case law governing the tort of invasion of privacy;[11] contract law;[12] and ethical rules of professional organizations such as the American Medical Association and the Hippocratic Oath.[13] In *Alberts v. Devine* in 1985, the court ruled that the duty of confidentiality arose from the fiduciary (trust) aspect of the physician-patient relationship independent of any contractual obligation the physician might have.[14] While such court decisions created well-deserved protection for patients' records where statutes had been lacking, they also made legal rules on release of medical information extremely confusing. Recent legislation in some states has attempted to clarify rules of confidentiality, but much of the older case law would still apply in a civil suit filed by a disgruntled patient.

In occupational medicine, traditional rules of confidentiality are complicated by the dual agency role of the medical provider and qualified (limited) privileges that may provide employers a defense against charges that the examining physician inappropriately released medical information. For example, in a 1992 Missouri case, an employee's tort claim of invasion of privacy was defeated, in part, by the existence of a qualified privilege that gave the employer a right of access to the employee's private medical information based on the employer's "business needs."[15]

When a private physician releases medical information to a plant physician without consent, exceptions of qualified privileges may excuse the conduct, especially if the plant physician has some role in the continuing care or protection of the patient's welfare in the work environment. Such qualified privileges may therefore negate tort actions for invasion of privacy as well as statutory restrictions on release of information.[16] Importantly, these exceptions often presume that the company doctor also owes the patient-employee a duty of confidentiality and therefore will not redisclose the information within the company.[17] This is consistent with the Uniform Health–Care Information Act (UHCIA), which permits the transfer of confidential information from one treating physician to another without specific written consent of the patient.[18]

By contrast, release of confidential medical information to a company's medical director, who was part of management and *not* responsible for direct patient care, was ruled a violation of confidentiality.[19] The First Circuit rejected the defense of business privilege and held that, because the medical director was not a treating physician, he had no right to the information without the employee's consent.

Finally, the handling of medical records in the practice of occupational medicine also may be influenced by federal and state regulations that govern the release of private medical information in the workplace. To varying degrees, the physician-patient confidentiality has been waived, abolished, or deemed to have never existed. This makes it even more difficult to know what kinds of information are truly confidential.

STATUTES AND REGULATIONS ON DISCLOSURE OF MEDICAL INFORMATION

The Uniform Health–Care Information Act

Most states have statutes governing the release of confidential medical records, with various requirements for consent by the patient to the release of the information. Beyond the UHCIA,[20] there has not been an attempt to achieve uniformity among the states. The UHCIA provides a model for state legislatures concerned with control and release of medical records in either general or occupational medical practice. Thus far, the UHCIA has been adopted only by Montana and Washington,[21] but because it was modeled, in part, after existing law from several states, it provides a general overview of rules governing release of medical records in the U.S.

In occupational medical practice, the UHCIA or a comparable state confidentiality statute, if adopted, would control the release of records only when another applicable state or federal law does not supercede. The difficulty in ascertaining which law controls the release of medical records in a particular situation makes it desirable for all releases of medical information to conform to the basic state requirements in *addition* to all other state and federal laws that may apply in a specific jurisdiction.

According to the UHCIA, a disclosure authorization to a health care provider must meet at least three requirements. It must (1) be in writing, dated, and signed by the patient, (2) identify the nature of the information to be disclosed, and (3) identify the person to whom the information is to be disclosed.[22] The provider must retain each authorization or revocation received from the patient.[23] Although each state may adopt a different rule, the model rule states that the duration of an authorization for release of information may not exceed 30 months. Washington state has a limit of only 90 days except for release to third-party payors.[24]

Under the UHCIA, circumstances under which disclosures may be made without consent of the patient include (1) transmission to professionals who require information to render health care to the patient, (2) transmission to previous health care providers, to the extent necessary to provide health care to the patient, (3) transmission for specified quality assurance, peer review, administrative, or legal purposes, (4) transmission to avoid or minimize imminent danger to the patient or another individual, (5) transmission to immediate family members and other close individuals, if not contrary to the instructions of the patient, (6) transmission for use in research projects, (7) transmission where required by public health authorities, and (8) transmission in accordance with compulsory process.[25] Because the UHCIA has not been widely adopted, most states recognize only a few of the above exceptions when consent is not required.

Providers must ensure that only the records specifically described in the release are disclosed. Moreover, a general release will be inadequate if another federal or state law requires a specific release for particularly sensitive medical records, such as those containing references to HIV status or substance abuse.

Workers' Compensation Statutes and Case Law

In general, all of a worker's medical records related to an occupational injury or illness are available to the insurer, employer, or state fund responsible for paying the medical bills and time loss compensation. There are some variations on this rule among the states, however, and recent decisions interpreting applicable workers' compensation statutes have emphasized the importance of obtaining a signed release from each patient despite a presumed absence of physician-patient privilege.

Some states grant the third-party payor complete access to all written reports but prohibit any oral ex parte[26] (private) communications with the treating physician in the absence of specific written consent of the claimant. For example, the West Virginia Supreme Court of Appeals recently held that the fiduciary relationship between the treating physician and the claimant required the physician to obtain authorization for oral discussions with an employer concerning the claimant's medical condition.[27] The claimant had previously signed a "release" acknowledging that state law permitted transmission of medical information by a physician to the employer or the employer's representative.[28] The court ruled, however, that the only permissible ex parte contacts would be the occasional verbal contact between the employer and the treating physician, limited to information contained within the written medical reports required by statute or other routine inquiries not involving the exchange of confidential information.[29] For example, ex parte oral communications regarding administrative matters such as when the claimant might be released for work would not be confidential and would therefore be permissible.[30] By contrast, the employer would not be allowed, under West Virginia law, to contact the physician to persuade him or her to alter the course of treatment or recommendations.[31] New Mexico appears to have a similar rule prohibiting oral ex part contacts as well as the release of documents not reasonably related to the worker's disability claim.[32]

The state of Washington prohibits ex parte contact between a treating physician and a representative of the opposing party in personal injury litigation. By contrast, the Supreme Court of Washington has ruled that ex parte communications between the claimant's treating physician and the employer or the employer's attorney is permissible in a workers' compensation claim.[33] The court reasoned that in a personal injury suit, the physician-patient privilege is waived to a limited extent, whereas in workers' compensation law, the physician-patient privilege is deemed abolished.[34] Oregon law is similar in stating that no physician-patient privilege is applicable in workers' compensation cases.[35] The intent of the law is to prevent delay in the flow of relevant medical information during the processing of the claim.[36] In Iowa, ex parte communications are permitted as long as the information released is "relative to the claim." In workers' compensation cases, Iowa courts deem the physician-patient privilege to be waived rather than abolished.[37]

When particularly sensitive information is relevant to a workers' compensation claim, the law becomes even more unpredictable. In 1991, a California court ruled that release of information regarding positive HIV status by a neurologist performing an independent medical examination to counsel for the workers' compensation carrier violated the state constitutionally guaranteed right of privacy.[38] The court held that the HIV status (which had been revealed by the claimant to a nurse at the culmination of an electromyography procedure because the claimant was concerned about possible contamination of electrodes) was extraneous to the doctor's opinion that the claimant's neurologic symptoms were psychosomatic and unrelated to the on-the-job injury.

A Georgia court ruled in 1992 that a psychiatrist who performed an independent medical examination on a patient with a work-related head injury was not liable for releasing the test results to the claimant's own doctor. The court implied, however, that in some instances there might be liability.[39] The court noted that the physician releasing the information was performing an IME at the request of the workers' compensation carrier and was not providing counseling of the type that *would* make the evaluation privileged.[40] This suggests that some confidences might indeed by protected from disclosure by a treating psychiatrist.

A New York physician released a medical record indicating positive HIV status in response to a subpoena issued by a Pennsylvania workers' compensation board. A New York court held in 1993 that the physician had violated state law by failing to use a special consent form to obtain permission to release information related to HIV status.[41]

The above decisions emphasize the importance of obtaining specific consent prior to release of information even in workers' compensation cases. Occupational physicians must also become aware of the significant limits that may be placed on communications of medical information to either employers or the state.

The Americans with Disabilities Act

Adding to the patchwork of state statutes and regulations supplementing court decisions, Congress has enacted various laws that affect the handling of employee medical records. The most important of these is the Americans with Disabilities Act of 1990. The ADA prohibits medical examinations of employees or applicants except in limited circumstances.[42] Preemployment physical examinations are no longer permissible. However, an employer may require an "employment entrance examination" after an offer of employment but before the individual has begun working in the position offered.[43] ADA requires that any information obtained be kept *confidential* with specific limitations on disclosure.[44] The provisions apply to employers working either directly or through contractors.[45] The ADA also prohibits interference with the exercise or enjoyment of any right granted or protected by the act.[46] Consequently, the employer may not request, persuade, or coerce an employee to disclose confidential medical information except as explicitly permitted by the law.[47]

The ADA does not contain specific requirements for the handling of a confidential medical record. Importantly, there is no requirement that medical personnel maintain custody of the records. However, medical information, including medical history, must be collected and maintained on separate forms and in separate files.[48] Personnel forms may not be used to collect medical data, and once compiled, medical data must be stored in a separate filing cabinet from other personnel records. The records custodian may not be the supervisor or manager. Supervisors and managers may be informed only of necessary restrictions or accommodations, and first aid and safety personnel may be informed if the disability might require emergency treatment.[49]

Government officials investigating compliance with ADA must also be given access to "relevant information on request."[50] Medical information may be submitted to state workers' compensation offices, second injury funds, or workers' compensation insurance carriers, in accordance with state law,[51] and state workers' compensation laws are not preempted in regard to confidentiality of medical records.[52]

Congress contemplated other uses of medical information by employers. Prior to passage of the legislation, the house committee noted that "medical information obtained in an examination ... may be used by the employer as baseline data to assist the employer in measuring physical changes attributable to on-the-job exposures."[53] This encompasses the use of x-rays, laboratory values, audiograms, and other data by the employer. However, release of this type of information to employers is unnecessary since the health care provider can maintain custody of the records and perform the necessary comparisons of data.

Regarding the assessment of employees or job applicants, the Equal Employment Opportunity Commission has focused on two issues: (1) whether the person is currently able to perform the essential job functions, either with or without accommodation, and (2) whether the person can perform the job without posing a "direct threat" to the health or safety of that person or others.[54]

EEOC policy states that "employers should provide doctors who conduct employment examinations with specific information about the job."[55] Access to detailed job descriptions listing essential job functions should enable examiners to perform evaluations without revealing confidential medical information. The EEOC also states, "The doctor's role should be limited to advising the employer about an individual's functional abilities and limitations in relation to job functions, and about whether the individual meets the employer's health and safety requirements."[56]

If the individual requests a "reasonable accommodation," the employer must decide if an accommodation is possible.[57] This decision requires some information about the condition being accommodated. Thus, the physician may have to release a few details to the employer at the request of the applicant or employee.

If the employer agrees that all medical records shall remain in the custody of the doctor, confidentiality is readily assured. The physician will be responsible, however, for keeping records of periodic examinations required by OSHA (see below) as well as for providing records to interested parties in accordance with workers' compensation laws.

In contrast, if the employer is a large corporation with a separate medical department, the examining physician may be asked to provide the entire medical record generated during a company-paid examination. Legal and ethical protections exist that offer some assurance that embarrassing details contained within the medical record will not be disseminated to non-medical personnel within the corporation.[58] Although ADA does not require medical personnel to maintain custody of the confidential employee medical records,[59] health care practitioners within the corporation would also be subject to medical practice and professional ethical rules[60] as well as state law controlling the release of medical records.

The ADA does not specifically address recordkeeping in smaller companies that do not have a medical department. These employers frequently delegate to human resources or safety personnel the maintenance of medical data related to workplace hazards, environmental monitoring, and preplacement examinations. Because smaller employers often shop around for medical services and change providers frequently, they may not want to delegate recordkeeping to one private practitioner, but instead may require that records be maintained on their own premises. This is consistent with OSHA's mandate that the employer is ultimately responsible for maintaining appropriate records for the required length of time (see below).

Because testing for the presence of illicit drugs is not a "medical examination" under the ADA,[61] drug testing can be undertaken before a job offer is made. The ADA is silent on the transfer of information related to substance abuse testing and does not appear to subject it to confidentiality requirements applicable to other medical information. Nevertheless, the results of substance abuse testing are still subject to other state and federal rules on confidentiality of medical records and drug test results. Much of the litigation alleging inappropriate release of confidential medical information to employers prior to the ADA had involved positive drug test results,[62] and it is reasonable to assume that this trend will continue. Consequently, physicians and their staff must obtain adequate consent not only to perform drug testing but also to release the results to the employer.

Regulations Pursuant to the Occupational Safety and Health Act

Pursuant to the Occupational Safety and Health Act,[63] the Occupational Safety and Health Administration, the National Institute for Occupational Safety and Health, the employee, labor unions, and employer all have rights of access to some or all of the employee's medical records. The general rule controlling OSHA and employer access to employee records is defined in 29 CFR § 1910.20. NIOSH access, while also based on the Occupational Safety and Health Act, is regulated by the Department of Health and Human Services rather than the Department of Labor.[64] In addition, other rules governing exposure to specific substances may contain provisions regarding release of medical records.

29 CFR § 1910.20 guarantees the right of the employee to review his or her records maintained by the employer.[65] OSHA also has a right to the exposure and medical records of all current and former employees. Consent of the employees is not required,[66] and inspections or examinations of records do not have to be mandated by specific OSHA standards.[67] Records from an employee assistance program are excluded from this access rule if they are maintained separately from the employer's medical program and its records.[68]

An employee's designated representative, including a recognized or certified collective bargaining agent without written authorization, also may have access to an employee's exposure records.[69] Requests by designated representatives for unconsented access to employee exposure records must be in writing and must specify the occupational health need for them.[70] Requests for access based on consent must comply with specific requirements listed in the OSHA rules.[71]

In general, courts have affirmed the right of access of federal agencies to employee medical records. In *U.S. v. Westinghouse Electric Corp.*, the United States Court of Appeals for the Third Circuit ruled that NIOSH was entitled to examine records related to the purpose of a NIOSH investigation, even if those records were not maintained pursuant to specific regulations.[72] NIOSH sought preemployment physical examinations, including medical history forms, unrelated to exposure to the substance under investigation. NIOSH wanted pulmonary function tests as well as descriptions of allergic and pulmonary symptoms prior to start of employment. The court ruled that NIOSH should have access to the entire record maintained at Westinghouse.[73] Employees, however, were entitled to prior notice by NIOSH so that objections to release of information could be weighed by the court.[74]

Meanwhile, the United States Court of Appeals for the District of Columbia Circuit addressed analogous rules of access to medical records contained within the lead standard (29 CFR § 1910.1025).[75] That court ruled that OSHA and NIOSH could have access to "all records of all medical examinations and tests of employees conducted pursuant to the [lead] standard" without consent of the employees.[76] The court also ruled that disclosure of medical removal records and the results of environmental and biologic monitoring to representatives of labor unions did not violate the privacy rights of the employees.[77] The court based its decision on *Whalen v. Roe*,[78] which held that there was no violation of the "zone of privacy" where detailed protections against unwarranted disclosures existed.[79]

OSHA's rules do not define what happens when OSHA or an employer wants access to employee medical records that are in the possession of a private physician. Both the general rule and the specific rule contained within the lead standard indicate that the employer must ensure that the examining physician maintains the necessary records for the required time.[80] It is the employer who is required to make records available to OSHA and NIOSH.[81] However, if authorizations for release of medical records to the employer have long since expired, a transfer of records from the physician to the employer could arguably violate state law on confidentiality of medical records. OSHA rules clearly state that they are not intended to supersede or displace existing legal and ethical obligations concerning the maintenance and confidentiality of employee medical information.[82] Although this implies that physician-patient confidentiality still applies in many instances, the point at which state law on confidentiality becomes preempted by OSHA requirements remains unclear.

In *General Motors v. NIOSH*, the Sixth Circuit rejected a claim of privacy for medical records in the possession of a plant physician. The court ruled that a physician-patient privilege under state law did not apply to a subpoena issued by a federal agency under a federal statute. Furthermore, there is no federal common law physician-patient privilege.[83] Soon thereafter, a federal district court held that NIOSH has the power to subpoena records in the custody of third parties.[84] These decisions imply that although a physician may violate state law by voluntarily transmitting records to the employer after an authorization for release of records has expired, OSHA or NIOSH can subpoena the records directly from the physician, and a federal court will presumably enforce the subpoena if the agency's request is supported by genuine need for the records that outweigh the individual's privacy interest.

Federal Law on Substance Abuse Records

Federal law codified at 42 USC § 29Odd-2 severely restricts disclosure of records concerning a patient's substance abuse. This federal statute mandates the confidentiality of "records of the identity, diagnosis, prognosis, or treatment of any patient which are maintained in connection with the performance of any program or activity relating to substance abuse education, prevention, training, treatment, rehabilitation or research, which is conducted, regulated, or directly or indirectly assisted by any department or agency of the United States."[85]

The content of any record regarding substance abuse may be released only to the extent and for the purposes authorized by the law, regardless of the patient's consent.[86] "Records" means any patient-related information in the possession of a federally assisted alcohol or drug program.[87] The term "program" has been broadly defined to include persons or entities that in whole or in part provide substance abuse diagnosis, treatment, or referral for treatment. A general medical facility itself may be a "program" if it has an identified unit or medical personnel whose primary function is to provide substance abuse diagnosis, treatment, or referral for treatment. Moreover, analogous requirements of confidentiality under 38 USC § 4132 have been applied to an emergency room of a Veterans Administration facility that maintains a substance abuse treatment unit.[88]

Substance abuse records may be released (without consent) to physicians in a bona fide medical emergency and pursuant to an appropriate order of a court.[89] Regulations specify, however, that if a health care provider receives a subpoena for such records, a response to that subpoena is not permitted unless a court order authorizes it.[90] A court order alone authorizes disclosure by the practitioner but does not compel disclosure unless accompanied by the subpoena.[91]

Federal law provides for consent by the patient to the release of substance abuse medical records. The required elements of the written consent form are described in 42 CFR § 2.31 and are similar to those of the consent forms under OSHA and the Uniform Health–Care Information Act. A general authorization for the release of medical records is not sufficient. The law also requires that a notice of prohibition of redisclosure appear on each disclosure.[92]

The confidentiality requirements for substance abuse patient records clearly apply to most hospitals, because federal assistance has been interpreted to include aid in the form of tax credits or deductions, tax-exempt status, Medicare payments, government contracts, and funds obtained indirectly from the federal government through a local government unit via revenue sharing.[93] Moreover, programs connected to substance abuse prevention have been broadly defined and are not limited to rehabilitation units. Regulations from the Department of Health and Human Services and court decisions make it clear that the confidentiality rules apply not only to hospitals or units designed to treat substance abuse, but also to employee assistance programs and private practitioners who offer or provide substance abuse diagnosis, treatment, or referral for treatment if they are federally assisted in any manner.[94]

Even occupational physicians who do not specialize in substance abuse may, if practicing in federally assisted large multispecialty clinics or hospital systems with substance abuse units or personnel specializing in substance abuse, be subject to these regulations. Corporations probably qualify as "programs" if they have an employee assistance program, even if their federal aid is limited to tax deductions rather than government contracts. Hence, the confidentiality provisions most likely apply to drug testing undertaken by an employer who seeks to prevent substance abuse.

Although the Americans with Disabilities Act states that testing for illegal drug use is not a medical examination for purposes of that act, the ADA does not remove the confidentiality requirements that apply to testing for evidence of substance abuse. A physician practicing in a setting (or program) covered by these rules still must have valid consent in order to notify the employer of a positive drug test. Criminal penalties for violation of these provisions include fines up to $5,000.[95]

If employee drug testing is performed pursuant to federal authority, additional federal regulations may control the handling of test results. Numerous federal agencies mandate drug-testing programs with specific rules on confidentiality, which most likely preempt other federal rules and state law.[96] For example, the Federal Highway Administration mandates that the medical review officer maintain custody of drug test results and report positive test results to the employer and certain government agencies.[97] The Federal Aviation Administration requires that positive results from airmen tested pursuant to FAA regulations be reported to the Federal Air Surgeon.[98] Mandatory drug testing of unionized workers is often controlled by a collective bargaining agreement whose provisions are subject to the Labor Management Relations Act, which preempts state law claims alleging violation of privacy rights.[99] Finally, state or local law may regulate the handling of test results if not contrary to applicable federal law.

ETHICAL ASPECTS OF MANAGING CONFIDENTIAL MEDICAL RECORDS

Beyond the legal issues involved in handling confidential medical records are some ethical considerations that are relevant to the practice of occupational medicine. In 1993, the Board of Directors of the American College of Occupational and Environmental Medicine approved a new code of ethics, revising the code originally adopted in 1976.[100] The chairman of the Committee on Ethical Practice in Occupational Medicine noted: "Ethical standards are necessary because, as opposed to laws, they do not vary according to temporal and regional standards and customs. Ethical standards involve higher issues than legal standards and deal with what is right."[101]

Two of the eight provisions in the ethical code address confidentiality of employee medical records, and state:

> Physicians should:
> 5. Keep confidential all individual medical information, releasing such information only when required by law or overriding public health considerations, or to other physicians according to accepted medical practices, or to others at the request of the individual;
> 6. recognize that employers may be entitled to counsel about an individual's medical work fitness, but not to diagnoses or specific details, except in compliance with laws and regulations.[102]

The above provisions had formerly been contained within paragraph 7 of the 1976 version of the code.

Most, if not all, of the ethical dilemmas in occupational medicine arise from the physician's role as a dual agent.[103] For services on behalf of the employer, the physician receives compensation either directly or indirectly (through a workers' compensation fund) from that employer. At the same time, the physician has obligations to the patient that are influenced by traditional concepts of the physician-patient relationship. Some obligations to the employer and employee may be compatible, such as the rendering of high quality medical care. By contrast, the perceived need to release medical information creates fundamentally incompatible obligations for the physician. The employee may hope that sensitive medical information will remain confidential, whereas the employer (or other third party payor, such as the state) may want access to as much medical information as possible for reasons that may be contrary to the interests of the employee. These include gathering facts that would support denial of an employee's workers' compensation claim, or help the company screen out individuals perceived to be at higher risk for on-the-job injuries, absenteeism, medical claims, or poor productivity. Such individuals might include current or former abusers of alcohol or controlled substances and workers with a history of prior compensation claims, hidden physical disabilities, positive HIV status, or AIDS.

While the employee's rights to confidentiality are partially protected by the ADA and other state and federal laws, many legal protections can be bypassed by securing the employee's consent for the release of information. Workers, especially when nonunionized, have unequal bargaining power, and if threatened with termination for refusal to consent, would probably agree to release of information.

ACOEM noted that ADA rules regarding the release of information have been "alternatively interpreted as being very permissive in permitting employers access to all employee medical information or as affording new privacy protection."[104] Although the ADA is perceived as protecting the employee/applicant from release of personal medical information, a careful reading of the act reveals that the law permits such a disclosure as long as the information is treated as "confidential medical information" by the employer. In view of this ambiguity, occupational medicine physicians have an ethical duty to preserve the patient's confidentiality as much as possible. Physicians should help to educate employers as to why they should not solicit this information, thereby incurring the burden of proof that the knowledge was not used illegally.[105] Considering the ambiguities of the law and the subtle coercion often used to secure consent to the release of information, the obligation to control the release of medical information to employers and others rests squarely on the occupational medicine physician.[106]

SUMMARY

The conflict between the demands of third party payors and the physician's ethical obligations to patients, complicated by a multitude of laws controlling the disclosure of confidential information, continues to provide a source of confusion in occupational medicine. Although, in theory, an attorney could review all requests for release of medical information on patients, the best approach for a physician may be to treat all information as confidential and to obtain adequate consents for release that fulfill the requirements of all potentially applicable state and federal laws, even when the physician-patient privilege appears to be waived or abolished. This would protect the practitioner from the inadvertent release of privileged information, whether it be an unauthorized ex parte communication or information related to sexually transmitted diseases, HIV status, or substance abuse.

REFERENCES

1. Simonsen v. Swenson, 14 Neb. 224, 177 N.W. 831, 832 (1920).
2. Quarles v. Sutherland, 215 Tenn. 651, 389 S.W.2d 249, 250-1 (1965).
3. Quarles, at 250-1 (discussing Duchess of Kingston's Trial, 20 How. St. Tr. 355, 573 (1776)).
4. *See infra* note 80 and accompanying text.
5. Quarles at 252.
6. *Id.* at 251.
7. *Id.*
8. Hammonds v. Aetna Casualty & Surety Co., 243 F. Supp. 793, 797 (N.D. Ohio 1965).
9. Schaffer v. Spicer, 215 N.W.2d 134 (1974); *but see,* Simonsen.
10. Clark v. Geraci, 29 Misc. 2d 791, 208 N.Y.S.2d 564, 567 (1960).
11. Horne v. Patton, 291 Ala. 701, 287 So. 2d 824 (1974); Doe v. Roe, 93 Misc. 2d 201, 400 N.Y.S.2d 668, 674 (1977); Neal v. Corning Glass Works Corp., 745 F. Supp. 1294 (S.D. Ohio 1989); Bratt v. IBM Corp., 785 F.2d 352 (1st Cir. 1986); Hammonds v. Aetna Casualty & Surety Co.; *but see,* Humphers v. First Interstate Bank, 298 Or. 706, 696 P.2d 527 (1985).
12. Horne v. Patton; MacDonald v. Clinger, 84 A.D.2d 482, 446 N.Y.S.2d 801 (1982).
13. Hammonds v. Aetna Casualty & Surety Co., 243 F. Supp. at 797; *see,* Alberts v. Devine, 395 Mass. 59, 479 N.E.2d 113, 119 (1985); Carroll v. Alberts, 474 U.S. 113, 88 L. Ed. 2d 474, 106 S. Ct. 546 (1985); *see also,* Horne v. Patton.
14. Alberts v. Devine, 479 N.E.2d at 120; *see also,* Hammonds, 243 F. Supp. at 802-3; Horne v. Patton.
15. Childs v. Williams, 825 S.W.2d 4 (Mo. App. 1992); *but see,* Alberts v. Devine (rejecting exception permitting disclosure to employer).
16. *See,* Neal v. Corning Glass Works Corp., 745 F. Supp. at 1297.
17. *Id.*
18. *See infra* note 20 and accompanying text.
19. Bratt v. IBM Corp.
20. Unif. Health-Care Information Act, 9 ULA pt. I, 478-52 (West 1988 & Supp. 1995).
21. Mont. Code Ann. §§ 50-16-501–50-16-553; Rev. Code Wash. §§ 70.02.005–70.02.904.
22. UHCIA § 2-101(c) (3).
23. UHCIA §§ 2-101(b), 2-102(e).
24. Rev. Code Wash. § 70.02.030(6) (1994).
25. UHCIA §§ 2-104, 2-105.
26. *See* Black's Law Dictionary at 517 (5th ed. West 1979) (*"ex parte"* means for one side or party only).
27. Morris v. Consolidation Coal Co., 191 W. Va. 426, 446 S.E.2d 648, 652-3 (1994).
28. *Id.,* 446 S.E.2d at 652.
29. *Id.* at 653.
30. *Id.* at 654.
31. *Id.*
32. Church's Fried Chicken No. 1040 v. Hanson, 114 N.M. 730, 845 P.2d 824 (1992).
33. Holbrook v. Weyerhaeuser Co., 118 Wash. 2d 306, 822 P.2d 271 (1992).
34. Holbrook, 118 Wash. 2d 306, 822 P.2d 271, 274 (1992).
35. Booth v. Tektronix, 312 Or. 463, 823 P.2d 402, 406 (1991).
36. Booth, 823 P.2d at 408.
37. Morrison v. Century Engineering, 434 N.W.2d 874, 876-7 (Iowa 1989).

38. Urbaniak v. Newton, 277 Cal. Rptr. 354 (1991).
39. Jarallah v. Schwartz, 22 Ga. App. 32, 413 S.E.2d 210 (1992).
40. *Id.*
41. Doe v. Roe, 190 A.2d. 463, 599 NYS 2d. 350 (1993).
42. 42 USCA § 12112(d) (1) (West 1994).
43. *Id.* at § 12112(d) (3).
44. *Id.* at § 12112(d) (3) (B).
45. *See id.* at § 12182(b) (1) (D).
46. *Id.* at § 12203(b).
47. EEOC Compliance Manual, No. 187, at 23 (1994).
48. 42 USCA § 12112(d) (3) (B) (1994).
49. *Id.* at § 12112(d) (3) (B) (i), (ii).
50. *Id.* at § 12112(d) (3) (B) (iii).
51. 42 USCA § 12201(b) (West 1994); 29 C.F.R. § 1630.14(b) (1994).
52. 29 CFR § 1630, app. at 412 (1994) (interpreting § 1630.14(b)).
53. HR Report 101-485, part 2 at 74.
54. A.L.I.-A.B.A., 18 EEOC Technical Assistance Manual, No. 6 at 39 (1992).
55. *Id.*
56. *Id.* at 38.
57. *Id.*
58. *See e.g.*, note 17 and accompanying text.
59. *See* notes 48 and 49, and accompanying text.
60. *See* note 102 and accompanying text.
61. 42 USCA § 12114(d) (1) (West 1994).
62. Crocker v. Synpol, 732 S.W.2d 429 (Tex. App. Beaumont 1987); Neal v. Corning Glass Works,
    Corp., (emergency room released results of urine drug screen to employer, and employee was
    terminated); *see infra* notes 93 and 94 and accompanying text.
63. 29 USC § 657 *et seq.*
64. 29 USC §§ 669(b), 671(c); 45 C.F.R. § 5.71.
65. 29 CFR § 1910.20(a) (1994).
66. *Id.* at § 1910.20(a), (c) (4).
67. *Id.* at § 1910.20(b) (2).
68. *Id.* at § 1910.20(c) (6) (ii) (D).
69. *Id.* at § 1910.20(c) (3).
70. *Id.* at § 1910.20(e).
71. 29 CFR § 1910.20(c) (12) (i) (1994).
72. U.S. v. Westinghouse Electric Corp., 638 F.2d 570 (3rd Cir. 1980).
73. *Id.* at 576; *but see*, Erie Bottling Corp. v. Donovan, 539 F. Supp. 600, 607, (D.C. Pa. 1982).
74. United States v. Westinghouse Electric Corp. at 581-2.
75. United Steelworkers v. Marshall, 647 F.2d 1189 (D.C. Cir. 1980), *cert. denied*, 453 U.S. 913 (1981).
76. *Id.* at 1240.
77. *Id.* at 1240-2.
78. Whalen v. Roe, 429 U.S. 589, 97 S. Ct. 869, 51 L. Ed. 2d 64 (1977).
79. United Steelworkers at 1241 (citing Whalen, 429 U.S. at 601, 605, 97 S. Ct. at 877, 879).
80. 29 CFR §§ 1910.20, 1910.1025(n) (2) (iii), (iv) (1994).
81. 29 CFR §§ 1910.20(a), 1910.1025(n) (4) (i) (1994).
82. 29 CFR § 1910.20(a) (1994).
83. General Motors v. NIOSH, 636 F.2d 163, 165 (6th Cir. 1980), *cert. denied*, 454 U.S. 877 (1981).
84. United States v. Amalgamated Life Insurance Co., 534 F. Supp. 676, 678 (S.D.N.Y. 1982).
85. 42 USCA § 29Odd-2 (West Cum. Supp. 1995).
86. 42 USCA § 29Odd-2(b) (1) (West Cum. Supp. 1995).
87. 42 CFR § 2.11 (1994).
88. United States v. Eide, 875 F.2d 1429 (9th Cir. 1989).
89. 42 USC § 29Odd-2(b) (2) (A)-(C) (West Cum. Supp. 1995).
90. 42 CFR § 2.61(a), (b) (1994).
91. *Id.*
92. 42 CFR § 2.32 (1994).
93. 42 CFR § 2.12(b) (1994); Town of Huntington v. N.Y. State Drug Abuse Control Commission, 84
    Misc. 2d 138, 373 N.Y.S.2d 728, 735 (1975); *see also*, Local 738 v. Certified Grocers Midwest,
    737 F. Supp. 1030 (N.D. Ill. 1990).
94. 42 CFR § 2.12(e) (1994); Jeanette "A" v. Condon, 728 F. Supp. 204, 205 (SDNY 1989).

95. 42 CFR § 2.4 (1994).
96. *See, e.g.*, 14 CFR § 121 (Federal Aviation Administration); 49 C.F.R. § 382 (Federal Highway Administration); 49 CFR § 219 (Federal Railroad Administration); 49 CFR § 653 (Federal Transit Administration); 49 CFR § 40 (Department of Transportation).
97. 49 CFR § 382.405–382.409.
98. 14 CFR § 121, App. I, VII, B, 3.
99. Laws v. Calmat, 852 F.2d 430 (9th Cir. 1988).
100. Teichman R: Introduction to the new ACOEM Code of Ethical Conduct. J Occup Med 36:27, 1994.
101. Teichman R, Wester M: The new ACOEM Code of Ethical Conduct. J Occup Med 36:27–30, 1994.
102. *Id.*
103. Brandt-Rauf P, Brandt-Rauf SJ, Fallon LF: Management of ethical issues in the practice of occupational medicine. Occup Med State Art Rev 4:171–176, 1989.
104. Committee Report: Commentaries on the Code of Ethical Conduct. I. J Occup Environ Med 37:201–206, 1995.
105. *Id.*
106. *Id.*

MARK A. ROTHSTEIN, JD

LEGAL AND ETHICAL ASPECTS OF MEDICAL SCREENING

From Health Law and Policy
    Institute
University of Houston
Houston, Texas

Reprint requests to:
Mark A. Rothstein, JD
Director, Health Law and Policy
    Institute
University of Houston
4800 Calhoun Road
Houston, TX 77204-6381

The responsibilities of occupational physicians have changed and expanded over time. These obligations now include hazard evaluation and control, regulatory compliance, biologic monitoring, medical surveillance, descriptive epidemiology, substance abuse programs, employee assistance programs, workers' compensation, and rehabilitation and accommodation of employees. Despite the importance of these roles, the paramount function of occupational physicians remains medical screening, the process by which a workforce is selected and maintained by application of medical criteria.[21] Medical screening is the defining role of the occupational physician. It is also the source of the most profound legal and ethical conflicts.

PHYSICIAN-EXAMINEE RELATIONSHIP

The "silent world"[14] in which the individual undergoes medical screening is permeated by the ill-defined and nebulous professional relationship between the physician and the individual. In their organization's codes of ethics and official pronouncements, physicians have been resolute in stating that there is no physician-patient relationship between a physician retained by an employer and an individual who is examined to determine his or her employability.

The absolute disavowal of any physician-patient relationship by physicians is understandable. The existence of the physician-patient relationship establishes the legal duty of care running from a physician to his or her patient. A breach of this duty provides the basis for an action in medical malpractice. If there were a physician-patient relationship, the physician would be required to "have and use the knowledge, skill and care ordinarily possessed and employed by members of the profession in good standing; and a doctor will be liable if harm results because he does not have them."[15]

The absence of a physician-patient relationship also relieves occupational physicians of other traditional obligations in medical practice, including informed consent for all medical tests, instructions on treatment options, referrals for follow-up, and the preservation of confidentiality of medical information. However, in many, if not most, instances, the examining physician does not inform the examinee of the contours of this unusual professional relationship.

Courts considering the issue have generally agreed that there is no physician-patient relationship in an employer-mandated medical examination performed for the purpose of determining fitness to work. Unless the purpose of the examination is to benefit the individual, or treatment is contemplated, there is no physician-patient relationship. This broad principle has been referred to by courts as the "benefit" and "treatment" rules.[20]

If there is no physician-patient relationship, what is the nature of the interaction between the employee or applicant and the examining physician? What obligations, if any, run between the physician and the person being examined? The law has taken a minimalist approach. In general, the physician's duty is merely not to injure the individual in the course of the examination. Unfortunately, the occupational medical profession has failed to delineate the ethical responsibilities of physicians conducting medical examinations of "nonpatients." Some proposed responsibilities are set out at the end of this chapter in the Bill of Rights of Examinees.

CONFLICTS OF INTEREST

In the traditional physician-patient relationship, the physician is the agent and fiduciary of the patient. This means that the physician owes a singular duty of loyalty to the patient and is bound to serve only the interests of the patient.[3] When a medical examination of an individual is conducted by an employer-retained physician and there is no physician-patient relationship, it is less clear whose interest—the employer's or the individual's—is given primary consideration by the physician. This reality, as well as the misperceptions surrounding the reality, gives rise to the "dual loyalty" concern that is the central ethical issue of occupational medicine.

Principle 1 of the American College of Occupational and Environmental Medicine Code of Ethical Conduct provides that "[p]hysicians should accord the highest priority to the health and safety of individuals in both the workplace and the environment."[1] This statement is inadequate, because "highest priority" can be read as merely describing a broad category of concerns all given highest priority, as opposed to a relative ranking of priorities.

Rather than a statement written as a vague absolute, what is needed is a statement in relative terms. The principle must directly answer the following question: When the interests of the individual examinee and the employer conflict, whose interests take precedence? It is not an easy question.

In the context of medical screening, if the examinee's interests take precedence, it could be asserted that the examinee has an absolute right to refuse to submit to certain medical tests or, after examination, to decide what health risks are acceptable. In effect, this would treat the examinee-physician relationship the same as the patient-physician relationship in private practice. By contrast, if the employer's interests are paramount, the employer could claim that managerial rather than medical personnel have a right to set medical criteria for employability and to evaluate all of the examinee's medical records and diagnostic information. In reality, neither of these extremes applies.

The lack of clarity regarding the ethical responsibilities of occupational physicians or the unwillingness of some employers to abide by them has shifted the focus to the legal constraints placed on medical screening and the use of medical information. However, as discussed below, the Americans with Disabilities Act and other laws have neither the purpose nor the effect of providing effective, comprehensive regulation of the practice of occupational medicine.

MEDICAL SCREENING UNDER THE AMERICANS WITH DISABILITIES ACT

A number of laws regulate at least some element of medical screening of workers. For example, specific health standards promulgated pursuant to the Occupational Safety and Health Act[24] mandate various preplacement and periodic medical examinations.[5] The Occupational Safety and Health Administration's Access to Employee Medical and Exposure Records regulation[6] sets forth the conditions under which employees and third parties may gain access to employee health records. The Department of Transportation has specific medical examination procedures for interstate truck drivers,[7] and the Federal Aviation Administration has specific provisions for medical examinations of flight crews.[4] Various state laws regulate HIV testing, genetic testing, and drug testing.[22]

By far, the most important law governing medical screening of workers is the Americans with Disabilities Act.[26] Previous laws prohibiting discrimination in employment on the basis of disability, including the Rehabilitation Act of 1973[25] and various state laws, established nondiscrimination principles, but the ADA is the first federal law that is comprehensive in coverage and detailed in responsibilities.

Although its primary goal is to prevent discrimination in employment against individuals with disabilities, the ADA also has established standards for lawful medical inquiries by employers. It is the first law to connect medical screening practices with disability-based discrimination. Accordingly, the ADA has mandated major changes in the way many companies conduct medical screening.

Definition of Medical Examination

Medical examinations are singled out for special treatment under the ADA. Because medical examinations and inquiries may take place only at certain times, it is important to define what tests are considered to be medical. The ADA itself provides little guidance, and in the absence of definitive court rulings, interpretations by the Equal Employment Opportunity Commission become the starting point in deciding the issue.

According to the EEOC, "Medical examinations are procedures or tests that seek information about the existence, nature, or severity of an individual's physical or mental impairment, or that seek information regarding an individual's physical or psychological health."[9] To determine whether any particular test is medical, answers to the following eight questions are sought: (1) Is the test administered by a health care professional or trainee? (2) Are the results of the test interpreted by a health care professional or trainee? (3) Is the test designed to reveal an impairment or the state of an individual's physical or psychological health? (4) Is the test given for the purpose of revealing an impairment or the state of an individual's physical or psychological health? (5) Is the test invasive? (Are samples of blood, urine, or breath required?) (6) Does the test measure physiologic or psychological responses (as opposed to performance of a task)? (7) Is the test routinely performed in a medical setting? (8) Are medical devices or equipment used for the test?

Tests of skill or physical agility are not considered medical examinations. However, if these tests tend to screen out individuals on the basis of disability, the employer has the burden of proving that the tests are job-related and consistent with business necessity. Psychological tests are considered medical examinations if they provide evidence of a mental disorder or impairment listed in the American Psychiatric Association's *Diagnostic and Statistical Manual of Mental Disorders (DSM-IV).*[9]

Preemployment Examinations

Under the ADA, medical examinations and inquiries can occur in three contexts: preemployment, preplacement, and employment. At the preemployment stage, while the employer is assessing the applicant's qualifications and before any offer has been extended, it is unlawful for an employer or the employer's agent to require the applicant to complete a medical questionnaire or to conduct a medical examination or to ask about the existence, nature, or severity of any disability. By contrast, an employer may ask the applicant whether he or she is able, with or without reasonable accommodation, to perform essential job-related functions.

Preplacement Examinations

In extending an offer of employment, an employer can make the successful completion of a medical examination a condition of employment. Consequently, the "conditional offeree" may be required to take a preplacement examination or what the ADA calls an "employment entrance examination."

Under the ADA, preplacement examinations must satisfy three requirements. First, all entering employees in the same job category must be subject to examination regardless of disability. This prevents the employer from requiring examinations only of individuals who seem to have obvious disabilities. The examinations, however, need not be identical. If, for example, one person relates a history of knee problems and the examining physician wants an x-ray of that person's knee, similar films need not be obtained for all people in the same job category.

Second, information obtained at the preplacement examination, as well as all other employee medical information, must be collected and maintained on separate forms and stored in separate medical files. The key is to prevent the storage of medical records in personnel files, where nonmedical personnel have access to them. In practice, for the few employers with in-house medical departments, this means storage in the medical department. For employers with a central medical facility, the records can be sent to the central office. For employers that use contract physicians, the records can be stored in the physician's office or, if they are returned to the employer, they can be stored in separate, locked files accessible only to medical personnel or pursuant to legal process.

The information in all medical records must be treated as confidential. Supervisors and managers, however, may be informed regarding necessary accommodations or restrictions on the work or duties of the employee. Similarly, first aid and safety personnel may be informed, when appropriate, if the disability might require emergency treatment. Finally, government officials investigating compliance with the ADA must be provided with relevant information on request.

Although many occupational physicians believe the ADA unnecessarily restricts or burdens the practice of medicine, the statute actually serves to confirm the independence and professional integrity of occupational medicine. For countless physicians, the most troublesome problem arises when management insists on obtaining specific diagnostic information about employees. Although the codes of ethics of the American Medical Association[8] and the American College of Occupational and Environmental Medicine[1] expressly prohibit such disclosures, some managers are indifferent to these professional canons.

It is too easy to say that physicians who make such disclosures are acting unethically. The punctiliously ethical occupational physician may be unemployable. With this provision of the ADA, however, occupational physicians have a new weapon to reinforce their professional ethics. Many employers, when reminded that they are subject to maximum damages of $50,000 to $300,000 (depending on employer size) for each violation of the ADA, will acquiesce and merely ask whether the individual is fit to work, unfit to work, or fit to work with restrictions or accommodations.

Some employers have attempted to circumvent restrictions on disclosure of medical information to management by requiring all individuals undergoing medical examinations to sign releases authorizing such disclosures. The EEOC has taken the position that, even though individuals may voluntarily disclose medical information to nonmedical personnel, the employer may not "request, persuade, coerce, or otherwise pressure the individual to disclose such information."[9] Therefore, it is probably unlawful to require the signing of such a release as a condition of employment.

Third, employers may not use medical criteria to screen out individuals with disabilities unless the medical criteria are job-related. Under the ADA, preplacement medical examinations may be of unlimited scope. An employer may require a comprehensive medical examination regardless of the job description. Similarly, the employer may make the release of all of the individual's medical records a valid condition of employment. Nevertheless, it is unlawful to withdraw a conditional offer of employment for any medical reason except that the individual is unable, even with reasonable accommodation, to perform the essential functions of the job.

This seemingly inexplicable provision resulted from legislative compromise during the passage of the ADA.[11] Some business groups were concerned that employers would be forced to limit the scope of their medical inquiries if each part of the examination had to be job-related. These fears were overstated. Medical examinations to obtain baseline health data of conditional offerees, an expressed concern of some employers, are clearly job-related. In Minnesota, which has the only state disability discrimination law that goes beyond the ADA to require that all medical examinations at any time must be strictly job-related,[17] employers have not reported any problems in complying. Moreover, it is questionable why employers would seek to possess information they legally could not use, especially when inadvertent disclosure of HIV, genetic tests, or other test results could lead to substantial legal liability.

Qualification Standards and Reasonable Accommodation

Under the ADA, medical screening is not an abstract exercise. Screening is designed to assess the individual's ability to perform specific functions related to a particular job. Therefore, exclusion of individuals based on generic medical criteria (reflecting the type of medical examination previously conducted at the preemployment stage) is unlawful under the ADA. The focus has now shifted to the ability to perform the essential functions of specific jobs. This means that the medical criteria also have changed, and the examining physician must understand the medical demands of the various positions at each work site.

The ADA prohibits discrimination against a qualified individual with a disability, defined to mean "an individual with a disability who, with or without reasonable accommodation, can perform the essential functions of the employment position that such individual holds or desires." Determining whether an individual is medically qualified is a two-step process. First, there must be an evaluation of the physical and mental demands of the job. Second, the individual must undergo a job-related medical assessment.

The ADA requires an individualized determination of fitness. Broad medical disqualification standards are inherently suspect. In matching job demands with individual abilities, the person need only to be able to perform the "essential functions" of the job. Individuals may not be excluded from employment because of an inability to perform "marginal functions." Whether a function is essential or marginal largely depends on the amount of time the person devotes to the activity and the effect on the business if he or she did not perform the function.

If a person cannot perform the essential functions of the job due to a disability, the employer must determine whether reasonable accommodation would enable that person to perform those functions. Under the ADA, employers have a duty to make reasonable accommodations for the known physical or mental limitations of an otherwise qualified applicant or employee. Reasonable accommodation may include providing accessible facilities, job restructuring, part-time or modified work schedules, reassignment to a vacant position, acquisition or modification of equipment or devices, appropriate adjustment or modification of examinations, training materials or policies, and the provision of qualified readers or interpreters. Reasonable accommodation is not required if it will result in "undue hardship" to the employer, defined as "an action requiring significant difficulty or expense" in light of factors such as the nature and cost of the accommodation and the size and financial resources of the company,.

Medical screening must be integrated with other aspects of the employment process at each company. For contract physicians, this may create additional challenges, but medically effective, legally defensible screening requires that these physicians obtain substantially more information about job functions than they have in the past. Occupational physicians, both employer-salaried and contract, also must work effectively with managerial staff in human resources and other departments to screen effectively and in compliance with the ADA.

Examinations of Current Employees

Under the ADA, examinations of current employees must be either voluntary or job-related and consistent with business necessity. Consequently, the traditional, mandatory, comprehensive, annual medical examination is now unlawful under the ADA. Although early detection of illness occasioned by these examinations has saved numerous lives over the years, Congress decided that employee interests in privacy, autonomy, and nondiscrimination were of overriding importance.

For occupational physicians, the ADA means that examinations of current employees (as well as many preplacement examinations) will be of more limited scope than in the past. From both a legal and ethical standpoint, it is essential that this fact be conveyed to examinees. Some employees who lack a sophisticated understanding of medicine may erroneously believe that they received the regular check-up, when they were given a more limited examination. If they regard passing the examination as tantamount to a clean bill of health they may forego a regular examination by their family physician. An unfortunate result could be failure to diagnose serious illness at an early stage as well as a lawsuit for malpractice. One practical approach, which benefits both examinees and physicians, is to have the examinee sign and receive a copy of a statement that clearly sets out the scope and purpose of the examination.

What the ADA Does Not Require

Although the ADA seems to place new legal responsibilities on occupational physicians, it does not change the basic common law view that there is no physician-patient relationship. As a result, individuals subject to workplace medical screening need not be informed about what tests are being performed, the purpose of the tests, the results of the tests, how and to whom test results will be given, why a conditional offer of employment was withdrawn, or the risks of workplace exposure if an offer is not withdrawn.

LIABILITY ISSUES

Even though the absence of a physician-patient relationship prevents the filing of traditional medical malpractice actions against employer-retained physicians, there are five types of cases where liability may be premised on medical screening. A separate series of actions also may be brought based on alleged negligent treatment.[19]

First, legal actions have been brought for negligence in medical screening, where the result of the physician's alleged negligent assessment was the denial of employment opportunities.[2] These lawsuits are based on common law negligence rather than a violation of the ADA. Under the ADA, only the employer, the party alleged to have improperly refused to hire the individual, may be liable. An action for negligent screening is most likely to involve independent contractor physicians. It is unlikely that a court would hold a salaried physician liable independent of his or her employer.

Second, occupational physicians have been held liable for injuries that take place during the course of an examination. These are relatively rare cases, but they include both physical injuries, such as those caused by the negligent drawing of blood,[16] and sexual misconduct during the examination.[13]

Third, examinees have alleged that negligent medical assessment led to improper job placement, which caused the plaintiff to be injured on the job.[10] Actions against employer-salaried physicians and employers are likely to be barred by workers' compensation laws,[18] but actions against independent contractor physicians are possible.

Fourth, a physician may be liable if a negligent medical assessment causes injuries to a third party. For example, a man with numerous severe impairments was nevertheless certified as fit to drive a truck in interstate commerce. A subsequent collision caused by the truck driver resulted in one death and three serious injuries. After the trucking company paid the claim of the plaintiffs, the court ordered the physician to indemnify the trucking company, which had retained his services.[27]

The fifth and most important source of liability for medical screening is an action in which a plaintiff alleges negligent failure to diagnose a serious injury or illness. The resulting delay in treatment is alleged to have aggravated the individual's condition or decreased the likelihood of successful treatment. The traditional view was that in the absence of a physician-patient relationship, the physician did not owe a duty to the examinee.[23] The drastic consequences of medical negligence in these cases, however, has convinced a few courts to impose duties on the examining physicians even if there is no physician-patient relationship.

For example, an employer hired an independent contractor physician to conduct an annual physical examination of a cook who worked on an offshore oil rig. The physician failed to diagnose the early stages of lung cancer and the employee died. In a medical malpractice action brought by the employee's widow, the court held that the employee was still owed a duty of care.

> [W]hen an individual is required, as a condition of future or continued employment, to submit to a medical examination, that examination creates a relationship between the examining physician and the examinee, at least to the extent of the tests conducted. This relationship imposes upon the examining physician a duty to conduct the requested tests and diagnose the results thereof, exercising the level of care consistent with the doctor's professional training and expertise, and to take reasonable steps to make information available timely to the examinee of any findings that pose an imminent danger to the examinee's physical or mental well-being.[12]

BILL OF RIGHTS OF EXAMINEES

Many of the legal and ethical problems outlined above would be eased and the esteem of the profession would be enhanced if occupational physicians and their employers would subscribe to and disseminate to examinees the following bill of rights.

Bill of Rights of Examinees

Each individual subjected to a medical examination at the direction of his or her employer has a right:

1. To be told the purpose and scope of the examination.
2. To be told for whom the physician works.
3. To provide informed consent for all procedures.
4. To be told how examination results will be conveyed to management.
5. To be told about confidentiality protections.
6. To be told how to obtain access to medical information in the employee's file.
7. To be referred for medical follow-up if necessary.

These modest requirements are routinely met in many clinical environments, and they are unlikely to interfere with the practice of occupational medicine. To the contrary, the Bill of Rights of Examinees should enhance cooperation and respect from the examinee as well as prevent personnel or legal disputes.

CONCLUSION

Although the medical screening of workers has changed in recent years, many of the same legal and ethical issues remain. The relationship of the physician and the examinee is not well understood by either party, and the ethical obligations of physicians working for employers often is not well understood by their employers.

The Americans with Disabilities Act has changed a number of practices in medical screening. Above all, it prohibits preemployment examinations and mandates that examinations of current employees be voluntary or limited to job-related matters. This law indirectly influences the physician-examinee relationship, but it is primarily an antidiscrimination law, not a law designed to regulate occupational physicians. Adoption of the proposed Bill of Rights of Examinees could alleviate some of the mistrust and misunderstanding that currently permeate medical screening.

REFERENCES
1. American College of Occupational and Environmental Medicine: Code of Ethical Conduct, 1993.
2. Armstrong v. Morgan, 545 S.W.2d 45 (Tex. Ct. Civ. App. 1976).

3. Beauchamp TL, Childress JF: Principles of Biomedical Ethics. 4th ed. New York, Oxford University Press, 1994.
4. 14 CFR 67.1–67.31, 1995.
5. 29 CFR 1910.1001–1910.1050, 1995.
6. 29 CFR 1910.20, 1995.
7. 49 CFR 391.41–391.49, 1995.
8. Council on Ethical and Judicial Affairs: American Medical Association, Code of Medical Ethics, sec. 5.09, 1994.
9. Equal Employment Opportunity Commission: Enforcement guidance on pre-employment inquiries under the Americans with Disabilities Act, 1994.
10. Ewing v. St. Louis-Clayton Orthopedic Group, Inc. 790 F.2d 682 (8th Cir. 1986).
11. Feldblum C: Medical examinations and inquiries under the Americans with Disabilities Act: A view from the inside. Temple L Rev 64:521–549, 1991.
12. Green v. Walker, 910 F.2d 291, 296 (5th Cir. 1990).
13. Hagan v. Antonio, 297 S.E.2d (Va. 1990).
14. Katz J: The Silent World of Doctor and Patient. New York, Free Press, 1984.
15. Keeton WP, Dobbs DB, Keeton RE, Owen DG: Prosser and Keeton on the Law of Torts. 5th ed. St. Paul, MN, West Publishing, 1984.
16. Mrachek v. Sunshine Biscuit, Inc., 123 N.E. 801 (N.Y. 1954).
17. Minnesota Statutes Annotated, sec. 363.02(1) (8) (i), 1991.
18. Nolan v. Borkowski, 538 A.2d 1031 (Conn. 1988).
19. Nolan v. Jefferson Downs, Inc., 591 So. 2d 831 (La. Ct. App.)
20. Rothstein MA: Legal issues in the medical assessment of physical impairment by third-party physicians. J Legal Med 5:503–548, 1984.
21. Rothstein MA: Medical Screening of Workers. Washington, DC, BNA Books, 1984.
22. Rothstein MA, Craver CB, Schroeder EP, et al: Employment Law. Vol. 1. St. Paul, MN,. West Publishing, 1994, pp 111–135.
23. Tomko v. Marks, 602 A.2d 890 (Pa. Super. Ct. 1992).
24. 29 USC 651–678, 1994.
25. 29 USC 701–796i, 1994.
26. 42 USC 12101–12213, 1994.
27. Wharton Transport Corp. v. Bridges, 606 S.W.2d 521 (Tenn. 1980).

NINA G. STILLMAN, JD
KAREN TAYLOR DONMOYER, JD

OCCUPATIONAL HEALTH ISSUES UNDER EMPLOYMENT DISCRIMINATION LAW

From Vedder, Price, Kaufman &
  Kammholz
Chicago, Illinois

Reprint requests to:
Nina G. Stillman, JD
Vedder, Price, Kaufman &
  Kammholz
222 North LaSalle Street
Chicago, IL 60601-1003

During the past 30 years, major societal changes have translated into statutes and regulations that have significantly altered the nature of the American workplace. Although the underlying premise of these statutory trends is to improve the occupational environment, the statutes approach this goal from different perspectives and diverse motivations. While many of these trends cohabit comfortably, others conflict, thereby creating significant problems for the employer who must seek a balance between divergent governmental policies.

State and federal legislation enacted over the past three decades has imposed on employers substantial obligations to prevent discrimination against certain classes of employees and applicants for employment. As a result of this legislation, an important factor in an employer's decision to hire, discharge, promote, or otherwise place an employee or applicant must be whether the individual is a member of a legally protected class. To date, Congress has afforded specific protection to members of our society on the basis of race,[1] sex,[2] pregnancy,[3] religion,[4] disability,[5] age,[6] veteran status,[7] national origin,[8] and citizenship.[9] Most states also offer these protections,[10] and some provide even more expanded coverage.[11]

During this same period, another national concern—the desire to make workplaces safer and healthier—found its way onto the national legislative agenda with the passage of the Occupational Safety and Health Act of 1970.[12]

The focus of this chapter is the conflicts that have developed between employment discrimination and occupational safety and health laws and the manner in which the courts and enforcement agencies have attempted to harmonize these competing interests. The tensions between these interests have arisen in various circumstances. With respect to women, attention has been focused on the pregnant employee and on the fertile female placed in physically demanding or potentially fetotoxic occupational environments. With respect to the aging worker, the concern has been the physically stressful or public safety position. This conflict between health and safety concerns and the prevention of discrimination also has influenced resolution of workplace violence and ergonomic issues.

SEX DISCRIMINATION ISSUES

The employment discrimination laws of the last three decades reflect a complete turn-about from early 20th century state statutes designed to prevent employment abuses of a different sort. During the Industrial Revolution, a 72-hour work week was commonly imposed on all workers, including women and children, who often worked in such physically demanding jobs as mining, steel production, glass blowing, and textile manufacturing.

In 1905 the United States Supreme Court ruled that states could not prescribe working conditions for places of private employment.[13] Three years later, however, the court reversed itself in the landmark case of *Muller v. Oregon.*[14] By upholding a state statute imposing a 10-hour workday limit for women, the court in *Muller* invited the states to enact protective legislation not only for women but for all workers. The states were quick to react and within a few years many had enacted statutes regarding maximum hours, weight-lifting limits, and mandatory rest periods for women.

Looking back from a late 20th century perspective, some historians have come to view such protective legislation as thinly veiled discrimination against women workers. However, a more historically accurate analysis shows that passage of the early 20th century protective legislation for women was part of a larger struggle to improve working conditions for all employees. The leaders of this movement correctly recognized that initial efforts to improve working conditions for all were best directed at the plight of working women and children. Soon thereafter, the basic protections enacted for female workers were almost uniformly extended to males, although some pockets of gender-specific workplace regulation persisted.

Fifty years later, very different interests drove the enactment of current equal employment opportunity laws. With the passage of Title VII of the Civil Rights Act in 1964, including its prohibition against sex discrimination in employment, the Equal Employment Opportunity Commission began to undermine the protective state legislation that it viewed as an obstacle to full workplace equality for women.

Regulations promulgated by the EEOC explicitly provide that protective laws for women "conflict with and are superseded by Title VII" and "will not be considered a defense to an otherwise established unlawful employment practice or as a basis for the application of the bona fide occupational exception."[15] The EEOC's rationale, supported by the courts, is that state protective laws and regulations "do not take into account the capacities, preferences, and abilities of individual females and, therefore, discriminate on the basis of sex."[16]

The first conflict between the newly enacted sex discrimination laws and a perceived occupational health concern involved the assignment of women workers to physically demanding jobs. Musculoskeletal differences between men and women create demonstrable differences in strength and physical ability between the sexes. Due to general perceptions regarding these differences, employers tended to make conclusive presumptions regarding a woman's ability to perform specific tasks without considering each individual woman's unique capacities, preferences, and abilities. In making unwarranted conclusive presumptions, employers engaged in prohibited sex-based stereotyping.

In the first decade following passage of the Civil Rights Act, courts struck down broad employment policies against hiring women for positions involving heavy labor.[17] The courts similarly invalidated employers' minimum height and weight requirements that, without explicitly excluding women from eligibility for certain jobs, had the effect of excluding a disproportionate percentage of women and, in some cases, Hispanics and Asians.[18] In 1977, the United States Supreme Court, in *Dothard v. Rawlinson*, held that an employment policy imposing minimum height and weight requirements for the job of prison guard violated Title VII because the requirements disproportionately excluded women from eligibility for employment and the employer failed to establish a correlation between an applicant's height and weight and the amount of strength thought essential to job performance.[19]

Although the law does not permit employers to make conclusive presumptions about a woman's ability or preference, it also does not require the employer to hire a woman who is physically incapable of performing the job sought.[20] Thus, although courts will generally overturn height and weight requirements, an employer may require an employee or applicant to demonstrate that he or she is able to perform the job properly. This use of preplacement testing was virtually invited by the Supreme Court in its *Dothard* decision:

> If the job-related quality that the appellants identify is bona fide, their purpose could be achieved by adopting and validating a test for applicants that measures strength directly. Such a test, fairly administered, would fully satisfy the standards of Title VII because it would be one that *measures the person for the job and not the person in the abstract* [emphasis added].[21]

Courts have shown a willingness to uphold preplacement tests of physical agility and strength where they (a) are job related and consistent with business necessity, (b) are nondiscriminatorily administered,[22] and (c) can be validated through one of the legally acceptable validation methods.

Most of the cases thus far addressing the issue of physical testing have involved tests administered by local public employers in connection with police officer and firefighter positions. Typically, the employer expended considerable time, money, and effort developing what was thought to be a job-related test. Nevertheless, the courts reviewing such tests have struck them down where they disproportionately excluded women and the tests were not professionally validated in conformance with the Uniform Guidelines of Employee Selection Procedures jointly issued in 1977 by the Departments of Justice and Labor, the EEOC, and the United States Civil Service Commission.[23] Although formal validation studies are not required to satisfy the job-related/business necessity standard, an employer bears a greater burden of persuasion on this issue in the absence of such a study or analysis.[24]

The second battle between sex discrimination laws and occupational health concerns was fought for almost a decade over pregnant workers, resulting in passage of the Pregnancy Disability Act of 1978.[25] The PDA amends the Civil Rights Act of 1964 by making the Title VII prohibition of sex discrimination in employment specifically applicable to discrimination against pregnant women. The PDA's conclusion that discrimination on the basis of pregnancy is synonymous with discrimination on the basis of sex did not inevitably flow from the language of other sex discrimination statutes and regulations. In fact, it was not until 1972 that the EEOC expressly addressed the issue of pregnant workers in its Guidelines on Discrimination Because of Sex, taking the position that it was unlawful sex discrimination to exclude pregnancy-related disabilities from employer-provided disability insurance (wage continuation) plans.[26] In its 1972 guidelines, the EEOC reversed the position espoused by a former EEOC general counsel, who wrote in 1966 that the EEOC did not "believe that an employer must provide the same fringe benefits for pregnancy as he provides for illness."[27]

The law with respect to pregnancy evolved through a series of cases during the 1970s and was generally codified with the enactment of the PDA in 1978. However, the differing case results, depending on the specific issue presented, led to considerable confusion, if not frustration. For example, broad employment policies that imposed mandatory discharge or leave for pregnant employees generally did not withstand a sex discrimination challenge. Thus, in *Cleveland Board of Education v. LaFleur*,[28] the Supreme Court ruled unconstitutional a public employer's policy that required pregnant teachers to go on unpaid leave 5 months before the expected birth and not to return until 3 months after the birth. However, in *General Electric Co. v. Gilbert*,[29] the Supreme Court reversed the position taken by the EEOC in its 1972 guidelines, ruling that Title VII did not require employers to include pregnancy-related disabilities in their disability insurance plans. It was this climate of uncertainty that finally led to passage of the PDA with its expressed intent to address pregnancy as a sex discrimination issue.

The current state of the law with respect to pregnancy prohibits employment policies that make broad generalizations about the ability of pregnant workers to continue working. However, the law does not prohibit employers from making individualized evaluations of pregnant workers to determine their ability to carry out specific job-related tasks. For example, many employers had long required female workers to obtain certification from their personal physicians that they were physically able to continue their work while pregnant or to return to work after childbirth. The PDA does not require employers to discontinue this practice if—but only if—a similar practice is followed for all employees who have diabetes, epilepsy, angina pectoris, and other nonpregnant conditions that may affect their ability to work safely. If certification of fitness-for-duty is made optional, the employer must be careful not to exercise that option only in cases of pregnancy.

Employers may also require (a) that the certification of fitness obtained from a pregnant worker's personal physician be reviewed by another physician familiar with the stressors of the working environment; and/or (b) that workers submit to an independent medical examination and evaluation of their health and fitness by an occupational or other appropriate physician. Again, however, Title VII would prohibit a policy that requires only pregnant workers, and not workers with other potentially disabling conditions, to undergo this independent evaluation. If it is medically determined that maternity leave is necessary, employers must also provide disability benefits for the duration of the mandatory leave if such benefits would have been provided for any other disability.[30]

The third battleground pitting equal employment policies against occupational health policies involves workplace hazards to the fetus. Because some occupational exposures may alter the reproductive capabilities of male workers, this issue cannot be entirely confined to females. However, in workplaces that increase the risk of fetal exposure to teratogens or transplacental carcinogens or in those that present unique stressors to the developing fetus, any policy designed to protect the fetus will inevitably be sex-specific to the mother. The employer whose workplace contains the potential for fetotoxic exposure faces the potential for liability from a number of sources. First, even if the toxin is not regulated by a specific standard promulgated under the Occupational Safety and Health Act and even if no employee has suffered actual harm, the employer could be subject to a citation from the Occupational Safety and Health Administration for violation of the act's general duty clause, which obligates an employer to "furnish each of his employees employment and a place of employment which are free from recognized hazards that are causing or are likely to cause death or serious physical harm to his employees."[31] Second, an employee who is injured by exposure to an agent in the workplace may seek recovery under a state worker's compensation statute or other state occupational illness law.

However, a more complicated issue of potential liability arises when it is the employee's unborn child, rather than the employee, who is injured by exposure to an occupational toxin. Injuries to a fetus, or even to an ultimately born child not yet conceived at the time of the damaging exposure, could subject an employer to substantial liability under a common law tort (personal injury) theory.[32] However, despite the significant health and safety concerns and the potential for liability presented by this situation, current sex discrimination laws substantially limit an employer's ability to take any protective action that will restrict the employment opportunities of the mother. Thus, while a number of courts have found that an airline's concern for passenger safety can justify an employment policy temporarily requiring pregnant flight attendants to take a leave of absence of transfer to ground duties,[33] these protective policies have been struck down as sexually discriminatory when only the employee's or her unborn child's safety is at issue.

Before the Supreme Court finally addressed the legality of fetal protection policies in *International Union, UAW v. Johnson Controls*,[34] five federal appellate courts considered the question of whether such policies violated sex discrimination laws. Two of these cases involved employer policies that required the termination of employment of pregnant x-ray technicians. The Fifth Circuit found that the employer's action violated Title VII; the court emphasized that less restrictive alternatives such as the temporary transfer of pregnant technicians were available.[35] The Eleventh Circuit similarly found that the employer violated Title VII, but this appellate court acknowledged that it would have accepted a discharge policy if the employer had limited the pregnant technicians' employment opportunities only in the event of an unreasonable risk to the fetus.[36]

The three other appellate decisions that predated the Supreme Court's *Johnson Controls* opinion all involved policies that excluded fertile female employees from specified jobs with potentially fetotoxic exposures. Although the Fourth and Sixth Circuits found the exclusionary policies before them to be discriminatory, they acknowledged that reasonable policies applying to all fertile women might be allowed.[37] Apparently believing it had such a policy before it, the Seventh Circuit, in its *Johnson Controls* decision, held that the battery manufacturer's fetal protection policy, which excluded women of childbearing capacity from jobs involving lead exposure, did not violate Title VII.[38] On appeal, however, the Supreme Court reversed, finding that the policy unlawfully discriminated against women on the basis of their sex in violation of Title VII.[39] The fact that the employer might ultimately be liable in tort to a damaged fetus was not considered by the Supreme Court to be a sufficiently compelling reason to justify the sexually discriminatory exclusion of women from the designated jobs. Although it acknowledged that many states recognized the right of a person to recover for prenatal injuries, the court rather cavalierly concluded that, if an employer were to follow applicable OSHA standards to minimize risks to fetuses and were to fully inform women of the potential risks of the job, its liability would appear "remote at best."[40]

Given the legal constraints on an employer's ability to mandate protective measures for its pregnant employees and their fetuses, an employer who discovers the existence of a fetotoxin in the working environment must determine whether protective measures are available (e.g., engineering or work practice controls or, as a last resort, personal protective equipment) to prevent or reduce the hazardous exposure short of employee exclusion. Furthermore, the employer, preferably with the assistance of a health care provider, must thoroughly educate and inform employees of the reproductive risks associated with the job and the availability of alternative measures to reduce those risks,[41] such as a temporary transfer without loss of pay or benefits to another "safe" or "low-risk" position.[42]

AGE DISCRIMINATION ISSUES

Due to advances in medicine and improvements in overall physical fitness, many workers are physically capable of remaining in the workforce longer than ever before. For reasons of personal preference or economic necessity, many older workers now seek to delay retirement. In response to this desire of older employees to continue working, Congress passed the Age Discrimination in Employment Act of 1967,[43] which prohibits employers from discriminating on the basis of age against employees or applicants older than 40.[44]

As with statutes that proscribe discrimination against women, the ADEA does not require an employer to hire an older person who is physically incapable of performing the available job. However, an employer cannot presume conclusively that an applicant, due to age, is incapable of performing a particular job.

A separate issue arises when an employer is confronted with an aging employee whose productivity has fallen or who can no longer perform more strenuous job tasks. The ADEA does not require that an employer retain an employee who is no longer physically able to perform adequately, but employers must avoid subjective age-based assumptions that relate age to job performance. Whenever possible, objective criteria and measures should be used to document that job performance has fallen below acceptable levels. For example, instead of relying on the unsupported opinion of an assembly-line supervisor regarding an older employee's infirmity, the employer should qualitatively or quantitatively compare the older employee's performance with that of the least acceptable younger coworker. Such a comparison would help to prevent the obviously discriminatory act of requiring a higher level of performance for an older worker than is required of a less productive, but still acceptable younger coworker.

As with the statutes that prohibit discrimination on the basis of sex, federal and state age discrimination statutes (as construed by the courts) recognize that in very limited situations age can be a bona fide occupational qualification (BFOQ) that an employer may assert in defense of a claim of age discrimination. The Supreme Court and lower federal courts have embraced a two-prong inquiry in evaluating a BFOQ defense in age cases.[45] First, an employer must establish that the job qualification it invokes to justify age discrimination is reasonably necessary to the essence of the business. The purpose of the reasonably necessary factor is to eliminate as rationales for age discrimination those job qualifications that are peripheral to the central mission of an employer's business.[46]

Under the second prong of the inquiry, an employer must demonstrate that it is compelled to rely on age as a proxy for the essential job qualifications validated by the first inquiry. This second prong can be established by showing either that (a) the employer had reasonable cause to believe (a factual basis for believing) that substantially all people over a particular age cannot safely or efficiently perform the duties in question or (b) it would be impossible or impractical to determine job fitness of those over the age limit on an individual basis.[47]

This BFOQ defense is quite limited and narrow.[48] However, when there is an overriding public safety concern, some courts have concluded that the level of proof required to establish the "reasonable necessity" of a BFOQ is lower.[49] Indeed, the greater the need for safety—measured by the likelihood of harm and the probable severity of that harm in the case of an accident—the more stringent the challenged job qualification may be.[50] Thus, virtually all successful invocations of the BFOQ defense have involved demonstrations that a particular age-related job qualification was reasonably necessary because public safety was the "essence" of the employer's business.[51] Not surprisingly, therefore, almost all the successful BFOQ cases have involved protective service (police and firefighters) or transportation (bus drivers and airplane pilots) jobs in which public safety concerns are highly correlated to an individual's ability to perform assigned tasks.

One of the first decisions to rely on this two-prong inquiry involved a challenge to a maximum age restriction on the hire of bus drivers. In that case, a commercial bus company successfully defended its blanket policy of refusing to hire interstate bus drivers over the age of 35 by convincing a federal court of appeals that its age-based policy was related to the essence of its business—the safety of its passengers.[52] The company presented convincing evidence that increasing age is accompanied by increased reflex time and degenerative physical changes that prevent older drivers from performing their duties optimally. Because pre-hire medical testing cannot practically and reliably measure these degenerative characteristics on an individual basis, the employer was entitled to rely on age as a proxy to exclude applicants older than 35.

Importantly, other employers of bus drivers cannot simply rely on the *Usery* decision to support the validity of their own age-based policies. A prior judicial determination that a specific age is a valid BFOQ for one employer-defendant does not control other actions under the ADEA.[53] Congress intended individualized determinations of the validity of a specific age as a BFOQ.[54] Thus, in other cases involving similar age restrictions for bus drivers, courts have rejected proffered BFOQs where employers failed to produce sufficient scientific or medical evidence that age was a necessary proxy for the job qualification.[55]

Employers also cannot merely rely on federal or state laws that mandate age restrictions for conclusive evidence of a BFOQ. They must provide independent factual evidence showing the need to rely on age as a proxy for a job requirement. For example, the Supreme Court found that a provision in the federal civil service statute requiring most federal firefighters to retire at age 55 excluded only federal firefighters from the protection of the ADEA and did not prove that age 55 was a BFOQ allowing a nonfederal employer to mandate retirement for its firefighters.[56] In rejecting the nonfederal employer's age limit, the court raised the possibility that the federal rule is not a BFOQ, but merely an example of "the sort of age stereotyping without factual basis that was one of the primary targets of the reforms of the Act."[57]

A rule promulgated by the Federal Aviation Administration mandating retirement of all commercial airline pilots at age 60 has been the source of much BFOQ litigation.[58] The FAA supports the rule as a safety measure for passengers because medical studies show that heart attacks or strokes are more frequent in men approaching age 60, and medical science cannot accurately detect or predict which men are at risk.[59] Appellate courts have upheld the rule's application in cases brought by covered pilots seeking exemptions,[60] but they have not yet permitted use of the rule as a sufficient legal basis for employers to mandate retirement of pilots not covered by it.[61] The Supreme Court has not addressed the validity of the rule as a BFOQ.

The validity of BFOQs based on state or local laws that mandate retirement for police and firefighters is also in a state of flux. In 1986, Congress exempted state and local agencies from claims of age discrimination if they had laws regarding mandatory retirement age for police and firefighters in effect as of March 3, 1983.[62] The exemption, however, expired on January 1, 1994, and Congress has not yet restored it.[63] Meanwhile, the EEOC has stated that "there is no certainty that the exemption will be restored" and, in the interim, has begun actively to challenge state and city age requirements for police and firefighters.[64]

Challenges to mandatory retirement policies have generally been unsuccessful when brought under the equal protection clause of the United States Constitution. For example, the Supreme Court upheld a Massachusetts statute that required state troopers to retire at age 50 even though the plaintiff trooper was in excellent physical condition.[65] The Supreme Court also has upheld a mandatory retirement provision of the Foreign Service Act of 1946.[66] The court reasoned that "the foreign service involves extended overseas duty under difficult and often hazardous conditions and that the wear and tear on members of this corps is such that there comes a time when these posts should be filled by younger persons. Mandatory retirement, it is said, minimizes the risk of less than superior performance by reason of poor health or lack of vitality."[67]

Because these decisions were based on equal protection grounds, the court focused on whether the age restriction was rationally related to a legitimate governmental purpose. Meeting the "rationale relationship" standard, however, may be easier than meeting the more demanding BFOQ standard under the ADEA. In fact, the plaintiffs in one case simultaneously sought relief under the ADEA and on equal protection grounds. Although the lower court dismissed both claims, the plaintiffs successfully resurrected their ADEA claim on appeal when the Supreme Court found that the challenged age requirement did not qualify as a BFOQ under the ADEA.[68]

As the law regarding age discrimination develops, older employees who are no longer physically able to perform the job due to infirmities brought on by age may be viewed as "disabled," thereby triggering protection under the Rehabilitation Act of 1973[63] or the Americans with Disabilities Act.[70] These laws require the employer to reasonably accommodate employees if doing so would not cause undue hardship to the employer's normal business. In the future, principals of reasonable accommodation could provide much broader protection to aging workers than is provided under the ADEA. For example, while an employer might be justified in terminating employment of an older worker under the ADEA when the employee is no longer physically able to perform his job, under the ADA the employer could be required to reasonably accommodate that same employee by modifying the job or possibly even transferring the employee.

DISABILITY DISCRIMINATION

The most recently enacted federal employment discrimination statute is the Americans with Disabilities Act, which protects qualified disabled individuals who can perform the essential functions of the job in question with a reasonable accommodation. This 1990 law has had significant impact on the American workplace. As with earlier employment discrimination legislation, the ADA has brought into conflict the goals of the EEOC (the agency charged with enforcement of the ADA) and OSHA (the agency with enforcement responsibility for the OSHAct). This problem of conflicting goals has been increasingly troublesome for those concerned with violence in the workplace and ergonomics.

In 1993, OSHA issued its first general duty clause citation for workplace violence. Thereafter, a number of similar citations issued against employers who, despite repeated warnings, failed to protect their employees from violence in the workplace. As part of the proposed abatement for these citations, OSHA recommended that employers implement programs to provide for early identification of individuals with a past history of violent or aggressive behavior. Unfortunately, some employers have discovered that pursuit of OSHA goals may lead to violations of the ADA.

Under the ADA, the employer must reasonably accommodate, and may not discriminate against, qualified individuals with disabilities. This includes mental or emotional disabilities. If, however, the qualified disabled person would pose a direct threat to his or her own health or safety[72] or the health or safety of others,[73] the individual need not be employed. The term *direct threat* is defined in the ADA as a significant risk of substantial harm that cannot be eliminated by reasonable accommodation.[74]

Any conclusion that an individual poses a direct threat must be based on (a) a careful review of the individual's current, actual condition and not upon generalizations or stereotypes about the disability,[75] (b) the current ability of the applicant or employee to safely perform in the position and not upon the likelihood that the risk might increase with the passage of time,[76] (c) "reasonable *medical* judgment that relies on the most current medical knowledge and/or the best available objective evidence,"[77] and (d) a consideration of reasonable accommodations that would eliminate the risk or reduce it to acceptable levels.[78] ADA regulations also provide a list of factors to be considered in determining whether an individual would pose a direct threat, including (1) the duration of the risk, (2) the nature and severity of the potential harm, (3) the likelihood that the harm will occur, and (4) the imminence of that harm.[79]

Accordingly, an employer who refuses to hire, or fires, a disabled person because of a risk of physical harm to other employees may be the target of an ADA lawsuit by that person. Recent cases highlight the problem of taking action against potential perpetrators of violence. For example, a federal district court held that the United States Postal Service violated the Rehabilitation Act of 1973 when it terminated employment of a postal worker with post-traumatic stress disorder because it feared the employee might become violent.[80] Even though one of the employee's supervisors and his subordinates described him as mentally unstable and capable of a shooting spree, the court found that the employee was coping appropriately with his stress and was otherwise qualified for his job. The court further found that he was dismissed solely because of his employer's fear that he could be violent. Since this fear was based on his employer's belief and not a medical opinion, the court concluded that the employer's fear was insufficient justification for the discharge.

By contrast, in *Gordon v. Runyon*,[81] a part-time mail handler at the post office was fired after he verbally assaulted a nurse, acted in a threatening manner, and was found to possess mace and a stun gun on postal property. Gordon sued under the Rehabilitation Act for wrongful discharge. The court granted the employer's motion for summary judgment because the employer successfully established that it could not reasonably accommodate the employee's mental disability without compromising safety in the workplace. The court agreed with the employer that Gordon was fired, not because of his mental disability, but because of his disruptive conduct and because he possessed a concealed, dangerous weapon in violation of federal law. The court concluded that Gordon presented an "increased potential threat to the safety of postal employees" by carrying the mace and the stun gun. The court also agreed with the employer that it would be unduly burdensome to accommodate Gordon's disability in light of his history of abusive and potentially threatening conduct toward supervisors and coworkers. (In the past, Gordon had hit his supervisor on the head with a parcel tub, used abusive language, and engaged in physically threatening behavior toward coworkers.) Thus, the court concluded that Gordon could not perform his job as a mail handler.

In *Hindman v. GTE Data Services, Inc.*,[82] the plaintiff was fired for unauthorized possession of a firearm after he arrived at work with a loaded gun. Suing under the ADA, Hindman claimed that he was fired for being "disabled" because he suffered from a chemical imbalance that resulted in a mental, psychological, and physiologic disorder. The district court denied the employer's motion for summary judgment.[83] The court rejected the employer's argument that Hindman merely exercised poor judgment in bringing the gun to work and that poor judgment was not a disability within the meaning of the ADA. Personality traits such as poor judgment are considered disabilities when they are symptoms of a mental or psychological disorder that is a disability under the ADA. The court held that the question of whether Hindman's misconduct (bringing the gun to work) was caused by his disability was a question of fact to be decided at trial. The court also rejected the employer's argument that Hindman was not qualified for his job because he posed a "direct threat" to the health and safety of others. The court noted that a successful "direct threat" defense requires an employer to prove that an employee poses "a significant risk as opposed to a slightly increased risk of substantial harm to the health or safety of the individual or others that cannot be eliminated or reduced by reasonable accommodation."[84] The court held that whether Hindman posed a direct threat was a factual issue for a jury to determine. Based on the court's ruling, the case proceeded to trial. After the plaintiff presented his evidence, the court ruled for the employer because there was no legally sufficient basis for a reasonable jury to find that the employer violated the ADA.[85] Rejecting the plaintiff's claim that he suffered from a chemical imbalance, the court relied on the fact that the employee violated his employer's work rules. Moreover, the court noted that the employer did not know of Hindman's alleged disability until after it decided to discharge him.

Ergonomics is the second major area where employers find themselves caught between the Scylla of workplace safety and Charybdis of disability accommodation. The impact of law on ergonomics began in the mid 1980s when state industrial commissions began to uphold claims that employees' carpal tunnel syndrome, epicondylitis, tendinitis, trigger finger, tenosynovitis, ganglion cyst, and other so-called cumulative trauma disorders (CTDs) or repetitive strain injuries (RSIs) were work-related and therefore compensable.

With the recognition of such injuries or illnesses as work-related by state workers' compensation commissions, employers felt compelled to record these claims on their OSHA 200 logs or risk liability under the OSHAct for failing to meet OSHA's record-keeping obligations.[86] The sudden, dramatic increase of such recorded injuries and illnesses inevitably attracted the attention of OSHA. In the late 1980s, the agency began its ergonomics initiative, focusing initially on the meatpacking industry, then the baking, poultry, and auto industries, and eventually extended to general industry, including retailing and financial services.

Although an OSHA standard has not yet been promulgated to regulate alleged ergonomic hazards, OSHA has used the general duty clause as the legal predicate for the agency's enforcement effort.[87] However, ADA places employers in another vise between the conflicting goals of two federal enforcement agencies.

For example, OSHA has expressly advocated that employers screen applicants for susceptibility to CTDs and not return employees to the same job in which they purportedly experienced a CTD.[88] However, employers who attempt to comply with these OSHA mandates will now find themselves at risk of ADA liability.

Under the ADA, employers cannot medically screen applicants for the heightened potential of illness or injury in the workplace.[89] Furthermore, if the treating physician states that a previously injured employee may return to work without restrictions, the ADA requires the employer to return that employee to the job unless it can prove that the releasing physician does not understand the stressors of the job that pose a direct threat to the employee's residual medical condition.[90] Although the ADA provides an exemption for medical examinations mandated by a specific OSHA standard,[91] there is no OSHA ergonomics standard at this time. Thus, the ADA exemption does not apply.

A second ADA/OSHAct conflict arises when employers attempt to limit their OSH Act and workers' compensation liability by screening for carpal tunnel syndrome—a position clearly endorsed by OSHA during the late 1980s.[92] (The agency now somewhat disingenuously states that screening for carpal tunnel syndrome should not be used for exclusionary purposes.) However, unless an employer has a vast reservoir of jobs (particularly entry level jobs) that do not involve activities and operations identified by OSHA as ergonomic hazards or stressors, there is little purpose in such screening other than for selection and for exclusion. Indeed, the EEOC has concluded that such screening is a violation of the ADA.[93]

CONCLUSION

This chapter identifies some of the problems created for employers when different national goals—equal employment opportunity and occupational safety and health—collide. Although the resulting legal conflicts were largely unintended, this is of no comfort to the employer who is caught between the competing policy agendas. Employment law is, however, constantly evolving and altering the relationship between employers and employees, often in unexpected and sometimes in conflicting ways. Arguably, this body of law presently overemphasizes the individual's desire and immediate capacity to work at the expense of perceived hazards to the future health of the employee or his or her progeny. However, in favoring the short-term desires of the employee, current law correctly condemns subjective employer presumptions—whether from the basest prejudice or the sincerest concern—that an individual in a protected class cannot, or should not, be placed in the working environment for which he or she is qualified. In any event, until the conflicts addressed in this chapter are resolved, any decision to exclude a protected class member from eligibility for certain employment based on health or safety considerations must be supported by a reasonable medical opinion in light of the specific facts involved. Any approach short of this will place an employer at substantial risk of liability.

REFERENCES

1. Title VII of the Civil Rights Act of 1964, as amended, 42 USC §§ 2000e *et seq.*; Civil Rights Act of 1866, 42 USC § 1981; Exec. Order No. 11246, as amended.
2. Equal Pay Act of 1963, 29 USC § 206; Title VII of the Civil Rights Act of 1964, as amended, 42 USC §§ 2000e *et seq.*; Executive Order No. 11246, as amended.
3. 42 USC § 2000e(k).
4. Title VII of the Civil Rights Act of 1964, as amended, 42 USC §§ 2000e *et seq.*; Exec. Order No. 11246, as amended.
5. Rehabilitation Act of 1973, 29 USC §§ 701 *et seq.*; Americans with Disabilities Act of 1990; 42 USC §§ 12101 *et seq.*
6. Age Discrimination in Employment Act of 1967, 29 USC §§ 621 *et seq.*, as amended.
7. Uniformed Services Employment and Reemployment Rights Act of 1994, 38 USC §§ 4301 *et seq.*
8. Title VII of Civil Rights Act of 1964, as amended, 42 USC §§ 2000e *et seq.*; Exec. Order No. 11246, as amended.
9. Immigration Reform and Control Act of 1986, 8 USC § 1324b.
10. See state fair employment laws set forth in Fair Empl. Prac. Manual (BNA) (State Law Guide).
11. For example, Illinois prohibits discrimination on the basis of marital status and unfavorable military discharge. 775 ICLS §§ 5/101 *et seq.* Florida, Louisiana and North Carolina prohibit discrimination in employment based on the sickle cell trait. Fla. Stat. Ann. §§ 448.075 *et seq.*; La. Rev. Stat. Ann. §§ 23:1001 *et seq.*; N.C. Gen. Stat. § 95-28.1.
12. 29 USC § 651 *et seq.*
13. *Lochner v. New York*, 198 US 45 (1905).
14. 208 US 412 (1908).
15. 29 CFR § 1604.2(b)(1). A bona fide occupational qualification (BFOQ) is an exception Title VII carves out where a particular sex, religion or national origin "is a bona fide occupational qualification reasonably necessary to the normal operation of that particular business or enterprise" (42 USC 2000e-2(e)(1)). In the case of sex discrimination, the EEOC narrowly authorizes a BFOQ "[w]here it is necessary for the purpose of authenticity or genuineness . . . e.g., an actor or actress" (29 CFR § 1604.2(a)(iii)(2)).
16. *Id.*
17. *Weeks v. Southern Bell Telephone & Telegraph Co.*, 408 F.2d 228, (5th Cir. 1969) (court struck down policy against hiring women for switch operator position because job required routine lifting of 30-pound weights); *see also Rosenfeld v. Southern Pacific Co.*, 444 F.2d 1219 (9th Cir. 1971) (court found employment policy of denying women certain jobs because of their arduous nature to be violative of Title VII); *Local 246, Util. Worker's Union of Am., AFL-CIO v. Southern California Edison Co.*, 320 F. Supp. 1262 (C.D. Cal. 1970) (California statute prohibiting female employees from lifting over 50 pounds is invalid).
18. *Meadows v. Ford Motor Co.*, 62 FRD 98 (W.D. Ky. 1973), *cert. denied*, 425 US 998 (150 pound minimum weight requirement for production line job is discriminatory); *Horace v. City of Pontiac*, 624 F.2d 765 (6th Cir. 1980) (minimum height requirement for police officers found discriminatory against women); *US v. City of Buffalo*, 457 F. Supp. 612 (W.D. N.Y. 1978), *aff'd as modified*, 633 F.2d 643 (2nd Cir. 1980) (height and weight requirements, although revised to reflect relative differences between men and women, found to have adverse impact on women and Hispanics and were not validated as job-related); *Officers for Justice v. The Civil Serv. Comm'n*, 473 F. Supp. 801 (N.D. Cal. 1979), *aff'd*, 688 F.2d 615 (1982), *cert. denied*, 459 US 1217 (1983) (minimum height requirement presented *prima facie* case of discrimination against women, Hispanics, and Asians).
19. *Dothard v. Rawlinson*, 433 US 321, 332, (1977).
20. The Americans with Disabilities Act, discussed later in this chapter and in other chapters of this book, requires employers to reasonably accommodate qualified disabled persons of either sex.
21. 433 US at 332 (1977).
22. For example, if the position sought requires frequent lifting of 30-pound weights, an employer might reasonably require that the employee or applicant for employment show that he or she can lift 30-pound weights with regularity; however, an employer would be vulnerable to a charge of discrimination if this preplacement strength test were required only of female applicants.
23. 142 Fed Reg 65542 (Dec. 30, 1977). The three basic studies used to validate tests are the content va-

lidity study, the construct validity study, and the criterion-related study. The content validity study is used where a test directly measures an ability that is a prerequisite for entry-level job performance, i.e., a typing test for a typist position. This study, accordingly, focuses on the skill content of the job and a test will likely be regarded as valid if the performance required by the test is essentially the same as that required on the job. The criterion-related study uses empirical data to demonstrate that "the selection procedure is predictive of or significantly correlated with important elements of job performance." In other words, a test is likely to be validated if it is a good predictor of success on the job. The construct validity study is used with respect to tests that measure abstract, unquantifiable qualities. A test subject to this study will likely be validated if it "measures the degree to which candidates have identifiable characteristics which have been determined to be important to successful performance of the job."

24. *LeGault v. Russo*, 842 F. Supp. 1479 (D.C. N.H. 1994) (in injunctive proceedings, court noted that fire department's agility and obstacle course tests which had a disparate impact on women were not content valid where job analysis was primarily based on several-year-old job specification that described fire fighter duties generally); *US v. Wichita Falls*, 704 F. Supp. 709 (N.D. Tex. 1988) (police test that faithfully imitated the crucial tasks performed by police officers was upheld despite the lack of a formal, written validation study where test contained all elements required by a formal content validation study: subjects were typical candidates for the job, the standard could be satisfied by current police officers, current officers were subjected to the same test and their scores recorded, and the tests were administered in controlled conditions); *Burnet v. City of Columbus*, 642 F. Supp. 1214 (S.D. Ohio 1986) (physical test that narrowly focused on strength rather than the range of abilities involved in the job performance of a fire fighter was struck down); *US v. City and County of San Francisco*, 51 Fair Empl. Prac. Cas. (BNA) 1187 (N.D. Cal. 1986) (in injunctive proceedings, court recognized likelihood that fire department's physical skills examination which had disparate impact on women was not job-related where in formulating test, interviews rather than actual observation and measurement were used to assess physical requirements of job); *Thomas v. City of Evanston*, 610 F. Suppl. 422 (N.D. Ill. 1985) (physical agility test for police positions which had disparate impact on women was struck down where employer failed to demonstrate or document that it had conducted a thorough job analysis in creating the test).

25. 42 USC § 2000e(k).
26. 37 Fed Reg 6835.
27. This EEOC opinion letter, dated November 15, 1966, was identified and placed into evidence by former EEOC General Counsel Charles Duncan during the trial of *Gilbert v. General Electric Co.*, 375 F. Supp. 367 (E.D. Va. 1974), *aff'd*, 519 F.2d 661 (4th Cir. 1975), *rev'd*, 429 US 125 (1976). It stated, in part:

> The Commission's policy with respect to pregnancy does not seek to compare an employer's treatment of illness or injury with his treatment of maternity, since maternity is a temporary disability unique to the female sex and more or less to be anticipated during the working life of most women employees . . . We do not believe that an employer must provide the same fringe benefits for pregnancy as he provides for illness.

28. 414 US 632 (1974).
29. 429 US 125 (1976).
30. EEOC Guidelines on Sex Discrimination, 29 CFR § 1604 "Questions and Answers on the Pregnancy Discrimination Act."
31. 29 USC § 654(a)(1).
32. *See, e.g., Thompson v. Pizza Hut of Am., Inc.*, 767 F. Supp. 916, 917-18 (N.D. Ill. 1991) (personal injury action to recover for injuries allegedly suffered in vitro by child when mother exposed to carbon monoxide fumes at work); *Jarvis v. Providence Hosp.*, 444 N.W.2d 236, 238 (Mich. Ct. App. 1989) (tort action for fetal death allegedly resulting from mother's contraction of hepatitis while working in laboratory during pregnancy).
33. *Levin v. Delta Airlines*, 730 F.2d 994 (5th Cir. 1984); *Burell v. Eastern Airlines*, 633 F.2d 361 (4th Cir. 1980), *cert. denied*, 450 US 965 (1981); *Harriss v. Pan American World Airways, Inc.*, 649 F.2d 670 (9th Cir. 1980); *MacLennan v. American Airlines*, 440 F. Supp. 466 (E.D. Va. 1977).
34. *Intern. Union, UAW v. Johnson Controls, Inc.*, 499 US 187 (1991).
35. *Zvinga v. Kleberg County Hosp.*, 692 F.2d 986 (1982).
36. *Hayes v. Shelby Memorial Hosp.*, 726 F.2d 1543 (11th Cir. 1984).
37. *Grant v. General Motors Corp.*, 908 F.2d 1303 (6th Cir. 1990); *Wright v. Olin*, 697 F.2d 1172 (4th Cir. 1982).
38. *Intern. Union, UAW v. Johnson Controls, Inc.* 886 F.2d 871, 901 (7th Cir. 1989) (en banc), *rev'd*, 499 US 187 (1991).

39. *Johnson Controls, Inc.*, 499 US 187 (1991).
40. *Id.* Arguably, this decision leaves open the question of whether a strong likelihood of substantial tort liability would provide a basis for a BFOQ defense.
41. As a consequence of being more fully apprised of risks by their employers, employees are unfortunately, more likely to point the finger at their employers if they or their unborn children suffer illness or injury that could be tied to workplace exposures.
42. It is unlikely, given the Supreme Court's decision in *Johnson Controls*, that an employer could "require" employees to transfer, but obviously a transfer would be made more attractive if it were into a position at the same rate of pay and without loss of seniority.
43. 29 USC §§ 621-634.
44. Originally, the act prohibited discrimination against individuals between the ages of 40 and 70. In 1986, however, Congress deleted the upper age limit, thereby extending the act's protection to all individuals older than 40. 29 USC § 631(a).
45. *Western Air Lines v. Criswell*, 472 US 400, 416-17 (1985). See also, 29 CFR § 1625.6(b), wherein the Equal Employment Opportunity Commission adopts the same two-part BFOQ test for the act's regulatory guidelines.
46. *Criswell*, 472 US at 413, *supra*.
47. *Id.* at 413.
48. *Id.* at 412.
49. *Touhy v. Ford Motor Co.*, 675 F.2d 842, 845-46 (6th Cir. 1982).
50. *Usery v. Tamiami*, 531 F.2d 224, 236 (5th Cir. 1976).
51. See, Robert L. Fishman, *The BFOQ Defense in ADEA Suits: The Scope of "Duties of the Job"*, 85 Mich. L. Rev. 330, 333 (1986) (the interests of "public-safety" are found in nearly all litigated BFOQ cases).
52. *Usery*, 531 F.2d at 236, *supra*.
53. *Criswell*, 472 US at 411, *supra*.
54. *Id.*
55. *See, e.g., Tullis v. Lear School, Inc.*, 874 F.2d 1489 (11th Cir. 1989) (mandatory age limit of 65 for bus drivers insufficiently supported); *E.E.O.C. v. KDM School Bus Co.*, 612 F. Supp. 369 (S.D. N.Y. 1985).
56. *Johnson v. Baltimore*, 472 US 353 (1985).
57. *Id.* at 366.
58. 14 CFR §121.383(c).
59. *Air Line Pilots Ass'n, Intern. v. Quesada*, 276 F.2d 892, 898 (2nd Cir. 1960).
60. *Baker v. F.A.A.*, 917 F.2d 318 (7th Cir. 1990), *cert. denied*, 499 US 936 (1991) (court upheld FAA's refusal to grant exemptions from age 60 rule); *Rombough v. F.A.A.*, 594 F.2d 893 (2d Cir. 1979).
61. *E.E.O.C. v. Boeing Co.*, 843 F.2d 1213 (9th Cir. 1988), *cert. denied*, 488 US 889 (1988) (FAA rule is merely some evidence, not conclusive evidence, in establishing BFOQ for aircraft manufacturer's policy of retiring test pilots at age sixty); *Williams v. Hughes Helicopters*, 806 F.2d 1387 (9th Cir. 1986); *Tuohy v. Ford Motor Co.*, 675 F.2d 842 (6th Cir. 1982); *EEOC v. Lockheed Corp.*, 54 Fair Empl. Prac. Cas. (BNA) 1632 (C.D. Cal. 1991). *But c.f., Gathercole v. Global Associates*, 727 F.2d 1485 (9th Cir. 1984) *cert. denied*, 469 US 1087 (1984); *Hoefelman v. Conservation Comm'n of Missouri*, 718 F.2d 281 (8th Cir. 1983); *Rasberg v. Nationwide Life Ins. Co.*, 671 F. Supp. 494 (S.D. Ohio 1987).

The continued viability of the age 60 rule as a BFOQ is currently in doubt. Many pilot organizations and airlines continue to try to convince the FAA to modify the rule to allow pilots to continue flying after 60. Beatrice K. Barklow, *Rethinking the Age Sixty Mandatory Retirement Rule: A Look at the Newest Movement*, 60 Air L. & Com 329, 335 (Fall 1994) (Opponents of the FAA rule claim the rule is unnecessary because the FAA requires pilots to be in top physical shape and to undergo semi-annual comprehensive medical exam.)

Although the FAA is currently reviewing whether it should maintain the rule or allow pilots to fly past 60, it is proposing that the rule also be applied to another class of pilots. Commuter Operations and General Certification and Operations Requirements, 60 Fed Reg 16230, 16237 (1995) (to be codified 14 CFR Parts 119, 121, 125, 127, and 135) (proposed March 29, 1995). Regardless of the FAA's final determination, employers should be aware that the EEOC continues to challenge employers who try to use the rule to justify BFOQ's for non-commercial pilots. *Discrimination: International Paper Violated ADEA With Pilots' Age Limit, Jury Finds*, Daily Labor Report (BNA), No. 110, at A-8 (June 8, 1995). *Part 135 Upgrade Proposal Draws Concerns About Cost, Safety Issues*, The

Weekly of Business Aviation, July 3, 1995 (excerpts from EEOC comments submitted to FAA regarding proposed expansion of the rule).

62. 29 USC §623(i).
63. *Discrimination: E.E.O.C. Sues Boston Fire Department Charging Forced Retirement Violations.* Daily Labor Report (BNA), No. 100, at A-6 (May 24, 1995).
64. *Id.*
65. *Massachusetts Bd. of Retirement v. Murgia,* 427 US 307 (1976).
66. 22 USC §1002.
67. *Vance v. Bradley,* 440 US 93, 103-4 (1979).
68. *Johnson v. Baltimore,* 731 F.2d 209 (4th Cir. 1984), *rev'd.* and *rem'd,* 472 US 353 (1985).
69. 29 USC §§ 701 *et seq.*
70. 42 USC §§ 1201 *et seq.*
71. Daniel F. Frier, *Age Discrimination and the ADA: How the Act May Be Used To Arm Older Americans Against Age Discrimination by Employers Who Would Otherwise Escape Liability Under the ADEA,* 66 Temple L. Rev. 173 (Spring 1993).
72. 29 CFR 1630.2(r).
73. 42 USC § 12113(b).
74. 42 USC § 12111(3); 29 CFR § 1630.2(r).
75. Guidelines, 56 Fed Reg 35,745.
76. House Judiciary Committee Report, H. Rept. 101-485, Part 3, pp. 45-46 (1990).
77. 29 CFR § 1630.2(r) (emph. added).
78. Guidelines, 56 Fed Reg 35,745.
79. 29 CFR § 1630.2(r).
80. *Lussier v. Brown,* 3 A.D. Cases 223 (D. Me. 1994). Employers covered by the ADA should look to judicial decisions and regulations under the Rehabilitation Act in construing the language of the ADA. 42 USC §12201(a).
81. 3 A.D. Cases 284 (E.D. Pa. 1994), *aff'd,* 43 F.3d 1461 (3d Cir. 1994).
82. 3 A.D. Cases 641 (M.D. Fla. 1994).
83. *Hindman v. GTE Data Services, Inc.,* 4 A.D. Cases 182 (M.D. Fla. 1995).
84. 29 CFR § 1630.2(r).
85. *Hindman, supra.*
86. 29 CFR § 1904.
87. See, supra, p. 8. OSHA has drafted an ergonomics standard that it originally scheduled for release in late 1994. However, with the Republican control of Congress after the November 1994 elections and strong opposition from Republican congressmen, the agency (as of late 1995) has elected not to proceed with rulemaking and, instead, continues to seek enforcement of its ergonomics initiative through use of the general duty clause.
88. See, e.g., citation underlying *Secretary v. Pepperidge Farm, Inc.,* OSHRC Docket No. 89-0265 (ALJ 1993).
89. 42 USC § 12112(d); Equal Employment Opportunity Commission Policy Guidance on Pre-employment Inquiries.
90. *See,* USC § 12113(b); 29 CFR § 1630(r).
91. EEOC Technical Assistance Manual on the Employment Provisions (Tile I) of the Americans With Disabilities Act.
92. *Pepperidge Farm, Inc., supra.*
93. *See,* EEOC Policy Guidance on Pre-employment Inquiries, *supra.*

DEBORA L. JONES, RN, COHN, MPH

OCCUPATIONAL HEALTH SERVICES AND OSHA COMPLIANCE

From The Darien Group
Glen Mills, Pennsylvania

Reprint requests to:
Debora L. Jones, RN, COHN, MPH
President
The Darien Group, Ltd.
12 Regency Plaza
Glen Mills, PA 19342-1000

Providers of occupational health services function in an interdependent relationship with employers and employees with regard to compliance with the requirements of the Occupational Safety and Health Act. When functioning on behalf of employers, it is critical for occupational health service providers to understand the regulatory drivers and the parameters of the employer's duty to comply. This chapter offers a brief overview of the Occupational Safety and Heath Administration and its approach to enforcement; a discussion of the interdependent compliance duties of employers, employees, and providers of occupational health services; and a review of OSHA general industry standards applicable to providers of occupational health services, highlighting areas of responsibility for OSHA compliance.

THE OCCUPATIONAL SAFETY AND HEALTH ACT

Scope and Applicability

The Williams-Steiger Occupational Safety and Health Act of 1970 became effective April 28, 1971, "to assure so far as possible every working man and woman in the Nation safe and healthful working conditions and to preserve our human resources." The act was born out of an awareness of an increasing incidence of worker injury, occupational illness, and death deemed unacceptable for a leading industrialized nation. Responding to the safety and health status of the American worker, the 91st Congress passed the act, which established the Occupational Safety and Health Administration (OSHA) within the

Department of Labor. At the same time, the act established the National Institute for Occupational Safety and Health (NIOSH) in the Department of Health and Human Services. OSHA was authorized to promulgate legally enforceable standards and to promote compliance with the act. NIOSH was created to undertake safety and health research and training.

Generally, the OSHAct applies to "all businesses affecting interstate commerce" except for federal, state and local governments, self-employed persons, farms at which only immediate members of the farm employers family are employed, and working conditions regulated by other federal agencies. In addition, workplaces located in states that have an OSHA-approved state plan are not covered by the OSHAct. Approved state plans must be "at least as effective" as the federal program, and states must cooperate with periodic federal monitoring and evaluation of their plans. Safety and health programs functioning under an OSHA-approved state plan receive up to 50% of the program's operating costs. Table 1 lists the states currently functioning under OSHA-approved plans. With these few exceptions, the act provides universal coverage of the health and safety of approximately 6 million workplaces in the 50 states, the District of Columbia, Puerto Rico, and all other territories of the United States.

Enforcement of the Act

Standards promulgated by OSHA provide the regulatory basis for promoting worker protection. There are four major categories of OSHA standards: general industry, maritime, construction, and agriculture. These standards provide detailed information for employers regarding their obligations in providing safe and healthful working conditions.

OSHA enforcement of standards is accomplished through worksite inspections. Recognizing that not all of the 6 million workplaces covered by OSHA can be inspected, OSHA ranks the agency's inspection activities in the following order:[5]

1. Imminent Danger: hazards that may cause death or serious physical harm immediately or before the danger can be eliminated through normal enforcement procedures.

2. Catastrophes and Fatal Accidents: job fatalities and accidents hospitalizing 5 or more employees.

3. Complaints: written and signed complaints by current employees or their representatives regarding hazards that threaten serious physical harm to workers.

TABLE 1.   Jurisdictions with OSHA-Approved Plans

Alaska	New York*
Arizona	North Carolina
California	Oregon
Connecticut*	Puerto Rico
Hawaii	South Carolina
Indiana	Tennessee
Iowa	Utah
Kentucky	Vermont
Maryland	Virgin Islands
Michigan	Virginia
Minnesota	Washington
Nevada	Wyoming
New Mexico	

* Covers public sector (state and local government) workplaces only. All other state plans cover private and public sector workplaces.

Complaints from occupational health service providers may also prompt OSHA to perform a workplace inspection.

4. Programmed Inspections: routine inspections of high-hazard industries, identified from injury and illness rates and related data. Businesses with 10 or fewer employees are exempt from this category of inspections.

The OSHAct requires OSHA to issue citations for violations of safety and health standards that are identified as a result of any worksite inspection. When issued, a written citation will include a description of the violation; the proposed penalty, if any; and the date by which the hazard must be corrected.[5] The latter is a legally enforceable abatement requirement, and compliance with abatement may be verified through follow-up inspections by OSHA. Penalties for violations of OSHA standards may be as high as $70,000 for each willful or repeated violation, $7,000 for each serious or other-than-serious violation, $7,000 for each violation of posting requirements, and $7,000 for each day beyond a stated abatement date for failure to correct a violation.[6] This penalty structure applies to all citations issued as a result of inspections initiated after March 1, 1991.

Employer and Employee Responsibilities

The act establishes "separate but dependent responsibilities and rights" for employers and employees. Employer responsibilities are detailed within applicable OSHA standards. When no specific standard defines employer obligations for worker health and safety with regard to a particular workplace hazard, employers must comply with their general duty to "furnish a workplace free from recognized hazards that are causing or are likely to cause death or serious physical harm to employees." Interpretive guidance provided by the Occupational Safety and Health Administration identifies 18 general responsibilities that are assigned to employers by the OSHAct[4] (Table 2).

OSHA also interprets employer responsibilities through the *Safety and Health Management Guidelines* issued on January 26, 1989. Although voluntary, these guidelines represent OSHA's view of that which every worksite should have in place to protect workers from occupational hazards. The guidelines specify a four-point workplace program as the best means of ensuring workplace health and safety:

1. Management commitment and employee involvement
2. Worksite analysis
3. Hazard prevention and control
4. Training for employees, supervisors and managers

In fulfilling the responsibilities assigned by the act, individual standards, and OSHA's voluntary guidelines, employers must understand the responsibilities of employees for OSHA compliance.

Consistent with the dependent nature of employer-employee responsibilities for compliance under the act, employees are informed that they "shall comply with all occupational safety and health standards and all rules, regulations, and orders issued under the act." Importantly, there is no mechanism within the act for issuing citations or penalties to employees that do not comply; the employer is ultimately accountable for workplace safety and health compliance. Nevertheless, the Occupational Safety and Health Administration identifies seven essential employee responsibilities for OSHA compliance[4] (Table 3).

OSHA's voluntary *Safety and Health Management Guidelines* promotes active employee involvement in all components of the recommended four-point workplace program. This active employee role indicates that employees share in

TABLE 2.   Employer Responsibilities for OSHA Compliance

1. Meet the general duty responsibility to provide a workplace free from recognized hazards that are likely to cause death or serious physical harm to employees, and comply with standards, rules and regulations issued under the act.

2. Be familiar with mandatory OSHA standards and make copies available to employees for review upon request.

3. Inform all employees about OSHA.

4. Examine workplace conditions to make sure they conform to applicable standards.

5. Minimize or reduce hazards.

6. Make sure employees have and use safe tools and equipment (including appropriate personal protective equipment) and that such equipment is properly maintained.

7. Use color codes, posters, labels or signs when needed to warn employees of potential hazards.

8. Provide medical examinations when required by OSHA standards.

9. Provide training required by OSHA standards (e.g., hazard communication, lead, etc.).

10. Report to the nearest OSHA office within 48 hours any fatal accident or one that results in the hospitalization of five or more employees.

11. Keep OSHA-required records of work-related injuries and illnesses, and post a copy of the totals from the last page of OSHA No. 200 during the entire month of February each year. (This applies to employers with 11 or more employees.)

12. Post, at a prominent location within the workplace, the OSHA poster (OSHA 2203) informing employees of their rights and responsibilities. (In states operating OSHA-approved job safety and health programs, the state's equivalent poster and/or OSHA 2203 may be required.)

13. Provide employees, former employees and their representatives access to the log and Summary of Occupational Injuries and Illnesses (OSHA No. 200) in a reasonable manner.

14. Provide access to employee medical records and exposure records to employees or their authorized representatives.

15. Cooperate with the OSHA compliance officer by furnishing names of authorized employee representatives who may be asked to accompany the compliance officer during an inspection. (If none, the compliance officer will consult with a reasonable number of employees concerning safety and health in the workplace.)

16. Avoid discrimination against employees who properly exercise their rights under the act.

17. Post OSHA citations at or near the worksite involved. Each citation, or copy thereof, must remain posted until the violation has been abated, or for three working days, whichever is longer.

18. Abate cited violations within the prescribed period.

the responsibility for establishing and maintaining an effective worksite safety and health program.

OSHA-MANDATED MEDICAL SURVEILLANCE

Employers must provide medical evaluations to exposed employees. OSHA has determined that the employer may designate the physician who will perform mandated medical examinations. The employer also has access to the results of the examination.[8] Employees can refuse to participate in the employer-sponsored medical surveillance program, but they are not protected by OSHA if an employer makes participation in the program a condition of employment.[8]

Responsibilities of Providers of Occupational Health Services

Although OSHA does not assign specific responsibilities to providers of occupational health services, it is clear that employer and employee compliance with OSHA is facilitated by the significant and expanding role of health care providers in

TABLE 3. Employee Responsibilities for OSHA Compliance

1. Read the OSHA poster at the job site.
2. Comply with all applicable OSHA standards.
3. Follow all employer safety and health rules and regulations, and wear or use prescribed protective equipment while engaged in work.
4. Report hazardous conditions to the supervisor.
5. Report any job-related injury or illness to the employer and seek treatment promptly.
6. Cooperate with the OSHA compliance officer conducting an inspection if he or she inquires about safety and health conditions in the workplace.
7. Exercise employee rights under the act in a responsible manner.

the delivery of occupational health services. This interdependent role for the occupational health provider presents regulatory considerations not typical of standard health care practice. These regulatory considerations may be viewed as responsibilities of all providers of occupational health services who function on behalf of the employer. Generally, these responsibilities include the following:[1]

1. Being familiar with applicable OSHA standards
2. Providing medical examinations as required by OSHA
3. Providing information for OSHA-related recordkeeping of work-related injuries and illnesses
4. Cooperating with employers who must grant employees access to medical records
5. Exercising the right of access to chemical information when appropriate for employee evaluation, treatment, or medical surveillance
6. Assisting employers in the identification of health hazards

When providers of occupational health services do not fulfill their duties, the result can be employer noncompliance with OSHA. If identified by OSHA in an inspection, this noncompliance can lead to citations and penalties issued against the employer.[7] In theory, civil actions based in tort or contract may be filed against the physician or occupational health service by employers or employees who have been substantially harmed.

Occupational Health Service Providers and Medical Records

The OSHA standard addressing medical record access (29 CFR 1910.20) defines a health professional as "a physician, occupational health nurse, industrial hygienist, toxicologist or epidemiologist providing medical or other occupational health services to exposed employees." The term *exposed employees* is broadly defined as "employees exposed to toxic substances or harmful physical agents." This broad definition suggests that, with few exceptions, health professionals who provide care on behalf of employers must comply with the standard's medical records requirements in a number of settings, including the following:

- Industry-based occupational health programs (employed staff)
- Contracted, industry-based occupational health programs
- Corporate occupational health programs
- Hospital-based and free-standing occupational health programs providing services to business and industry
- Hospital emergency departments
- Physician offices (occupational environmental medicine, family practice, general internists, and others)

• Mobile occupational health services (medical and screening services)
• Occupational health consultants (providing recommendations for medical services and OSHA compliance)

Occupational health professionals seeking to facilitate employer compliance with OSHA standards must understand those standards. Therefore, the following sections provide a brief overview of several of the applicable OSHA general industry standards.

GENERAL INDUSTRY STANDARDS

Recording and Reporting Occupational Illnesses and Injuries

Employers must maintain an annual record of work-related illnesses and injuries on an OSHA 200 log or equivalent form. Recordable cases must be documented as soon as feasible after an employer learns the facts but not later than 6 working days after receiving information that an illness or injury has occurred.

The employer must determine if a work-related illness or injury is recordable as defined by OSHA. Guidance documents from the agency indicate that all work-related fatalities are recordable; all recognized or diagnosed work-related illnesses are recordable; and all work-related injuries requiring medical treatment or involving loss of consciousness, restriction of work or motion, or transfer to another job are recordable.

Occupational health service professionals who assist in the maintenance of OSHA 200 logs must distinguish medical treatment from first aid. Episodes requiring medical treatment are recordable, and first aid cases are not. By OSHA definition, medical treatment includes treatment administered by a physician or by registered health care professional under the standing orders of a physician. Medical treatment does not include first aid even if first aid is provided by a physician or registered health care professional. By contrast, first aid is any one-time treatment and any follow-up visit for observation of minor scratches, cuts, burns and splinters that do not ordinarily require medical care. Such treatment and observation are considered first aid even though provided by a physician or registered health care professional.

Employers frequently ask health professionals to help them reach determinations of work-relatedness, first aid versus medical care, and illness versus injury.[3] The advice and documentation provided by occupational health service providers is often the primary basis for employer decisions regarding recordability of work-related illnesses and injuries.

In summary, the essential recordkeeping responsibilities of occupational health service providers include familiarity with OSHA's recordkeeping requirements, timely documentation of employee evaluation and treatment (within 6 days), documentation that enables the employer to distinguish first aid from medical care in determining recordability, and timely assistance to employers in resolving work-relatedness, recordability, injury versus illness, and medical versus first aid issues.

Access to Employee Exposure and Medical Records

OSHA standards mandate that employees or their representative(s) have access to medical and workplace exposure information. These access requirements apply to all exposure and medical records of employees exposed to toxic substances or harmful physical agents. Access is required even if exposure and medical monitoring are not mandated by a particular OSHA standard. Therefore, any medical records of patients evaluated at a medical facility or site or by a physician at the employer's request are covered by this standard.[3]

Although the access standard specifies that compliance is the responsibility of the employer, the day-to-day management of access may be delegated to occupational health service providers functioning on behalf of the employer. Providers with delegated duties must be aware that this standard applies to a broad definition of medical records; specifies the content of a written authorization for release of medical records; requires that the employee or his representative be granted access to the requested medical record within 15 days of the request, and requires maintenance of medical records for the duration of employment plus 30 years, unless a particular OSHA standard specifies otherwise.

Employers must advise employees of their rights to access medical and exposure records at the time of employment and annually thereafter. Access by health professionals to information regarding chemical identity and trade secrets is also addressed. When knowledge of chemical identity is required for appropriate treatment by a physician or nurse, the employer must release that information immediately. In the absence of an emergency, a written request may be made for release of a chemical identity if the health professional is treating an exposed employee or performing baseline or periodic medical surveillance.

In summary, the essential responsibilities of occupational health service providers regarding access include familiarity with OSHA's definition of medical records and access to those records, reasonable efforts to assure that procedures and forms for release of medical records meet OSHA requirements, reasonable efforts to assure that records are maintained for the duration of employment plus 30 years, and familiarity with the right to request and receive chemical identity information if required for the provision of emergency or non-emergency medical care for exposed employees.

Occupational Noise Exposure

Employees exposed (on the average) 8 hours per day 5 days per week to noise at 85 dBA or above must be included in a hearing conservation program that includes baseline and annual audiometry. Baseline testing must be performed within 6 months of the employee's first noise exposure unless testing is performed by a mobile unit. For mobile unit testing, a baseline exam is acceptable if obtained within one year of initial exposure to noise. Audiometry must be repeated at least annually to detect any shift or change in hearing when compared to the baseline test. OSHA defines a threshold shift as a change in hearing threshold relative to the baseline audiogram of 10 dB or more (on average) at 2,000, 3,000, and 4,000 Hz in either ear.

The noise standard specifies background noise levels for the testing area, audiometric test frequencies, and parameters for retesting, equipment calibration, interpretation of results, and adjustment of results for presbycusis. Audiometry that complies with the OSHA standard must incorporate these specifications into the screening, interpretation, and documentation of the hearing evaluation performed by the occupational health service.

In summary, the essential responsibilities of the occupational health service regarding noise include review of the occupational noise exposure standard and documentation that audiometry services comply with that standard, documentation that audiometry either is or is not being performed to demonstrate compliance with noise standards, and referral of employers to other providers when hearing tests designed to demonstrate compliance with noise standards do not otherwise meet OSHA requirements.

Hazardous Waste Operations and Emergency Response

Employees exposed to hazardous waste associated with government-mandated clean-up operations; treatment, storage, and disposal of hazardous waste; and/or participation in emergency response must be included in a medical surveillance program if employees are exposed to hazardous substances at or above the permissible exposure limits (PEL) or, if no PEL applies, exposed to published exposure limits for the substance, or employees wear a respirator for 30 days or more per year, or an employee is injured or ill due to possible exposure to hazardous substances or an employee is a member of a HazMat team.

The hazardous waste operations standard indicates that medical monitoring of hazardous waste workers requires preplacement, periodic, and termination examinations. The periodic examinations must be performed at least once every year unless the examining physician recommends an alternative schedule, which cannot be less than every two years.

Physical examinations are also required if an employee manifests signs or symptoms that may be related to hazardous waste exposure or if an emergency incident results in employee exposure above the PEL or published exposure limits.

The examining physician must determine the content of the physical examination. The standard advises that guidance for physicians who must determine examination content can be found in the NIOSH publication *Occupational Safety and Health Guidance Manual for Hazardous Waste Site Activities*. The standard indicates that the examination must be performed by or under the supervision of a licensed physician, preferably a physician knowledgeable in occupational medicine.

Employers must provide a copy of the standard and appendices to the examining physician. For each examinee, the physician must have access to a description of the employee's duties related to exposure, the employee's exposure levels, a description of personal protective equipment to be used by the employee, and information from previous medical examinations, if not readily available to the examining physician.

Following the examination, the physician must document any medical conditions that would contraindicate work in hazardous waste operations and any limitations in performing this work. The physician must also state that the employee has been informed of the results of the medical examination.

In summary, the OSHA hazardous waste standard requires that occupational health service providers be familiar with the standard and with information compiled by NIOSH in the *Occupational Safety and Health Guidance Manual for Hazardous Waste Site Activities*, review and understand employee duties, exposures, and required use of personal protective equipment, and provide a written opinion addressing only those conditions and limitations that are clearly related to occupational exposures.

Respiratory Protection

Employers may provide and require use of respirators to decrease inhalational exposure to airborne contaminants associated with occupational disorders. If respirators are used in the workplace, employers must implement an acceptable respiratory protection program, as defined by the standard. Occupational health service providers must verify that employees are physically capable of working while using respiratory equipment. Medical evaluations must be completed prior to initial use of a respirator and periodically thereafter (annual exams are recommended).

In summary, occupational health service providers must know the type of respirator to be used by the employee and the type of work to be performed while wearing the respirator and understand the relevant medical and physical conditions associated with appropriate use as well as contraindications for use of respiratory protective equipment.

Medical Services and First Aid

Employers must assure that medical personnel are readily available to advise and consult regarding employee health. In instances in which medical services are geographically removed from the workplace, the employer must have personnel trained in first aid on site. First aid supplies maintained at the workplace must be approved by the company's consulting physician.

Thus, occupational health service providers must be familiar with the workplace and understand the activities of first aid personnel to facilitate approval of supplies that are consistent with first aid training.

Hazard Communication

This standard requires that all employers inform employees about workplace chemical hazards through a comprehensive hazard communication program. In general, this program must include chemical labeling and hazard warnings; training of employees regarding the hazards associated with workplace chemicals; and availability of material safety data sheets (MSDS) for use by employees, supervisors and medical providers. MSDSs typically provide information about chemicals and their health effects. This information may be useful in medical evaluation and treatment of workers, in recommending appropriate medical surveillance, and in advising employees regarding long-term risk of cancer and the potential for adverse pregnancy outcomes related to workplace exposures.[2] The MSDS, however, does not have to disclose information reasonably viewed as a trade secret by the manufacturer or supplier.

Physicians are assured access to chemical information, including trade secrets, when a medical emergency follows exposure to a particular chemical. Trade secret information may also be available to physicians in the absence of an emergency, as long as the information is related to medical treatment or surveillance and the clinician submits a written justification of need and signs an agreement of confidentiality.

Regarding hazard communication, occupational health services providers must be familiar with the general format and content of material safety data sheets, know how to assert the right to chemical information that is related to treatment or surveillance of an exposed employee, and appreciate the right of the manufacturer to protect trade secrets.

Toxic and Hazardous Substances

Subpart Z of OSHA's general industry standards contains 27 standards that address specific toxic or hazardous exposures (Table 4). These standards define employer duties and guide health professionals who must implement medical surveillance for each of the regulated substances. Although each standard addresses a specific exposure, several duties are common to virtually all of the Subpart Z standards. For example,

• Physical examinations, if required, must be performed by or under the supervision of a licensed physician.

TABLE 4. Toxic and Hazardous Substances under Subpart Z
of OSHA's General Industry Standards

CFR Section	Substance	CFR Section	Substance
1910.1001	Asbestos	1910.1017	Vinyl chloride
1910.1003	4-Nitrobiphenyl	1910.1018	Inorganic arsenic
1910.1004	alpha-Napththylamine	1910.1025	Lead
1910.1006	Methyl chloromethyl ether	1910.1027	Cadmium
1910.1007	3,3'-Dichlorobenzidine	1910.1028	Benzene
1910.1008	bis-Chloromethyl ether	1910.1029	Coke oven emissions
1910.1009	beta-Napththylamine	1910.1030	Bloodborne pathogens
1910.1010	Benzidine	1910.1043	Cotton dust
1910.1011	4-Aminodiphenyl	1910.1044	1,2-dibromo-3-chloropropane
1910.1012	Ethyleneimine	1910.1045	Acrylonitrile
1910.1013	beta-Propiolactone	1910.1047	Ethylene oxide
1910.1014	2-Acetylaminofluorene	1910.1048	Formaldehyde
1910.1015	4-Dimethylaminoazobenzene	1910.1050	Methylenedianiline
1910.1016	N-Nitrosodimethylamine	1910.1450	Hazardous chemicals in laboratories

• Physical examinations, when required, must be provided by the employer at a reasonable time and place and at no cost to the employee.

• The physician's written statement of findings and recommendations should not discuss findings or diagnoses unrelated to the occupational exposure under consideration.

• Nonphysicians who administer pulmonary function tests must complete a training course in spirometry sponsored by an appropriate academic or professional institution.

Table 5 provides an overview of several standards to illustrate the considerable variability between standards, the type of guidance provided, and some of the special requirements that are unique to individual standards.

Most of the standards specify that the employer must provide a copy of the relevant standard and appendices to the physician performing mandated medical surveillance. In turn, the health professional must provide services that are consistent with the requirements of the respective standard(s).

CONCLUSION

Employers and corporate medical directors acting on behalf of employers obtain occupational health services anticipating that providers understand regulatory "drivers" and employer responsibilities for compliance. When acting on behalf of employers, providers have an interdependent function and responsibility for compliance. When OSHA standards are not met, the outcome may be citations and penalties against the company and civil liability for the occupational health service provider.

Hospitals, clinics, and physicians' offices have joined the traditional, industry-based employee health unit as delivery sites for occupational health services. Unlike the majority of company-based occupational health and occupational medical professionals, the typical community-based provider is a general practitioner, nurse, or technician practicing occupational health without the benefit of specialized training. Many of these providers offer mandated medical services, including OSHA compliance services. Those who provide, and those who purchase these services, must understand their respective roles and responsibilities in complying with OSHA requirements.

TABLE 5.   Medical Surveillance Programs for Selected Toxic and Hazardous Substances

Standard	Medical Surveillance Program
1910.1001 Asbestos	**Initial evaluation:** Medical and work history; standardized respiratory disease questionnaire; complete physical with emphasis on the respiratory, cardiovascular and digestive systems; chest x-ray and classification; pulmonary function testing **Periodic evaluation:** As per initial evaluation, performed annually with exception of chest x-ray (schedule provided) **Physician's written statement:** Must include statement that employee was informed of increased risk of lung cancer attributable to the combined effect of smoking and asbestos fibers **Medical records:** To be maintained for length of employment plus 30 years **Special requirements:** Termination examination
1910.1003 4-Nitro- biphenyl	**Initial evaluation:** Physical examination including personal, family, and occupational history, including genetic and environmental factors **Periodic evaluation:** As per initial evaluation, not less than annually **Physician's written statement:** Required to provide a statement of the employee's suitability for employment in the specific exposure **Medical records:** To be maintained for the duration of employment and then forwarded via registered mail to the director **Special requirements:** In all physicals, consideration is to be given to conditions of increased risk to 4-nitrobiphenyl
1910.1017 Vinyl chloride	**Initial evaluation:** General physical with attention to the liver, spleen, kidneys, skin, connective tissues and pulmonary system; medical history including alcohol intake, history of hepatitis, history of exposure to potential hepatotoxic agents, past history of hospitalizations and blood transfusions; serum testing of total bilirubin, alkaline phosphatase, SGOT, SGPT, and gamma glustamyl transpeptidase. **Periodic evaluation:** Every 6 months for employees who have worked in vinyl chloride for 10 years or longer; annually for all other exposed employees **Physician's written statement:** To address employee suitability for continued exposure to vinyl chloride, use of protective equipment and respirators **Medical records:** Must be maintained for the duration of employment plus 20 years, or 30 years, whichever is longer **Special requirements:** Physician may recommend alternative examination; must provide equal assurance of detecting pertinent medical conditions; must be documented in writing to employer
1910.1018 Inorganic arsenic	**Initial evaluation:** Work and medical history including smoking history, respiratory symptoms; nasal and skin exam; chest x-ray, sputum cytology and other exams believed appropriate by examining physician **Periodic evaluation:** As above, annually for employees less than 45 years old with less than 10 years exposure; at least semiannually for all others **Physician's written statement:** To include results of exam and tests, opinion as to whether employee has detected medical conditions placing employee at increased risk due to exposure to inorganic arsenic, any recommended limitations in exposure or use of protective equipment, employee informed of results **Medical records:** To be maintained for at least 40 years, or for the duration of employment plus 20 years, whichever is longer **Special requirements:** Specifications for maintaining chest x-rays and cytologic examination slides
1910.1025 Lead	**Initial evaluation:** Exam with attention to the teeth, gums, hematologic, gastrointestinal, renal, cardiovascular, and neurological systems; blood pressure; blood sample for blood lead; hemoglobin and hematocrit, red cell indices and peripheral smear morphology, zinc protoporphyrin, BUN, serum creatinine; routine U/A **Periodic evaluation:** Biological monitoring of blood lead and ZPP every 6 months or every 2 months if last blood lead at or above 40 µg/100 g of whole blood; monthly during medical removal; exams annually for any employee with blood lead at or above 40 µg/100 g during the preceding 12 months **Physician's written statement:** To include recommended special protective measures or limitations to be placed upon employee **Medical records:** To be maintained for at least the duration of the employee's employment **Special requirements:** Allows for multiple physician review mechanism; provides medical removal protection; prohibits prophylactic chelation

REFERENCES

1. Godefroi R, McCunney RJ: The role of regulatory agencies. In McCunney RJ (ed): Handbook of Occupational Medicine. Boston, Little, Brown & Co., 1988, pp 37–46.
2. Himmelstein JS, Frumkin H: The right to know about toxic exposures—implications for physicians. N Engl J Med 312:687–690, 1985.
3. McElveen JC: Legal and ethical issues. In McCunney RJ (ed): Handbook of Occupational Medicine. Boston, Little, Brown & Co., 1988, pp 21–35.
4. Occupational Safety and Health Administration: All about OSHA. OSHA 2056, 1994.
5. Occupational Safety and Health Administration: Inspecting for job safety and health hazards. Fact sheet no. OSHA 92-02.
6. Occupational Safety and Health Administration: New OSHA civil penalties policy. Fact sheet no. OSHA 91-36.
7. Postal LP: Suing the doctor: Lawsuits by injured workers against the occupational physician. J Occup Med 31:891–896, 1989.
8. Rothstein MA: Legal considerations in worker fitness evaluations. Occup Med State Art Rev 3:209–218, 1988.
9. Sandler HM: Legal aspects of occupational medicine. In Rom WN (ed): Environmental and Occupational Medicine. 2nd ed. Boston, Little, Brown & Co., 1992, pp 1347–1350.

MICHAEL BARAM, LLB

GENERIC STRATEGIES FOR PROTECTING WORKER HEALTH AND SAFETY

OSHA's General Duty Clause and Hazard Communication Standard

From the Center for Law and
   Technology
Boston University School of Law
Boston, Massachusetts

Reprint requests to:
Michael Baram, LLB
Center for Law and Technology
Boston University School of Law
765 Commonwealth Ave.
Boston, MA 02215

The Occupational Safety and Health Act of 1970 (OSHAct) authorizes the Occupational Safety and Health Administration (OSHA) to employ various strategies to protect worker health and safety in the private sector.[1] These strategies include use of prescriptive standards, each designed to reduce a specific chemical or physical hazard in designated industries,[2] and use of rules to compel employers to report hazard information.[3]

This chapter discusses a third approach, OSHA use of a "generic strategy" to address a set of hazardous conditions that may be found in any workplace subject to OSHA authority. Generic strategies are used to hold employers accountable for failure to prevent the hazardous conditions irrespective of actual harm and thereby have significant influence on how employers manage workplace health and safety. Two prominent generic strategies are addressed: OSHA's program for enforcing the "general duty" clause and OSHA's application of its "hazard communication" standard. Both programs exert pervasive influence in the workplace and secure protections for workers that could not be achieved using other strategies.

THE GENERAL DUTY CLAUSE

The OSHAct provides that each employer "shall furnish to each of his employees employment and a place of employment which are free from recognized hazards that are causing or are likely to cause death or serious harm to his employees."[4] This brief statement has been construed by OSHA, its review commission (OSHRC), and the courts as a general duty imposed by Congress on private sector employers that is self-executing and thereby legally enforceable by OSHA without need for standards or other regulatory action by the agency. To enforce the general duty, the OSHAct authorizes OSHA to enter and inspect private workplaces, investigate conditions, question employers and workers, and issue citations and impose penalties if it finds violations of the general duty.[5] Violators can appeal OSHA citations and sanctions to the agency's review commission and ultimately to a federal court.[6]

By contrast, issuance of prescriptive standards is cumbersome, consuming substantial monetary and human resources in a regulatory process that typically requires 6–10 years. Not surprisingly, the agency has been able to set specific standards for only a few dozen of the thousands of toxic substances that may pose hazards in American workplaces. Reliance on the general duty clause, however, has substantially enhanced the agency's ability to protect workers over the past 25 years.

Because the parameters of the general duty are ambiguous, OSHA's reliance on the clause has sparked significant controversy. Many companies have appealed OSHA citations to OSHRC and the courts, enabling these bodies to have a decisive role in defining what the general duty requires of employers and how the agency should enforce it.[7] One result of this continuing oversight is a legal consensus that the general duty clause does not impose strict or no-fault liability. Rather, the clause imposes a narrower fault-based liability on employers who fail to eliminate or reduce a workplace "hazard" that is "recognized," "serious," and "abatable by feasible means." In practice, this consensus means that enforcement by OSHA requires the agency to develop findings of fact that prove that a particular hazard meets the "recognized-serious-abatable by feasible means" criteria.[8]

Since 1970, OSHRC and court decisions have narrowed the applicability of the general duty clause. To reduce the risk that its citations and penalties will be challenged and overturned, OSHA continuously revises its enforcement guidelines to reflect new rulings by the oversight tribunals.[9] At the same time, however, OSHA also attempts to preserve the breadth of the general duty and to retain considerable discretion in applying the duty to an ever-expanding universe of workplace hazards. Not surprisingly, the fundamental tension between employer desires to vitiate and agency desires to maintain or expand the scope of the general duty continues to generate litigation.

What is a "hazard"? According to OSHRC and the courts, a hazard consists of processes or materials that cause injury or disease by operating directly on employees as they engage in work or work-related activities.[10] Thus, to preserve its discretion to hold a company accountable for virtually any type of threat to worker health or safety, OSHA loosely defines hazard as "a danger which threatens physical harm to employees."[11]

When is a hazard "serious"? Reflecting the language of the OSHAct, OSHA holds that a hazard is serious when its "likely" or actual consequences include "death or serious physical harm to employees." Importantly, this definition of serious hazard includes chronic illnesses "which require the passage of a substantial period of time to occur."[12] OSHA has applied this definition in holding companies accountable for diverse hazards, including job functions that can or do cause ergonomic injuries; job conditions of heat stress that cause or are likely to cause worker drowsiness, fainting, falls, brain damage, and stroke; and job processes that involve worker exposure to toxic chemicals.[13]

OSHRC and the courts have upheld OSHA's authority to punish companies for hazards whose consequences are deemed "serious" by the agency on a scale ranging widely from temporary to permanent harm, from partial to total impairment, from sudden somatic to chronic harm, and from reversible injury to death. Furthermore, OSHA need only show that such "serious" consequences are "likely" or possible, and need not prove they are probable by some method such as risk assessment.[14]

When is a hazard "recognized"? In line with OSHRC and court decisions, OSHA holds that a recognized hazard is one that is known either to the employer or its employees, or to others who are knowledgeable about or belong to the same industrial sector.[15] This means an employer can violate the general duty clause if it had actual or constructive knowledge of the hazard.

OSHA provides that proof of actual knowledge may consist of "written or oral statements made by the employer . . . or supervisory personnel during or before the OSHA inspection" as well as other company documentation, including memoranda, safety rules, operating manuals, and procedures. Furthermore, collective bargaining agreements, accident or injury reports, workers' compensation claims, and certain types of employee complaints may provide the requisite proof.[16]

Regarding constructive knowledge, OSHA provides that recognition of a hazard can be imputed to an employer if it finds that others involved in the same industrial sector know of the hazard. Proof of such knowledge may be shown by

- warnings provided by the manufacturers or suppliers on equipment or materials used by the employer,
- relevant statements of safety and health experts,
- studies by other agencies, insurers, workers, or unions,
- hazard abatement methods used by other companies in the same industrial sector,
- state and local laws and regulations applicable to the hazard and enforceable against that industrial sector's member companies, and
- voluntary standards adopted by the relevant industrial sector.[17]

Journal articles distributed throughout the relevant industry also may be used to prove that a hazard is recognized, but "only to supplement other evidence which more clearly establishes recognition."[18] "Common sense," defined as that which "any reasonable person would have recognized" as a hazard, also provides a measure of a recognized hazard. However, OSHA has applied the common sense test only to hazards so conspicuous that they are "universally recognized," such as refueling trucks near open flame heaters.[19]

When is a hazard "abatable by feasible means"? According to a former OSHRC chairman, "feasibility of abatement . . . is an element not drawn directly from the language of the general duty clause but rather from the intent of Congress that the general duty be an achievable one . . . . [OSHA] must establish the type of employer conduct necessary to avoid citation and demonstrate the feasibility and likely utility of such conduct. To that end, the abatement method proposed must be shown to materially reduce the risk."[20] In other words, OSHA must prove "there was feasible means by which the employer could have eliminated or materially reduced the hazard."[21]

OSHA has defined its responsibility as proving that a hazard is "preventable" or can be "significantly reduced" by a specific method (or series of methods) that was "feasible and available" and existed *before* OSHA's inspection and citation.[22] The agency has also designated the types of evidence it will rely on, such as

- the employer's own policies and practices,
- private voluntary standards for abatement and abatement recommendations in trade journals,
- recommendations by suppliers of equipment or materials to the employer,
- evidence provided by experts,
- implementation of the method by other companies,
- implementation of the method by the cited employer after the occurrence of the injury that prompted OSHA investigation.[23]

Thus, OSHA must prove that a particular method was available, was capable of materially reducing the recognized hazard, and was feasible for use by the company in question. Feasibility involves both technical and economic considerations. For technical expertise, the agency gathers evidence of industry practice and seeks the opinions of safety engineers, equipment designers, behavioral and human factors analysts, and other experienced professionals.[24] For economic issues, OSHA has not established a clear-cut position because the agency has not yet reconciled two conflicting views at the federal bench. Courts have held that expense to the owner, per se, does not make an abatement method unfeasible, but they also have held that Congress did not intend that the general duty impose precautions on an employer that would clearly threaten its economic viability.[25] Thus, OSHA is challenged by the frequent need to establish economic feasibility in cases involving small businesses with limited resources as well as in cases involving larger employers with highly developed programs for workplace health and safety where the identified abatement methods would provide only a modest improvement at great cost.[26]

In proving feasibility, OSHA is guided by OSHRC and court decisions holding that the test is feasibility, not industry custom, and that an employer can be liable for lacking the requisite abatement method even though it is not used by other companies in the same business sector. Thus, an employer cannot rely on industry custom as a conclusive defense. To prevail, the company must contest the technical and economic feasibility of the specific method espoused by OSHA.[27]

Even if OSHA finds a hazard that meets the foregoing criteria, its enforcement of the general duty to abate the hazard may be thwarted by preemption doctrine. OSHRC and the courts have repeatedly held that Congress intended the general duty to be a "gap-filler"—an obligation to be imposed on an employer only when an OSHA standard is not available to abate the hazard.[28] Thus, if an OSHA standard applies to the hazard at the time of OSHA investigation (and the standard can be enforced to abate the hazard), that standard preempts enforcement of the general duty against that hazard. OSHA accordingly instructs its field inspectors that "the general duty provisions shall be used only when there is no standard that applies to the particular hazard involved."[29]

Employers frequently rely on the preemption doctrine when appealing OSHA citations for general duty violations. In these cases, OSHRC or a court must determine the precise nature of the hazard in question and whether an OSHA standard already applies to the same hazard in its entirety.[30] In some cases the standard argued by the employer as being applicable and having preemptive effect may nevertheless be inadequate to protect workers from the hazard. To deal with this situation, the courts have modified preemption doctrine, holding that

If . . . an employer knows a particular safety standard is inadequate to protect his worker against the specific hazard it is intended to address, or that the conditions in his place of employment are such that the safety standard will not adequately deal with the hazards to which his employees are exposed, he has a duty under section 5(a)(1) [the general duty clause] to take whatever measures may be required by the Act, over and above those mandated by the safety standard to safeguard his workers. . . . Scienter is the key.[31]

In a case involving worker exposure to freon in a confined workplace, OSHRC further limited preemption by interpreting the requirement that OSHA prove employer "knowledge" (or scienter) as one that can be met by producing evidence of the employer's actual knowledge or the knowledge of "industry in general."[32] Thus, the general duty is now subject to a less restrictive preemption test that provides that citation for a particular recognized hazard is *not preempted* by an applicable OSHA standard when the employer or industry in general knows that the standard fails to protect.[33]

Enforcement of the general duty clause has been hotly disputed since 1970. Companies view OSHA inspections as intrusive fishing expeditions designed to uncover multiple hazards, especially when tragic workplace accidents subject OSHA to media attention and labor pressure to punish the employer. Companies also resent the ambiguities that lead to inconsistent and unpredictable applications of the duty, and they prefer the due process and greater predictability provided by health and safety standards.

Unions and other advocates of worker safety believe the general duty clause establishes a fundamental standard of care similar to the negligence doctrine in tort law. They deplore Congressional failure to provide OSHA with sufficient resources for enforcement and the agency's predisposition to settle disputed penalties for meager amounts that fail to deter employers from maintaining unsafe workplaces.[34]

THE HAZARD COMMUNICATION STANDARD

The OSHAct authorizes OSHA to issue regulations requiring the use of "labels or other appropriate forms of warning . . . to insure that workers are appraised of all hazards to which they are exposed . . . and precautions for safe use."[35] Over the years, OSHA has issued labeling and warning requirements for specific substances, including compressed gases, flammable substances, and chemicals. The labels typically identify the substance, briefly state its hazardous properties (e.g., "flammable gas"), warn against certain behaviors (e.g., "no smoking, no open flames"), and provide safe use and storage instructions.[36]

Employers subject to these requirements expect that the companies that supply them with hazardous materials will provide the proper labels and warnings for use in the employer's workplace. However, the employer is ultimately responsible for complying with OSHA's requirements. Thus, most companies will review what the supplier provides and amplify it, as necessary, to assure compliance for the particular circumstances of each workplace.

Suppliers typically try to provide what the customer employer needs or demands because doing less loses customers to competing suppliers who do more. Thus, market forces reinforce OSHA labeling and warning requirements.[37] In addition, the common law of product liability encourages compliance because suppliers whose products injure workers employed by their customers may be found strictly liable for "failure to warn" such users of their products.[38]

Because substance-specific warning requirements were insufficient to protect workers from exposure to a multitude of other hazardous chemicals, OSHA enacted the hazard communication standard in 1983.[39] Adopting the concept that workers have "a need and right to know the hazards and identities of the chemicals they are exposed to when working,"[40] OSHA completed a 10-year process by issuing this generic strategy for warning workers, a step that has been described as "the most significant regulatory action ever taken by the agency."[41]

The hazard communication standard (HCS) imposes duties on the "upstream" manufacturer, distributor, and importer of hazardous chemicals to furnish their "downstream" customers with labels and a data sheet for each hazardous chemical they purchase. The HCS then requires both the upstream and downstream companies, as employers, to provide this information to their own employees who are exposed to the chemicals, together with special education and training for employees in order to prevent harmful exposures. The HCS now applies to virtually all private sector workplaces, including those in the manufacturing and construction sectors of business.

The HCS grants exposed employees the "right to know" such information about the chemicals to which they are exposed in the workplace. The cornerstone of this right is an enforceable program of hazard communication and training to protect worker health and safety throughout the commercial life cycle of each hazardous chemical.

The generic aspect of the HCS arises from its applicability to more than 2,000 hazardous chemicals listed by OSHA and to any other chemicals that meet detailed criteria found in appendices to the HCS. Because the criteria require only one statistically significant study "conducted in accordance with established scientific principles" to establish that a chemical is "hazardous" under HCS, more than 60,000 substances may fall into the criteria-based hazardous chemical category.[42] The HCS specifically exempts some workplaces (e.g., laboratories), some chemicals (e.g., pesticides, foods, drugs, and many consumer products), and "mixtures" that contain hazardous materials at extremely low, designated concentrations.[43]

Another significant feature of the HCS is the absence of any exemption for hazardous chemicals that pose a de minimis risk (in terms of incidence) to worker health or safety. OSHA's rationale for not affording this exemption is that upstream manufacturers and importers, who have the burden of identifying the hazardous agents and developing the labels and data sheets, have no way of knowing with certainty how downstream customers will use the purchased chemicals. Moreover, manufacturers cannot readily determine which customer uses will pose a significant risk. OSHA's position has been affirmed by federal courts.[44]

The HCS requires manufacturers and importers to
- identify hazardous chemicals according to OSHA's list and criteria,
- label all containers of these chemicals with the identity of the chemical, appropriate hazard warnings, and the name and address of the supplier,
- prepare a material safety data sheet (MSDS) for each hazardous chemical, designating the substance's identity, commercial source, physical and chemical properties, contents of mixtures, health and safety hazards, appropriate methods for protecting safety and health, and emergency and first aid procedures, and
- provide the MSDS to all downstream employers who purchase the hazardous chemical.

Regarding hazards, the MSDS must address
- physical hazards such as flammability, reactivity, radioactivity, and explosiveness,
- health hazards such as corrosivity, toxicity, carcinogenicity, and capacity to cause irritant, sensitizer, or target organ effects. The health effects covered in the MSDS must be based on animal data; human epidemiologic data; evidence of carcinogenicity; designation as a carcinogen by IARC, NTP, or other expert bodies; or other studies conducted under established scientific principles, and
- symptoms of exposure, primary routes of exposure, and exposure limits set by OSHA or other authorities.

The HCS thereafter requires all employers, whether upstream suppliers or downstream customers, to retain the MSDS, notify their own employees of its availability and location for review, and make the MSDS accessible to employees upon request at any time. Each employer also must train its workers about the hazards posed by the chemicals. At a minimum, workers should learn hazard detection methods, safe handling and use procedures, and appropriate measures for self-protection.

To summarize, the HCS contains three essential components:

- **labeling** to provide immediate and obvious warning of the most serious hazards posed by a chemical,
- an **MSDS** to provide detailed information on the full set of hazards and on appropriate preventive and remedial measures, and
- mandatory **training** to assure that employees understand the information and improve their ability to prevent, mitigate, and respond to hazards.

Although the HCS sets forth a uniform MSDS format, the substantive content is left to each manufacturer or importer. As a result, MSDSs provided by different suppliers of the same chemical vary in content and quality and may range from a minimal information MSDS of two pages to an information-loaded MSDS of 20 pages or more. Many suppliers voluntarily provide additional information to help downstream customers in various ways. For example, they may furnish

- videos and documents that the downstream employers can used to comply with mandatory training requirement under the HCS,
- information on other state and federal regulations that apply to the chemicals they have purchased,
- guidance to customers on how to comply with the HCS and other standards that apply to the chemicals in question, and
- experts to assist customers either as consultants or as a value-added feature of a purchase.[45]

Manufacturers and other suppliers of hazardous chemicals undertake these amplifications of the basic HCS to more effectively compete for and retain customer loyalty and to avoid both strict liability and negligence-based liability for failure to warn downstream users who may suffer injurious exposure. Thus, market forces and liability doctrines combine to promote compliance with several of the HCS requirements.

Despite these incentives, OSHA continues to find many companies in violation of the HCS. Many companies fail to notify and train employees adequately, or they provide inadequate material safety data sheets. Nevertheless, most assessments of this generic OSHA strategy are favorable; commentators typically suggest only incremental reforms.

The HCS is a hybrid regulation. Some of its features demand strict adherence to OSHA prescriptions for compliance. Other features allow each company to determine what it must do to achieve compliance. The prescriptive features that mandate uniform response across all workplaces (despite greatly varying chemical hazards, employee safety programs, and conditions of exposure) are inevitably over-inclusive and uncomfortably rigid. The performance features raise many issues of interpretation and compliance uncertainty. What seems needed is an OSHA mechanism that follows a principled approach to permit suitable variances from the uniform prescriptions. Also needed is guidance that attempts to reduce the ambiguities of the performance features of the HCS. Currently, these stresses become apparent when a company appeals an OSHA penalty for violation of the HCS, and are resolved by OSHRC and the courts on a case-by-case basis.[46]

REFERENCES

1. 29 USC §651; Public Law 91-596 (Dec. 29, 1970).

2. See OSHAct, section 6(b) for OSHA's mandate to set prescriptive standards, and section 6(c) for issuing "emergency standards" to protect employees from "grave danger." Once an emergency standard takes effect, it must be followed by a final version within six months.

3. Authorized by section 8(c).

4. Section 5(a)(1).

5. See discussion in *National Realty and Construction Co. v. OSHRC*, 489 F.2d 1257 (DC Cir. 1973) and *International Union v. General Dynamics Land Division*, 815 F.2d 1570 (DC Cir. 1987). Enforcement authority is provided by sections 8, 9, 10, and 17 of the OSHAct.

6. Section 11 (of the OSHAct).

7. For full compilation of the OSHRC and court decisions on the general duty clause, see Occupational Safety and Health Reporter, Bureau of National Affairs, Inc. A useful review of legal developments is provided in Rothstein M, Occupational Safety and Health Law, West Publishing Co. (1990).

8. See *OSHRC v. Duriron Co.*, 750 F.2d 28 (6th Cir. 1984). Congress has referred to this decision as the most appropriate judicial interpretation of its general duty mandate. See S. Rep. No. 228, 101st Congress, 1st Sess. 208, 209 (1989).

9. OSHA Instruction CPL 2.45 B CH-3, OSHA Office of General Industry Compliance Assistance (June 15, 1992) and subsequent modifications thereto.

10. Rothstein M, supra note 7, at p. 187, citing *OCAW v. American Cyanamid Co.*, 741 F.2d 444 (DC Cir. 1984).

11. OSHA Instruction, supra note 9, at section A.2.b(1)(a).

12. OSHA Instruction, supra note 9, at section A.2.b.(3)(c), which further requires that expert testimony be used to establish that a chronic illness likely to cause death or serious physical harm could arise from "regular and continuing employee exposure at the workplace to the toxic substance at the measured levels."

13. See *International Union v. General Dynamics Land Division*, 815 F.2d 1570 (DC Cir. 1987), and Kolesar D: Cumulative Trauma Disorder: OSHA's General Duty Clause and the Need for an Ergonomics Standard, Michigan Law Rev 90:2079.

14. OSHRC has required a "possibility test" in lieu of a more demanding "reasonable foreseeability test" for establishing the requisite serious consequences of a workplace hazard. See discussion in Foulke E, Beck T: The General Duty Clause of the Occupational Safety and Health Act of 1970, Labor Law J, 44(3):133, 1993. Courts have also held that a mathematical test of probability is not required of the agency. See *Illinois Power Co. v. OSHRC*, 632 F.2d 25 (7th Cir. 1980) and *Usery v. Marquette Cement Co.*, 568 F.2d 902 (2nd Cir. 1977).

15. OSHA Instruction, supra note 9, at section A.2.b.(2). See also *National Realty and Construction Co. v. OSHRC*, 489 F.2d 1257 (DC Cir. 1973).

16. OSHA Instruction, supra note 9, at section A.2.b.(2)(b). The employer's failure to complete a corrective action prior to OSHA investigation may also suffice.

17. OSHA Instruction, supra note 9, at section A.2.b.(2)(a).

18. Id.

19. OSHA Instruction, supra note 9, at section A.2.b.(2)(c); applied in *Eddy's Bakeries Co.*, 1981 OSHD §25,604 (Rev. Commission 1981).

20. Foulke E, Beck T, supra note 14, at p. 138, citing *National Realty* and other cases.

21. See *Duriron*, supra note 8.

22. OSHA Instruction, supra note 9, at section A.2.b.(4) and A.2.b.(4)(a).

23. Id.

24. Id.

25. See *National Realty*, supra note 5, at p. 1266, n. 37.

26. As discussed in Koselar D: OSHA's General Duty Clause and the Need for an Ergonomics Standard. Michigan Law Rev 90:2079.

27. See *International Union and National Realty*, supra note 5.

28. For review of these determinations on preemption, see Foulke E, Beck T, supra note 14, at p. 139. See also Morgan D, Duvall M: OSHA's General Duty Clause: An Analysis of its Use and Abuse. Ind Rel Law 5:283, 1983, at p. 311.

29. OSHA Instruction, supra note 9, at sections A.2.c. and A.2.d. See also 29 CFR 1910.5(f).

30. See eg, *Tampa Shipyards, Inc.*, 1992 OSHRC Lexis 28 (Mar. 10, 1992) regarding deaths caused by a crane, and OSHRC's lengthy evaluation of OSHA's crane standards to determine if they had preemptive effect on the agency's use of the general duty clause against Tampa.

31. *International Union v. General Dynamics Land Division*, 815 F.2d 1570 (DC Cir. 1987); 13 OSHC 1201, at 1205, 1207; cert denied, 108 S. Ct. 485 (1987).

32. 15 OSHC 1275, at 1285. However, in ultimately affirming the general duty citation, OSHRC relied on evidence of the employer's actual knowledge based on actual harm to its employees following exposure to freon in confined spaces, and also on formal grievances filed by the union and General Dynamics' posting of freon safety advisories at its facility.
33. See *International Union*, supra note 31.
34. OSHA's victory in *International Union v. General Dynamics* resulted in an OSHRC-reduced penalty of only $900 against the employer. For many years, OSHA has based its penalties on the number of general duty violations. In 1995, OSHA tried to impose higher penalties by calculating an employer's liability on the basis of the number of workers exposed to the hazard. For example, OSHA cited the Arcadian Corporation for 87 violations following a urea reactor explosion at the company's fertilizer plant. A fine of $4.3 million was proposed for 87 endangered lives. OSHRC, however, held that the agency lacked authority under OSHAct to impose liability on the basis of head counts. *Secretary of Labor v. Arcadian Corp.*, OSHRC, No. 93-3270 (Sept. 15, 1995); 17 OSHC 1345 (1995).

    Some members of Congress seek to dismantle OSHA. To assure its survival, the agency has ameliorated its enforcement policies. See OSHA Draft Compliance Directives on Penalty and Citation Policies (Aug. 14, 1995), in which the agency proposes to reduce penalties and, in some circumstances, eliminate penalties for small- and medium-sized employers.
35. 29 USC 655(b)(7).
36. See 29 CFR 1910.101–1910.111 and O'Connor C, Lirtzman S: Handbook of Chemical Industry Labeling (1986).
37. Begley R: Buyer's Green Demands Challenge Suppliers, Chemical Week (Aug. 23, 1995), p. 43.
38. Zoll D: Product Liability and Labels, in Handbook of Chemical Industry Labeling, supra note 36.
39. 29 CFR 1910.1200.
40. Baram M: Risk Communication as a Regulatory Alternative for Protecting Health, Safety, and Environment, Report to the Administrative Conference of the United States—Part II (1989).
41. Tyson P: The Preemptive Effect of the OSHA Hazard Communication Standard on State and Community Right-to-Know Laws, Notre Dame Law Rev 62:1010, 1011, 1987.
42. 29 CFR 1910.1200(d)(2).
43. 29 CFR 1910.1200(b)(3) and (b)(4), and 29 CFR 1910.1200(d)(5).
44. Fed Reg 48:53,295, 1983; see also *General Carbon v. OSHA*, 1988 LW 17401 (DC Cir. 1988).
45. See Begley R, supra note 37. See also Technology Transfer for Improving Chemical Risk Management (eight case studies), in Baram M, Dillon P, Ruffle B: Managing Chemical Risks, Lewis Publ. Co., 1992.
46. See Baram M, supra note 40.

GREGG M. STAVE, MD, JD, MPH

CONTROL OF BIOLOGIC HAZARDS

From the Occupational Health
Services
Glaxo Wellcome Inc.
Research Triangle Park, North
Carolina

Reprint requests to:
Gregg M. Stave, MD, JD, MPH
Associate Director
Occupational Health Services
Glaxo Wellcome Inc.
5 Moore Drive
Research Triangle Park, NC 27709

Biologic hazards are found in numerous workplace settings, including clinical and research laboratories, fermentation plants, patient care facilities, and the food, detergent, furniture, forestry, veterinary, and biotechnology industries. The diversity of sources of biologic hazards requires various prevention strategies. Local, state, and federal governments have recognized that biologic hazards represent significant public and workplace health issues. Attempts to control these hazards have produced a patchwork of overlapping state and federal statutes and regulations.

OSHA STANDARDS AND GUIDELINES

The Bloodborne Pathogen Standard

The Occupational Safety and Health Administration has issued only one standard addressing biologic hazards in the workplace. The Bloodborne Pathogen Standard[1] was issued in December 1991 and became effective in March 1992. The standard applies to all employers with employees that may be exposed to bloodborne pathogens, which are defined as pathogenic microorganisms that are present in human blood and can cause disease. These pathogens include but are not limited to hepatitis B virus and human immunodeficiency virus. The standard applies not only to hospitals, doctors' offices, and dental suites, but also to clinical and research laboratories, mortuaries, emergency response units, lifeguarding, and medical equipment maintenance.

The first requirement of the Bloodborne Pathogen Standard is the performance of an "exposure determination." Employers must evaluate the potential for employees to be exposed to bloodborne pathogens. The term *occupational exposure* refers to the *potential* for occupational exposure under the standard. Occupational exposure means reasonably anticipated skin, eye, mucous membrane, or parenteral contact with potentially infectious materials on the job. Employees who use personal protective equipment such as gloves are considered to be exposed. If employees have the potential for occupational exposure to bloodborne pathogens, the employer must develop a written exposure control plan. Bloodborne pathogen exposure can occur from handling substances other than blood, such as semen, vaginal secretions, cerebrospinal fluid, pleural fluid, pericardial fluid, peritoneal fluid, amniotic fluid, saliva in dental procedures, and fluids that are visibly contaminated by blood. Also, body fluids from deceased individuals can be infectious. The standard also recognizes that unfixed human tissues are potentially infectious, as are "HIV-containing cell or tissue cultures, organ cultures, and HIV- or HBV-containing culture medium or other solution; and blood, organs, or other tissues from experimental animals infected with HIV or HBV." Some materials not mentioned in the standard may also be infectious, including non-human primate-derived materials as well as tissues or cell lines derived from human or primate sources. HIV should only be found in early generations of cell lines because it does not replicate outside the host. By contrast, HBV may persist.

An employee is at risk of exposure if he or she handles these biologic materials or substances. Whereas exposure risk is negligible for personnel who work in health care settings but do not handle body substances, the emergency response duties of worksite first aid teams may lead to contact with blood or body fluids of injured co-workers. For these personnel, the employer should provide appropriate training and personal protective equipment and offer the hepatitis B vaccine. (An OSHA ruling in June 1993 permits employers to delay the vaccination of first aid providers in specific situations. Employers considering this option should carefully review the practical implications of this policy.)

If workers can be exposed to bloodborne pathogens on the job, the employer's written exposure control plan must specify engineering controls, personal protective equipment, and work practice controls that focus on universal precautions. All blood and body fluids should be regarded at all times as potentially infectious.

Special requirements apply to facilities engaged in the culture, production, concentration, experimentation, and manipulation of HIV and HBV. The scale of these operations determines their classification as either research or production facilities.

The employer must provide training and annual retraining in the use of personal protective equipment, safe storage and transport of body fluids, safe disposal of potentially infectious wastes, effective decontamination of contaminated work surfaces, and prohibition of storage or consumption of food and drink in areas where there is a reasonable likelihood of exposure. Hepatitis B vaccine must be provided promptly by the employer at no cost to the employees at reasonable risk of exposure. Employees who refuse the vaccine should sign an OSHA-specified declination form. The standard also requires a procedure to evaluate employees who have had an exposure, to determine the potential infectivity of the source, and to provide appropriate medical care for the exposed worker. The employer must keep records documenting training, vaccination (or declination), and post-exposure evaluation.

Guidelines for Tuberculosis

In October 1993, OSHA issued mandatory guidelines for an enforcement policy intended to protect workers from tuberculosis.[2] This action was prompted by increasing reports of occupationally acquired TB infection among health care workers, including several deaths from multidrug-resistant TB. The OSHA guidelines are based on the Centers for Disease Control and Prevention's 1990 *Guidelines for Preventing the Transmission of Tuberculosis in Health-Care Settings, with Special Focus on HIV-Related Issues*.[3] The guidelines are primarily designed for health care facilities, correctional institutions, homeless shelters, long-term care facilities for the elderly, drug treatment centers, and other sites where workers are at increased risk of exposure.

OSHA has mandated that employers develop a TB infection control program. Elements of this program must include (1) a protocol for early identification of persons with active TB, (2) a medical surveillance program, (3) evaluation and management of workers with positive TB skin tests or evidence of active TB, (4) isolation of persons with suspected or confirmed TB in appropriate isolation rooms, and (5) employee training and information. The medical surveillance requirement includes pre-placement evaluations along with periodic administration and interpretation of TB skin tests. The frequency of testing depends on the risk of exposure. Medical surveillance and the evaluation and management of workers with positive Mantoux tests must be at no cost to the employee.

In October 1994, the CDC issued *Guidelines for Preventing the Transmission of Mycobacterium tuberculosis in Health-Care Facilities, 1994*.[4] The purpose of the recommendations is to reduce the risk of transmitting tuberculosis to health care workers and other personnel in health care facilities as well as to patients, volunteers, and visitors. The primary focus of the recommendations is the inpatient facility where health care is provided, i.e., hospitals, medical wards in correctional facilities, and nursing homes. Additional recommendations are made for ambulatory care facilities, emergency departments, home health care sites, emergency medical services, medical offices, and dental suites.

The CDC publication provides extensive detail on the development of a TB infection control plan. Components of the plan include (1) assigning responsibility for the program to specific persons, (2) conducting a risk assessment and periodically repeating the assessment, (3) developing a written TB infection control plan based on the risk assessment, (4) educating and training health care workers, and (5) designing a medical surveillance program that includes counseling and screening health care workers for TB. An infection control program should include measures for prompt identification, treatment, and isolation of infectious persons. Protection of workers should always include engineering controls and appropriate respiratory protection.

The October 1993 OSHA enforcement policy was intended as an interim measure. A formal OSHA compliance directive will be developed after OSHA completes a review of the CDC *Guidelines for Preventing the Transmission of Mycobacterium tuberculosis in Health-Care Facilities, 1994*. At least five unions have submitted petitions asking OSHA to develop a standard and to proceed with rulemaking.

STATE PUBLIC HEALTH LAWS

Infection Control

States addressing workplace hazards may enact public health laws that go beyond the requirements of OSHA. For example, North Carolina enacted Control Measures for Communicable Diseases in 1990.[5] This broad legislation essentially codified the recommendations and guidelines found in Control of Communicable

Diseases in Man, a publication of the American Public Health Association.[6] The statute also created specific requirements for control, diagnosis, treatment, follow-up, prevention, and reporting of HIV, HBV, other sexually transmitted diseases, and tuberculosis.

The North Carolina law focuses extensively on the prevention of transmission of HIV and HBV from infected health care workers to patients. Although this public health issue does not involve a hazard for the health care worker, it deserves mention because occupational health practitioners are frequently asked to provide assistance with this matter. In North Carolina, health care workers infected with HBV or HIV who perform or assist (in a manner in which patients may be exposed to their blood) in surgical, obstetric, or dental procedures must notify the state health director. The director must investigate the practice involved and the risk of transmission to patients. If the director determines that there is a significant risk, the information collected must be reviewed by an expert panel. The panel then makes recommendations to the director regarding restriction from work, identification of potentially exposed patients, and periodic review of the medical condition of the health care worker. Infected workers who are permitted to continue their work must take a course on infection control.

North Carolina also requires all health care workers, emergency responders, and funeral service personnel to follow blood and body precautions with all patients, but the law does not define blood and body precautions. It seems likely, however, that the definition would be adapted from Control of Communicable Diseases in Man, which equates blood and body precautions with universal precautions. Under this definition, blood and certain body fluids (any visibly bloody body secretion, semen, vaginal secretions, tissue, cerebrospinal fluid, and synovial, pleural, peritoneal, pericardial and amniotic fluids) of all patients are considered potentially infectious. This definition is similar but not identical to the definitions provided under OSHA's Bloodborne Pathogen Standard. For example, the OSHA standard specifies unfixed tissue or organs as potentially infectious instead of simply "tissue." The OSHA definition also includes saliva in dental procedures. Compliance with the state law and OSHA regulations would require the adoption of the broadest set of definitions.

Mandatory Reporting

To monitor public health concerns, all states have developed mandatory reporting laws for various conditions. These laws facilitate both investigation and surveillance of communicable diseases and other conditions of public health importance. Many infectious illnesses of occupational significance are included under these laws.

The North Carolina Administrative Code requires attending physicians to promptly report a long list of infections and other conditions that may represent public health concerns.[7] Potentially work-related infections listed in the statute include anthrax, foodborne illness, hepatitis A, hepatitis B, tularemia, blastomycosis, brucellosis, HIV, psittacosis, Q fever, tetanus, and Rocky Mountain spotted fever. Clinicians should be familiar with their own state's reporting requirements.

NIH RECOMBINANT DNA GUIDELINES

In the 1970s, recombinant DNA was a relatively new concept and technology. Its proponents argued that the tremendous power of the new technology would propel science forward to improved understanding of man and disease. Detractors countered that the safety of this technology was unproven and that recombinant

DNA had the potential to destroy mankind through the creation of virulent or cancer-causing organisms that could not be controlled. This debate raged in many places, including Cambridge, Massachusetts, home of MIT and Harvard University. As a result, the city of Cambridge declared a moratorium on recombinant DNA research that lasted for several years.

The concerns of prominent biologists and other critics of recombinant DNA research have led to the development of many controls and practices designed to prevent propagation of, and infection by, potentially harmful molecules and organisms.

For example, the National Institutes of Health has developed (and frequently revised) a series of guidelines that address recombinant DNA.[8] These guidelines specify appropriate practices for constructing and handling recombinant DNA molecules as well as organisms and viruses containing recombinant DNA molecules. The NIH guidelines specifically apply to all recombinant DNA research conducted or sponsored by an institution that receives funding from the NIH. However, these guidelines are generally considered to be the standard of practice and are adopted by most organizations conducting research involving recombinant DNA. The guidelines are detailed and complex and must be thoroughly understood by any institution involved in recombinant DNA research. Some of the unique aspects of the guidelines are discussed here in broad terms.

The guidelines include classifications of microorganisms according to the hazard presented. They also address physical containment recommendations (engineering controls). Importantly, the guidelines set up a series of administrative controls, which include the creation of an institutional biosafety committee (IBC), designation of a biological safety officer (BSO), and designation of specific responsibilities for principal investigators.

The IBC evolved from the early days of controversy about recombinant DNA. The IBC must have at least five members; at least two members not affiliated with the institution must "represent the interest of the surrounding community with respect to health protection and the environment." The BSO is also a member of the committee. Appointment of a BSO is required for any research conducted at Biosafety Level 3 or Biosafety Level 4, which are the levels requiring the greatest degree of containment.

The IBC must review and approve research that complies with the guidelines. The review must include an independent assessment of the appropriate containment level and documentation that persons conducting the research have the requisite facilities, procedures, practices, training, and expertise. The BSO must assess compliance through periodic laboratory inspections.

OTHER REGULATIONS

Immunization for Travel

International business travelers may acquire one or more infectious diseases. Many countries require proof of specific vaccinations before they will issue a visa. Vaccination information can be obtained through embassies, the CDC, the World Health Organization, and local public health departments.

Occupational physicians should be aware that legally mandated vaccination prior to travel represents only the minimum level of protection against infectious disease. Other vaccines or medications intended to protect personal health, including those directed against tetanus, polio, hepatitis A, and malaria, should not be neglected.

Biologic Waste

Biologic waste represents an occupational hazard for those who generate it, collect it, and dispose of it. Biologic waste can be categorized in various ways. Regulations often characterize waste as medical, infectious, pathologic, or microbiologic. Different regulations often describe requirements for waste handling and disposal using the same terminology but with different or overlapping definitions. In addition, complex and inconsistent federal, state, and local laws and regulations may apply in a particular jurisdiction.

OSHA's Bloodborne Pathogen Standard covers the handling of some wastes in the workplace but does not address the treatment and disposal of waste once it leaves the generating facility. The standard defines "regulated waste" as follows:

> liquid of semi-liquid blood or other potentially infectious material; contaminated items that would release blood or other potentially infectious materials in a liquid or semi-liquid state if compressed; items that are caked with dried blood or other potentially infectious materials and are capable of releasing these materials during handling; contaminated sharps; and pathological and microbiological wastes containing blood or other potentially infectious materials.

The specific requirements for handling regulated waste include specifications for containers. For example, containers for contaminated sharps must be closable, puncture-resistant, leakproof, and labeled, or color-coded.

States and localities differ on the regulation of waste disposal. For example, in North Carolina, the responsibility for medical waste regulation falls to the Solid Waste Section of the North Carolina Department of Environment, Health and Natural Resources.[9] This agency divides medical waste into "general waste," which includes sharps and blood and body fluids in volumes less than 20 ml, and "regulated medical waste," which includes blood and body fluids in individual containers greater than 20 ml, as well as microbiologic waste and pathologic waste. Regulated medical waste must be incinerated or treated prior to disposal.

Even though they use identical terms, the OSHA standard and the state definitions focus on different parts of the waste handling process. Regarding regulated medical waste, application of the OSHA definition to the waste disposal process in North Carolina would overclassify waste and increase handling costs. For example, used gloves, bloody gauze, dressings, and bandages would be handled not as general waste but as waste requiring incineration or treatment. However, the distinctions in the definitions of waste seem reasonable because the concerns relating to the workplace (OSHA regulations) differ from those relating to the environment and public health (EPA and state regulations). Moreover, the degree of work-related health risks may distinguish clinical worksites from waste treatment and disposal operations. For example, waste workers can use mechanical equipment, other engineering controls, and personal protective gear that would be inappropriate in the patient care environment. In any event, because uniformity in the use and meaning of terms related to waste is not likely to occur, those responsible for handling and disposal must pay close attention to defined terms if they are to understand the applicable laws and regulations.

REFERENCES

1. 29 CFR 1910.1030.
2. OSHA Directorate of Compliance Programs: Memorandum for Regional Administrators. Enforcement Policy and Procedures for Occupational Exposure to Tuberculosis. Washington, DC, Dept. of Labor, October 8, 1993.

3. Centers for Disease Control: Guidelines for preventing the transmission of tuberculosis in health-care settings, with special focus on HIV-related issues. MMWR 39(RR-17):1–29, 1990.
4. Centers for Disease Control and Prevention: Guidelines for preventing the transmission of Mycobacterium tuberculosis in health-care facilities, 1994. MMWR 43(RR-13): 1994.
5. North Carolina Administrative Code Title 15A Department of Environment, Health and Natural Resources, chapter 19. Health: Epidemiology, subchapter 19A Communicable Disease Control, Section .0200. Control Measures for Communicable Diseases.
6. American Public Health Association: Control of Communicable Diseases in Man. Washington, DC, American Public Health Association, 1990.
7. North Carolina Administrative Code Title 15A Department of Environment, Health and Natural Resources, chapter 19. Health: Epidemiology, subchapter 19A Communicable Disease Control, Section .0100. Reporting of Communicable Diseases.
8. National Institutes of Health: Guidelines for research involving recombinant DNA molecules (NIH Guidelines) June 1994. Federal Register July 5, 1994, Separate Part IV.
9. North Carolina Administrative Code Title 15A Department of Environment, Health and Natural Resources, chapter 13, subchapter 13B. Solid Waste Management. Section .1200. Medical Waste Management.

JACK W. SNYDER, MD, JD, PhD

JULIA E. KLEES, MD, MPH

DRUG TESTING PROGRAMS IN GOVERNMENT AGENCIES AND PRIVATE WORKPLACES

The Legal Challenge Continues

From Thomas Jefferson University
Philadelphia, Pennsylvania (JWS)
and
BASF Corporation (JEK)
Mt. Olive, New Jersey

Reprint requests to:
Jack W. Snyder, MD, JD, PhD
Associate Professor
Departments of Emergency
    Medicine and Laboratory
    Medicine
401 Pavilion
Thomas Jefferson University
    Hospital
125 South 11th Street
Philadelphia, PA 19107-4998

The belief that drug use is causally related to numerous social ills is widely held. In the workplace, employers perceive that diminished performance, decreased productivity, poor attendance, safety problems, theft, narcotic sales (and other undesirable or criminal acts), increased benefit awards, low morale, lack of customer confidence, and poor public relations represent significant costs related to employee substance abuse. As a result, many private and government organizations have sought to prevent drug abuse by conducting periodic and random drug testing of their employees. These efforts to detect licit and illicit substance use by employees have sparked significant controversy.[1]

Documented substance abuse in the United States military during the 1970s and detection of illicit substances in the body fluids of transportation workers involved in highly publicized accidents during 1980s led President Reagan to sign Executive Order 12564, which prohibited use of illegal drugs by federal employees and directed federal agencies to develop educational, assistance, and testing programs designed to achieve drug-free workplaces. At the request of Congress and President Reagan, the U.S. Department of Health and Human Services (DHHS) published *Mandatory Guidelines for Federal Workplace Drug Testing Programs*, and the Department of Transportation (DOT) published *Procedures for Transportation Workplace*

Drug Testing Programs.[2] In 1991, the Omnibus Transportation Employee Testing Act was signed by President Bush to mandate drug and alcohol testing of any individuals in the transportation industry who perform safety-sensitive functions; the Omnibus Act also codifies the DHHS guidelines.[3] Implementation of these laws has resulted in mandatory employee drug testing beyond the military. (As of 1996, nearly 10 million transportation and other workers must be tested by law.)

The federal government sought to increase the likelihood that verification of a positive result, that is, a "true positive" constituting evidence of illegal drug use, reflected accuracy and reliability in the laboratory as well as a reasonable balance between individual rights of privacy and corporate responsibilities to maintain a safe workplace. Drug testing sets the employer's responsibility to provide and maintain a safe workplace on a collision course with the individual's right of privacy. Employee drug testing, including the complex interplay of the regulatory agency, the court, the clinician, and the laboratory, contributes to the precarious balance between workplace needs and an individual's privacy.

THE LEGAL FRAMEWORK FOR DRUG TESTING

American physicians and employers contend with a significant lack of coordination among federal, state, and local laws regarding substance abuse testing. While federal laws require drug testing and substance abuse programs, inconsistent state and local laws restrict drug testing,[4] and court decisions have established conflicting standards for workplace testing. To assess the impact of law at any of the three stages of drug testing, the following questions must be addressed: Is the individual to be tested a public employee or subject to a government-mandated program in the private sector? Is the individual to be tested covered under the terms of a collective bargaining agreement? Is he or she subject to provisions of either a contract or a personnel manual? Is the person to be tested protected by the Americans with Disabilities Act or by state or federal rehabilitation laws? Is the purpose of drug testing to discriminate on the basis of race, religion, gender, or national origin (in violation of Title VII of the Civil Rights Act of 1964)? Does the person to be tested live or work in a jurisdiction where drug testing may violate public policy or breach covenants of good faith and fair dealing? In many states, the answers to these questions are complex or unknown, yet employers and their physician advisers must grapple with these issues to avoid unwanted legal entanglements that can derail a drug testing program.

Regulatory Requirements

When drug testing is required by the government, a government agency, or a private company or individual acting at the direction of the government, significant restrictions may be placed on the testing. These government entities, unlike private employers or persons, are viewed as agents of the state whose conduct is governed by constitutional protections of an individual's rights, including the right to privacy. By contrast, there are presently few constitutional limits on the parameters of drug testing in the private sector because, typically, only agencies or individuals acting on behalf of the state can infringe on constitutional rights.

Privacy rights are an issue in the context of drug testing because the Fourth Amendment to the United States Constitution prohibits unreasonable searches and seizures, and a drug test is a *search* of a person's body fluids. The concept of privacy must be balanced against a reasonable, legitimate governmental need to search. Court decisions interpreting the Fourth Amendment typically indicate that a search is not reasonable unless it is based on some level of suspicion;[5] they also indicate that the privacy interests of individuals are outweighed by the government's interest in detecting drug users and deterring them from acquiring safety- and security-sensitive positions.[6]

The United States Supreme Court has ruled that if government interests are sufficient, drug testing may not require any level of suspicion. Specifically, the court has held that mandatory and suspicionless testing of customs employees, railroad engineers, and voluntary student athletes is reasonable under the Fourth Amendment.[7] Thus, a positive drug test result obtained through random testing can, by itself, lead to loss of employment or athletic participation. Organized labor has vigorously opposed government-mandated drug testing, but its efforts so far have yielded only a requirement that split samples be collected. In practice, however, collecting split samples significantly increases costs, with only marginal benefit to employees.[8]

In 1995, federal appellate decisions on random drug testing can be placed on a spectrum awaiting a Supreme Court ruling.[9] Random testing programs have been upheld when public safety, national security, or school disciplinary concerns are deemed more important than an individual's expectation of privacy.[7,10] However, random testing programs such as those involving clerical workers or water meter readers have been struck down because they interfere with protected Fourth Amendment rights in the absence of any threat to public safety or security. Cases upholding random testing in the absence of any threat to public safety or security, have been decided where the individuals to be tested have had diminished expectations of privacy (e.g., jockeys or athletes).[11] Thus, it is important to analyze random drug testing cases from a job-specific viewpoint, focusing on safety or security issues to decide if testing is permissible.

Regulatory requirements in individual states add additional confusion to drug testing program implementation. The Omnibus Act and related 1994 regulations preempt local and state drug testing requirements for employees undergoing DOT-mandated substance abuse testing.[3] However, non-DOT drug and alcohol testing is subject to the diverse and local statutes summarized in Table 1.[4]

Substance Abuse Testing Program Design and Performance

Employers who are convinced of the need, value, and legal permissibility of drug testing must implement (in writing with advance notice to each employee) policies, procedures, and methods of testing that are reasonably related to and designed accomplish a legitimate purpose. At the analytic or testing stage, employers must address the following issues: Who should be tested (e.g., applicants, safety-sensitive personnel, all employees)? When should testing be performed (e.g., randomly, post-accident, reasonable suspicion)? Who will administer the program (e.g., human resources, corporate medical, or another corporate department)? Who will collect the urine specimens (e.g., nurse, doctor, technician)?[12] How will the urine specimens be collected (e.g., assess urine temperature, use blue toilet water, witnessed v. unwitnessed urination)? Will a SAMHSA-certified laboratory be used to perform the specimen analysis? What analytic technique or methodology will be used? Will the screening test be confirmed by gas chromatograph/mass spectrometry? Will the chain-of-custody be preserved (e.g., through proper labeling, sealing, and documentation)? Will a medical review officer be used for non-regulated testing? What employment options are available to employees who have a positive drug test result? Is there an opportunity for employees to explain, undergo retesting, provide split samples, or enter rehabilitation in lieu of termination of employment or discharge as part of a

TABLE 1.   Reference Table of State and Local Restrictions on Private Sector
(Non-mandated) Drug Testing

State	Required Drug Testing Procedure	Restrictions on Scope of Testing			
		Applicant Testing	Reasonable Suspicion	Post Accident	Random Testing
Alabama	No testing statute	✓	✓	✓	✓
Alaska	No testing statute	✓	✓	✓	Limited CS
Arizona (voluntary)	P/N, CL, COC, CON, CTR, OR	✓	✓	✓	✓
Arkansas	No testing statute	✓	✓	✓	✓
California	No testing statute	Uncertain CS	✓	Q1	Limited CS
CA, City of Berkeley	No testing statute	✓	✓	Q1	Prohibited S
CA, San Francisco	No testing statute	✓	✓	Q1	Prohibited S
Colorado	No testing statute	✓	✓	✓	✓
CO, Boulder	No testing statute	✓	✓	Q1	Prohibited S
Connecticut	CON, CTR, OR	✓	✓	Q1	Limited S/CS
Delaware	No testing statute	✓	✓	✓	✓
District of Columbia	No testing statute	✓	✓	✓	✓
Florida (voluntary)	P/N, CL, CO, COC, CON, CTR, MRO, OR, EAP, ET	✓	✓	✓	✓
Georgia (voluntary)	P/N, C/L, COC, CON, CTR, OR, EAP, ET	✓	✓	✓	✓
Hawaii	P/N, CL, CO, COC, CON, CTR, MRO	Q	Q	Q	Q2
Idaho	No testing statute	✓	✓	✓	✓
Illinois	No testing statute	✓	✓	✓	✓
Indiana	No testing statute	✓	✓	✓	✓
Iowa	P/N, CL, CO, COC, CON, CTR, OR, EAP	Q3	✓	Q1	Prohibited S
Kansas	No testing statute	✓	✓	✓	✓
Kentucky	No testing statute	✓	✓	✓	✓
Louisiana	P/N, CL, CO, COC, CON, MRO, RT, REP	Q	Q	Q	Q
Maine	P/N, CL, CO, COC, CON, MRO, RT, CTR	Q/CS	Q1	Q1	Limited S
Maryland	P/N, CL, CO, COC, CON, MRO, RT, CTR	✓	✓	✓	✓
Massachusetts	No testing statute	✓	✓	Q1	Limited CS
Michigan	No testing statute	✓	✓	✓	✓
Minnesota	P/N, CL, COC, CON, OR, RT, CTR, EAP	✓	✓	Q1	Limited CS
Mississippi (voluntary)	P/N, CL, CO, COC, CON, OR, RT, REP	✓	✓	✓	✓
Missouri		✓	✓	✓	✓
Montana	P/N, CL, CO, COC, CON, CTR, MRO, OR, RT	Q4	✓	Q1	Prohibited S
Nebraska	CL, COC, CON, CTR	✓	✓	✓	✓
Nevada	No testing statute	✓	✓	✓	✓
New Hampshire	No testing statute	✓	✓	✓	✓
New Jersey	No testing statute	✓	✓	✓	Uncertain
New Mexico	No testing statute	✓	✓	✓	✓
New York	No testing statute	Uncertain CS	✓	✓	Uncertain
North Carolina	CL, COC, CON, RT	Q	Q	Q	Q
North Dakota	No testing statute	✓	✓	✓	✓
Ohio	No testing statute	✓	✓	✓	✓
Oklahoma	P/N, CL, CO, COC, CON, CTR, OR, RT, EAP	Q	Q	Q	Q

(Continued on facing page)

TABLE 1.   Reference Table of State and Local Restrictions on Private Sector (Non-mandated) Drug Testing *(Continued)*

State	Required Drug Testing Procedures	Restrictions on Scope of Testing			
		Applicant Testing	Reasonable Suspicion	Post Accident	Random Testing
Oregon	CL, CON	✓	✓	✓	✓
Pennsylvania	No testing statute	✓	✓	✓	✓
Rhode Island	CON, OR, RT, EAP	✓	✓	Q1	Prohibited S
South Carolina	No testing statute	✓	✓	✓	✓
South Dakota	No testing statute	✓	✓	✓	✓
Tennessee	No testing statute	✓	✓	✓	✓
Texas	No testing statute	✓	✓	✓	✓
Utah (voluntary)	P/N, COC, CON, CTR	✓	✓	✓	✓
Vermont	P/N, CL, CO, COC, CON CTR, OR, RT, EAP	Q5	✓	Q1	Prohibited S
Virginia	No testing statute	✓	✓	✓	✓
Washington	No testing statute	✓	✓	✓	✓
West Virginia	No testing statute	✓	✓	Q1	Limited CS
Wisconsin	No testing statute	✓	✓	✓	✓
Wyoming	No testing statute	✓	✓	✓	✓

This table is provided as a quick reference. Policies and procedures should be reviewed by an attorney. (From Shults T: The state law mosaic—general considerations. MRO Alert 6(3):10–14, 1995; with permission.)

Voluntary statutes:
    Employers who voluntarily adopt the statutes' standards and procedures are provided with specific benefits such as lower worker compensation insurance premiums and legal protection from civil suits.

Required testing procedures:

PN   Policy and/or Notice. Statute requires written policy and/or specific notice to employees and or applicants. The notice typically requires specific information to be given, and in some cases is quite detailed. Maine is unique in that it requires that the employer must have the policy approved by a stage agency prior to testing.

CL   Certified Laboratory. Just using a SAMHSA certified laboratory may not fulfill the state requirement. Many of the state statutes specify the use of a state certified laboratory.

CO   Cut-off. Like DHHS's mandatory guidelines, some states mandate specific cut-off levels for the laboratory. This may imply a limited menu of drugs.

COC   Chain-of-Custody. Usually this requirement is fulfilled by following the DHHS/DOT guidelines. In many cases the statute does not provide any detail on how the COC requirement should be met. Florida has required a state approved COC form.

CON   Confirmation of all Initial Positives. This usually requires GC/MS confirmation.

CTR   Confidential Test Results. With the exception of Rhode Island, every state that has a drug testing statute, explicitly requires that the results be held confidentially.

MRO   Medical Review Officer. Oklahoma is the first state to require verification of test results by a review officer. The Oklahoma law also requires 12 hours of approved training for the MRO. Many of the state statutes were passed in the mid 1980s prior to the widespread use of MROs. Recent statutes have included this require-ment and/or the closely related "opportunity to rebut test results."

OR   Opportunity to Rebut Test Results.

PRV   Connecticut and Rhode Island prohibit the direct observation of collection. Minnesota, Montana, and North Carolina require consideration of individual privacy in the collection process.

RT   Opportunity to Retest.

EAP   Employee Assistance/Rehabilitation/SAP. Unlike the federal programs, some states mandate that the employer pay for these services.

ET   Education/Training for employees or supervisors.

Restrictions on Scope of Testing:

✓   See article on general considerations. No statutory restrictions.

CS   Case Law. There has been a judicial decision that has restricted or prohibited this type of testing.

S   Statute.

Q   Qualified. There are technical or procedural requirements in some category of testing.

Q1   Post-accident drug testing can only be performed when there is independent reasonable suspicion to believe that the individual involved was intoxicated or impaired and/or there is reasonable suspicion to believe that drugs or alcohols were involved in or resulted in the accident.

Q2   Restrictive testing bill pending in Hawaii state legislature.

Q3   Iowa—Applicant drug testing must be part of "physical"; there are also specific notice requirements under Iowa state law.

Q4   Montana—Permitted only in safety sensitive positions. See state for conditions and definition of safety sensitive positions.

Q5   Vermont—10 day advance notice of applicant test required. See state statute.

last chance agreement? Who will provide treatment if any is provided? If employees are represented by a union, how long will the union representative be allowed, once contacted, to advise an employee confronted with suspected drug use?

There are several contexts in which drug testing occurs, with varying levels of expectation of privacy. Applicant testing refers to either preemployment testing of an applicant prior to offering employment or as a prerequisite to offering regular employment to a temporary employee. Post-accident testing is defined as testing of employees involved in any accident at work that causes physical injury or property damage. Post-rehabilitation, or back-to-work testing, refers to testing of an employee without advance notice who has returned to work after having completed treatment for substance abuse, as part of a structured rehabilitation program. Reasonable suspicion testing occurs when the employer has a reasonable belief to suspect that an employee is using drugs or alcohol based on appearance, accident rate, performance problems, possession of drug paraphernalia on premises, or other reliable information. Finally, random testing or testing without suspicion implies testing an individual without having reasonable suspicion of drug use; it represents the greatest invasion of a person's constitutional privacy.

Physicians involved in drug testing should note that (a) consent forms signed by the testee decrease the physician's risk of liability for invasion of privacy while an employee's failure to sign consent forms could subject that person to discipline or discharge; (b) testees have separate privacy interests in the testing process, including the act of urination, the urine itself, and the information contained therein; (c) a positive urine drug test does not necessarily correlate with impairment, does not prove use of drugs at work, does not distinguish casual from habitual use, and does not always require treatment; and (d) immediate supervisors should not be told specific test results. Rather, one person should be designated by an employer to receive results, communicate with employees, and make referrals.

Interpretation of Results and Effects on Rights

ROLE OF THE LABORATORY

Approximately 78 laboratories in the U.S. are certified by the Substance Abuse and Mental Health Services Administration (SAMHSA) to perform federally mandated drug testing. To become certified, a drug testing laboratory must correctly identify and confirm the presence of specified drugs (typically marijuana, cocaine, codeine, morphine, phencyclidine, and amphetamines) in 90% of test samples submitted in each of three cycles of performance testing. The laboratory is immediately disqualified if it reports just one false positive test in any cycle. The laboratory also must accurately measure drug concentrations in 80% of test samples to within 20% of the known value for a given sample. Once certified, a lab must correctly analyze at least 10 samples bimonthly and be inspected twice per year.

As a matter of fundamental fairness and regardless of the nature of any contractual arrangement with an employer, at least one court has found that a drug testing laboratory owes a legal duty to both examinees and employers to ensure that the results reported to the employer are correct.[14] Negligent testing or a false positive result could wrongfully identify the employee as a drug user, harm the employee's reputation, or curtail future employment opportunities for that individual. Laboratories are in the best position to prevent harm because they are solely responsible for testing and quality control and can bear the financial burden better than the person maligned by a false positive report.

The national impact of this case, *Stinson v. Physicians Immediate Care,* remains to be determined. At least one federal court has held that laboratories are third party contractors that do not owe a duty of care to specimen donors; moreover, a drug test does not constitute medical treatment or a request for medical information. The same court indicated that a false positive test result cannot provide the basis for a libel action because consent is a complete defense; malice is not implied or presumed from the mere fact of publication of the test results.[15] On appeal, the ruling that laboratories have no legal duty to use reasonable care in performing drug tests was upheld by the Fifth Circuit.[16]

In Texas, a woman sued a laboratory after her job offer was withdrawn because she tested positive for opiates. The plaintiff maintained that in the days before the test, she had eaten several poppy seed muffins. She argued that the laboratory contracted to perform the preemployment drug test should have informed her and her prospective employer that eating poppy seeds could cause a positive urine test result. The Texas Supreme Court rejected this assertion because imposing such a duty would require the laboratory to inform each test subject of all possible causes of positive results and would charge the laboratory with a responsibility that belongs to its clients. Moreover, placing such a duty on the laboratory impinges on the liability of other professionals for services rendered. The court also concluded that a simpler duty to warn of the possibilities that information may be misinterpreted is unworkable. Finally, the Texas court endorsed the refusal of other courts to impose a duty on a drug testing laboratory to perform follow-up testing on weakly positive samples or to ensure competent medical interpretation of results in the absence of a contractual duty to do so.[17]

EVIDENTIAL BREATH TESTING

The DOT alcohol testing program requires employers to conduct reasonable suspicion, post-accident, random, return-to-duty, and follow-up testing with evidential breath testing for employees performing safety-sensitive functions. The use of alcohol is legal, except where regulated by the DOT; thus, alcohol testing must establish the amount of alcohol currently present in the bloodstream during the performance of a safety-sensitive or other covered function. Employers are permitted to use only breath testing, and not blood or urine testing, for determining an employee's blood alcohol concentration. The DOT states that "evidential breath testing is as accurate, faster, relatively less expensive, and less invasive and frightening than blood testing. It eliminates the need for elaborate procedures for packaging, chain of custody, and laboratory certification."[18] An evidential breath testing device has been approved by the National Highway Traffic Safety Administration (NHTSA) for use in DOT-regulated alcohol testing. Recently, the DOT authorized the use of nonevidential alcohol testing devices for the initial screen; nonevidential devices include saliva testing devices.[19] Nonevidential devices may not be used for confirmation, which requires use of an evidential testing device approved by the NHTSA.

Employers must provide both an initial and confirmatory test to ensure the accuracy of the results. If the initial test result indicates a breath alcohol concentration of 0.04 g/dl or greater, the employee must be retested (using a new mouthpiece) within 15–60 minutes. A confirmed result in excess of 0.04 g/dl forces the employer to remove the employee from his or her job and to take further specified actions. An employee testing above 0.02 g/dl but below 0.04 g/dl must be removed from his position until he tests below 0.02 g/dl.

A medical review officer (MRO) is a licensed physician with knowledge of substance abuse disorders who receives laboratory results generated by a drug testing program. The MRO has appropriate medical training to interpret and correlate an examinee's positive test result with his or her medical history and any other relevant information; the MRO has specific knowledge of the medical use of prescription drugs and the pharmacology and toxicology of illicit drugs.[20] Every employer who undertakes drug testing under federal regulations must use an MRO to review and interpret positive test results. (Negative test results must be administratively reviewed and the records for one year.) Although current federal regulations do not address private sector drug testing, many private employers have elected to follow federal procedures, including use of an MRO, who must determine whether a positive result is justified and whether alternative medical explanations account for the result. If there is not a legitimate explanation for a positive result after discussion with the donor, the MRO must confirm the test result as a verified or true positive, and documentation must be kept for 5 years. (The most commonly detected drugs are marijuana, cocaine, benzodiazepines, and opiates.)

Within 72 hours of being notified of a positive drug test result, an employee donor covered by DOT guidelines can request that a second sample or split specimen be tested. A negative result from the second sample may be used to exonerate and correct an erroneous or false positive result obtained from the first sample. In writing, the MRO must instruct the laboratory that performed the first test to send the second urine sample to another laboratory certified by SAMHSA.

MROs may perform several other functions. The MRO may determine if, or when, an employee is fit to return to duty following rehabilitation. The MRO also may be required to report to a designated corporate official safety issues that arise during physical examination of a specimen donor (e.g., needle marks, clinical signs of intoxication) even if the laboratory result is not ultimately verified as positive. Physicians with MRO experience may serve as advisors when issues of drug use in the workplace arise.

Beyond DOT regulatory guidance, there are few clear standards to guide MROs who assume the roles mentioned above. To decrease the risk of error or failure to meet expectations of the employer, laboratory, specimen donor, or injured third parties, MROs are well-advised to provide only those services defined by written contract with the employer. MROs should limit their activities to those they have agreed to perform and should obtain appropriate insurance to cover those activities. Physicians should not undertake the role of MRO without appropriate training.[21] Possession of a medical license and specialty board certification does not assure competency in the interpretation of drug test results. To avoid lawsuits and potential liability, physicians must understand the legal, ethical, economic, scientific, and medical issues that make the role of MRO so unique.

The Americans with Disabilities Act and related regulations present another challenger to individuals or corporations undertaking forensic urine drug testing.[22] The ADA prohibits discrimination based on physical and mental disabilities in both private and public sector employment as well as provision of public services by public or private entities. The ADA prohibits employers from discriminating against an employee or potential employee in the process of hiring, firing, compensation, advancement, training, or other terms, conditions, and privileges of employment.[23]

In the hiring process, the employer may inquire into an applicant's ability to perform job-related functions; however, prior to offering employment, employers cannot specifically ask about disabilities or about prescription drug use that may suggest a disability.[24] Employers must provide reasonable accommodation to persons with disabilities who can perform the essential functions of the job unless the accommodation would create undue hardship for the employer. If a disabled applicant meets the prerequisites for employment, an employer must consider whether the applicant can perform the essential function of the position with or without reasonable accommodation.[25]

The impact of the ADA on drug testing depends on who is to be tested and when. For applicants as well as current employees, the ADA term *individual with a disability* does not include one who presently engages in the illegal use of drugs.[26] Employees are not required to accommodate those who currently use or are under the influence of nonprescribed illegal drugs. Discrimination does not occur if an employer chooses not to hire an applicant who illegally uses drugs or if a current employee who illegally uses drugs is discharged regardless of work performance or is retained and held to the same standard as other workers. Recovering addicts are protected by the ADA if they have completed successful rehabilitation or currently participate in a drug rehabilitation program and no longer engage in the illegal use of drugs.[27] Employees and applicants who are erroneously regarded as illegal drug users are also protected.

Although the ADA protects recovering drug addicts, it is neutral on drug testing; the ADA does not encourage, prohibit, restrict, or authorize testing at any time for illegal drugs. Therefore, an applicant or employee is not considered disabled simply by having a positive drug test result. A positive test simply shows evidence of current use, which is not a disability that merits protection under the ADA.[28]

The ADA specifically prohibits employers from administering medical exams prior to making a job offer.[29] However, testing for illegal drugs is not considered a medical exam under the ADA; applicants can be required to submit urine for testing for illegal drugs prior to receiving a conditional offer of employment. By contrast, alcohol testing is a prohibited preemployment examination.[30] Employers cannot require that applicants be tested for alcohol until after a conditional offer of employment is made; all offerees for the same position must be given the same test. An employer who rescinds a job offer to an applicant who tests positive for alcohol must be able to prove that the candidate is not qualified to perform the essential functions of the job with or without accommodation. In practice, most employers do not test applicants for alcohol because the knowledge gained does little to inform the employer about the candidate's ability to do the job. At least one influential federal court has agreed with this practice by striking down the Department of Transportation's rule mandating preemployment alcohol testing of commercial drivers.[31]

The ADA distinguishes alcohol use and illegal drug use for purposes of reasonable suspicion and random testing of current employees. Alcohol testing of employees must be job-related and justified by business necessity.[32] Unlike other substance abuse disorders, alcoholism per se is a protected disability under the ADA. Unless job performance is affected, an alcoholic is protected under the ADA even if currently using alcohol; alcoholics are held to the same standards as other employees, even in the face of unsatisfactory performance that may be related to alcoholism. The ADA may require an employer to provide a leave of absence to an employee with an alcohol problem *if* the employer provided similar leave to other employees with disabilities and the leave was for the purpose of medical treatment that would enable the employee to safely perform his duties.[33]

IMPACT OF THE FAMILY AND MEDICAL LEAVE ACT

The Family and Medical Leave Act of 1993 (FMLA) requires employers to provide up to 12 weeks of unpaid family or medical leave, with continuation of health insurance benefits.[34] The employee may subsequently return from the FMLA leave to the same or an equivalent position, with restoration of all previous benefits. A medical leave may be taken by an eligible employee for a serious health condition (physical or mental) that involves a period of incapacity and/or continuing treatment that results in an absence from work of more than 3 days. FMLA leave is available for treatment of substance abuse for eligible employees; however, the FMLA does not require that an employer disregard preexisting work rules and established policy.[35] The FMLA does not prevent termination or other employment action against an employee for substance abuse if the action is taken pursuant to preexisting policy.

SOURCES OF POTENTIAL LIABILITY

Employers implementing substance abuse policies must consider local developments in the concepts of wrongful discharge, discrimination resulting from use of lawful products, and negligence. Communications regarding test results must be kept confidential; substantial liability may result from improper disclosure of findings or other information. Defamation of character and invasion of privacy are significant liability concerns. Liability for negligent hiring may arise if an injured party establishes that the employer failed to sue reasonable care in the selection and retention of the employee.[36]

LABOR AND EMPLOYMENT LAW

Issues concerning unions, collective bargaining, arbitration, handbooks, and wrongful discharge have arisen in the context of drug testing. For example, drug testing appears to be a mandatory subject of bargaining regardless of whether testing is characterized as a matter of employee discipline and job security. The scope of bargaining may be limited, however, at least in the public sector. In the Fifth Circuit, if the parties negotiate to an impasse, a company cannot unilaterally impose drug testing. Indeed, arbitration may be required at that point. The same federal court, however, more recently decided that a substance abuse policy mandating preemployment, for-cause, and random testing is a health and safety policy and therefore excluded from arbitration under a collective bargaining agreement.[37]

Analysis of arbitral decisions suggests that arbitrators in general agree with the National Labor Relations Board that drug testing is a mandatory subject of bargaining in the absence of a clear and unmistakable waiver of bargaining rights. When a drug testing policy has been unilaterally implemented by an employer, however, most arbitrators have ruled against these actions.[38] By contrast, there is little consensus among arbitrators regarding substantive issues such as invasion of privacy or disciplinary action for positive test results. Of note, arbitral decisions suggest that neutrals will likely hold that discharge due to off-duty use of drugs requires a showing that such use affects job performance or causes injury to the employer's reputation.[39]

Does the Federal Service Labor-Management Relations Act require federal agencies to incorporate the details of drug testing programs into collective bargaining agreements with unions? The D.C. Circuit said no, expressing concern that subjecting these details to the grievance process would allow challenges from anyone—whether adversely affected or not—well before any testing began.[40]

A public employee's access to the federal courts in drug and alcohol testing cases can be barred by the terms of a collective bargaining agreement with his or her employer. Even where a drug testing policy has been held to be constitutionally infirm, a public employee may not pursue a civil rights suit based on that infirmity where his union and his employer agree to operate under that policy.[41]

Does a last-chance agreement signed after failing a drug test waive an employee's right to arbitrate? Not necessarily. The Third Circuit has indicated that a waiver, to be enforceable, must be premised on last-chance documents that are very carefully worded to say what issues can or cannot be submitted to arbitration.[42]

Does the existence of an employer handbook providing for progressively harder punishment for drug use preclude the employer from summarily firing workers who violate rules concerning drugs? The Sixth Circuit said no, since the handbook did not create contract rights or invade privacy.[43] Indeed, the handbook made it clear that "the usual steps may not always be followed." Importantly, other courts have noted that the receipt of a copy of a personnel practice manual does not create an employment contract such that violation of a provision prohibiting drug use requires written notice or warning prior to termination. This result is even more likely if the employee has, without fraudulent inducement, signed a waiver stating that receipt of a manual does not create a contract.[44]

May at-will employees who are fired for refusing to submit to a drug test sue their employers for wrongful discharge? Under limited circumstances in a few states, the answer may be yes. For example, public policy exceptions to the at-will doctrine may support actions based on tortious invasion of privacy or intrusion on seclusion. These claims would require proof of activities such as visual monitoring of the process of urination or inappropriate use of the sample to detect a medical condition.

What constitutes a breach of a union duty's to provide fair representation to a member discharged after testing positive? The Sixth Circuit has ruled that a union representative's failure to challenge a laboratory's methods of handling urine samples did not amount to a breach of duty to provide fair representation.[46] Must a union represent a member at grievance proceeding when that person has violated a last-chance agreement? Although some have argued that last chance means what it says, namely *last* chance, the courts have yet to speak on this issue.

Finally, wrongful discharge of government workers is illustrated by a case in which a police officer reported fellow officers who received payments for tipping off massage parlors about raids. She successfully sued for reinstatement by proving retaliation and violation of First, Fourth, and Fourteenth Amendment rights when her random drug test result was shown to be the product of tampering.[47]

UNEMPLOYMENT AND WORKERS' COMPENSATION LAW

Can workers discharged for failing a drug test obtain unemployment benefits? In most states, the answer remains unclear. In the private sector, a positive drug test (indicating mere presence of a drug in the body) may be all that is required to prove an employee has violated a policy prohibiting work while under the influence of drugs. Even if the employer's policy banning work under the influence does not require physical symptoms or impairment or observable adverse effects, the verified positive result, by itself, not only can serve as the basis for dismissal but also may be viewed as misconduct negating unemployment compensation. Thus, several courts have characterized a positive drug test, standing alone, as per se misconduct that prevents an unemployment award.[48]

Although one court has arguably narrowed the definition of misconduct by holding that a positive test is noncompensable misconduct *unless* the worker can prove that his or her addiction represents a bona fide illness, other have broadened the definition of noncompensable misconduct to include conviction on drug charges, refusal to provide a specimen for testing, refusal to apply to an employee assistance program or to undergo substance abuse treatment, wanton or willful disregard of company policy or the employer's best interests, and violation of a last chance agreement with or without a positive drug test.[49] By contrast, misconduct may not lead to loss of unemployment benefits if an employee submits a specimen but refuses to sign a consent or does not apply to an EAP due to lack of notice.[50] Thus, in the absence of more explicit statutory or regulatory guidance, employers should articulate a drug-free workplace policy that clearly states the conditions under which employees may be discharged for testing positive.

Can workers' compensation be awarded following an accident on the job even though the employee had a verified positive drug test? The answer is often not clear, but, in a few states, the admissibility of test results may require proof of a written drug test policy. Thus, in the absence of an explicit policy, a worker may arguably be compensated even though state law prohibits awards for accidents when intoxication contributed to the event and a positive drug test creates a statutory presumption of intoxication.[51]

CONCLUSION

Emphasizing a lack of research on the effectiveness of drug testing, one national panel has recently called for further study not only of the effects of drug use on job performance but also the effects of testing on both costs and deterrence in the workplace.[52] Some have interpreted the panel's report as saying that the effectiveness of workplace drug testing programs has not been proven; others suggest that the report does not explicitly make such a conclusion. However, despite the lack of firm support in the literature for quantifiable benefits associated with drug testing, the National Academy of Sciences panel did offer the following points of consensus:

- A drug is defined as any substance that affects psychologic or physiologic behavior; this includes alcohol.
- Alcohol should be stressed as a priority in anti-drug programs.
- In drug testing, it is the urine collection process that is most vulnerable to tampering.
- All workplace drug testing, including preemployment testing, must include gas chromatography/mass spectrometry in its confirmation procedures.
- Paper-and-pencil tests such as personality profiles and honesty tests are not necessarily good predictors of drug use; use of these tests risks the false identification of some workers as drug users while missing actual drug users.
- If treatment is necessary, employee assistance programs should provide for long-term follow-up to prevent relapse.
- Not everyone who tests positive necessarily needs treatment.
- Regardless of whether drug use occurs on the premises, it has potential workplace effects (such as hangovers) that should be considered in antidrug programs.
- The federal laboratory certification program run by SAMHSA should be kept to ensure accuracy of drug test results.
- Those who interpret test results must have expertise in toxicology, pharmacology, and occupational medicine.

The American business community has concluded that workplace drug testing deters drug use, promotes public safety, and saves money. The evolution of a multibillion dollar industry supporting drug testing means that this endeavor is likely to continue, even if more direct measures of cognitive impairment or worker performance are eventually developed. Increased numbers of physicians will participate in a process where they do not serve as patient advocates. Therefore, physicians and occupational health professionals must acquire substantial knowledge of law if they hope to maintain the precarious balance between legitimate employer needs and personal privacy; to prevent liability for themselves, laboratories, and employers; and to exert greater influence on the entire drug testing phenomenon.

REFERENCES

1. See e.g., Lundqist LA: Weighing the factors of drug testing for Fourth Amendment balancing. Geo Wash Law Rev 60:1151–1231, 1992; Rothstein MA: Workplace drug testing: a case study in the misapplication of technology. Harv J Law Technol 5:65–93, 1991; Williams PW: Suspicionless drug testing after Skinner and Von Raab: constitutional adjudication in the courts of appeals. Univ Kans Law Rev 40:733–776, 1992.
2. DHHS-NIDA. Fed Reg 53:11979–11989, 1988; US-DOT. Fed Reg 54:49854–49876, 1989.
3. Omnibus Transportation Employee Testing Act of 1991, P.L. 102-143, 105 Stat. 917, Title 5.
4. Shults T: The state law mosaic—general considerations. MRO Alert 6(3):10–14, 1995; MRO Alert is published by Quadrangle Research LLC, Research Triangle Park, NC.
5. See *O'Connor v. Ortega*, 107 S.Ct. 1492 (1987).
6. See *National Treasury Employees Union v. Von Raab*, 489 U.S. 902, 109 S. Ct. 1384 (1989).
7. *National Treasury Employees Union v. Von Raab*, 109 S. Ct. 1384 (1989); *Skinner v. Railway Labor Executives Assn.*, 109 S.Ct. 1402 (1989); *Veronica School District 47J v. Acton*, NO. 94-590, 6-26-95 (U.S.S.Ct.).
8. See e.g., Broadwell DK: The evolution of workplace drug screening: a medical review officer's perspective. J Law Med Ethics 22:241–246, 1994.
9. See e.g., Weinberg DS: Another random drug test or the latest infringement on the Fourth Amendment rights of American workers? Northwestern U Law Rev 87:1087–1119, 1993.
10. See e.g., *Intl. Brd. of Teamsters v. Dept. of Transp.*, 932 F.2d 1292 (9th Cir. 1991) (commercial vehicle operators); *Intl. Brd. of Elec. Workers, Local 1245 v. Skinner*, 913 F.2d 1454 (9th Cir. 1990) (gas pipeline workers); *Transport Workers' Union, Local 234 v. SEPTA*, 884 F.2d 709(3d Cir. 1989) (mass transit); *Thomson v. Marsh*, 884 F.2d 484 (D.C. Cir. 1989) (train or customs service workers who carry firearms); and *Guiney v. Roache*, 873 F.2d 1557 (1st Cir.), cert. denied, 493 U.S. 963 (1989) (police dept. employees who carry firearms or interdict drugs).
11. See e.g., *Dimeo v. Griffin*, 943 F.2d 679 (7th Cir. 1991) (horse racing jockeys). But see *Univ. of Colorado v. Derdeyn*, No. 92-SC-86 (Colo S.Ct. 1993 (random testing unconstitutional despite diminished expectation of privacy of college athletes).
12. On July 14, 1995, the Food and Drug Administration cleared for use in drug abuse screening programs the first sweat patch to test for amphetamines, cocaine, and opiates. The patch, which is applied to the skin, is designed for use by trained drug abuse testing professionals in clinical and rehabilitation centers. The new testing technology has two components: the Sudormed Sweat Specimen Container, made by Sudormed, of Santa Barbara, Calif., and the EIA Microplate Assay, made by SolarCare Technologies Corporation, Bethlehem, Pa. The patch is a waterproof adhesive pad designed to be worn on the back, upper arm, or lower chest. The patch has a tamper-proof feature so that it may only be applied once and cannot be removed and reapplied later. Urine drug testing can typically detect drugs for up to 3 days after the last known use. By contrast, the sweat patch can be worn up to 7 days and is designed to detect drugs of abuse during that period.
13. See DHHS-ADAMHA. Scientific and technical guidelines for federal workplace drug testing programs; standards for certification of laboratories engaged in urine drug testing for federal agencies. Fed Reg 52:30637–30652, 1987; Finkle BS, Blanke RV, Walsh JM (eds): Technical, Scientific, and Procedural Issues of Employee Drug Testing. Rockville, MD, National Institute on Drug Abuse, 1990.
14. See *Stinson v. Physicians Immediate Care*, No. 2-94-0969, 2-16-95 (Ill. App. 2d Dist.).
15. To create common law tort liability for defamation, there generally must be a false and defamatory statement concerning another; an unprivileged publication to a third party; fault amounting at least to negligence on the part of the publisher; and either actionability of the statement irrespective of special harm, or the existence of special harm caused by the publication. In theory, private employees could successfully bring a defamation action against an employer who published a positive drug test result with the knowledge of its possible inaccuracy. See *Willis v. Roche Biomedical Laboratories, Inc.*, CA No. H-91-2360, U.S.D.C .(S.D. Tex. 1993).

16. See *Willis v. Roche Biomedical Laboratories, Inc.*, No. 92-2361, 5th Circuit, 8/2/95.
17. See *SmithKline Beecham Corp. v. Doe*, No. D-4131, Texas S.Ct., 7/21/95.
18. Federal Register, Feb 15, 1994, at 7301–7625.
19. 49 CFR 40.91.
20. See e.g., Procedures for Transportation Workplace Drug and Alcohol Testing Programs (CFR § 40), Fed Reg 59(31):7347, 1994.
21. Although specific education and certification are not yet required of physicians participating in federally-mandated or private sector testing, both the American College of Occupational and Environmental Medicine and the American Association of Medical Review Officers offer 2-day courses and certification exams.
22. 42 USCA §§ 12101 to 12213 (West. Supp. 1992).
23. 42 USCA § 12112(a).
24. 42 USCA § 12112(d)(2) at (A) & (B).
25. 42 USCA § 12114(a).
26. 42 USCA § 12114(a).
27. 42 USCA § 12110(b).
28. 42 USCA § 12114(d).
29. 42 USCA § 12112(d).
30. 42 USCA § 12112(d); EEOC Enforcement Guidance: Preemployment, Disability-Related Inquiries and Medical Examinations under the Americans with Disabilities Act of 1990, No. 915.002(5-19-94) at 36.
31. See *American Trucking Associations, Inc. v. Federal Highway Admin.*, No. 94-1209, 4-5-95 (4th Cir.).
32. 42 USCA § 12112(d)(4)(A).
33. See *Schmidt v. Safeway, Inc.*, 864 F. Supp. 991 (D. Ore. 1994).
34. Family and Medical Leave Act of 1993, 29 USC §§2601–2654, and Final Rules implementing the FMLA at 29 CFR §825.100-800.
35. See Fed Reg 60:2195, 1995 (Jan. 6, 1995).
36. See *Guillermo v. Brennan*, 691 F. Supp. 1151 (N.D. Ill. 1988).
37. NLRB General Counsel's Memorandum on Drug and Alcohol Testing, Memorandum GC 87-5 (September 8, 1987): See *Oil, Chemical & Atomic Workers International Union v. Phillips 66 Co.*, No. 91-6212, USCA 5th Cir. (1992); *Oil, Chemical & Atomic Workers' International Union v. Shell Oil Co.*, No. 92-9582, USCA 5th Cir. (1993).
38. *The Harshaw/Filtrol Partnership v. International Chemical Workers Union*, Local 73, 89-1 ARB ¶8089; *Donaldson Mining Company v. United Mine Workers of America, District 17, Local 340*, 89-1, ARB ¶8089.
39. See Redel CL, Abbey A: The arbitration of drug use and testing in the workplace. Arbitration Journal 48:80–85, 1993.
40. See *US Department of Interior v. Federal Labor Relations Authority*, No. 91-1218, USCA D.C. Cir. (1992).
41. See *Dykes v. Southeastern Pennsylvania Transportation Authority*, No. 95-1032, Third Circuit, 11/7/95.
42. See *United Steelworkers of America v. Lukens Steel Co.*, No. 91-1540, Third Circuit (1992).
43. *Baggs v. Eagle-Picher Industries, Inc.*, No. 90-1949, USCA 6th Cir.., cert. denied, No. 92-513, US S.Ct. (1992).
44. See, e.g., *Mansourou v. John Crane Inc.*, No. 1-92-2260, Ill. App. Ct. (1993).
45. *Borse v. Piece Goods Shop, Inc.*, 963 F.2d 611 (3d Cir. 1992) (at-will employee discharged for refusing to consent to random drug testing and personal property searches may have a cause of action for wrongful discharge under Pennsylvania law if such testing tortiously invaded her common law right to privacy).
46. *Walk v. P.I.E. Nationwide Inc.*, No. 90-2097, USCA 6th Cir. (1992).
47. See *Pike v. Gallagher*, CA No. 91-0891, USDC (D.N.M. 1993).
48. See, e.g., *Farm Fresh Dairy, Inc. v. Blackburn*, No. 74,905, S.Ct. Okla. (1992); but see *Wenzel v. Rissler & McMurry, Inc.*, 887 P.2d 686 (Wyo. 1992) (no misconduct if employer does not follow its policy and procedures).
49. See, e.g., *Kaminski v. Texas Employment Commission*, No. A14-92-00352-CV, Tex.Ct.App., 14th Dist. (1993) (refusal to undergo test); *Reigelsberger v. Employment Appeal Board*, No. 164/92-890, Iowa S.Ct. (1993) (refusal to undergo substance abuse treatment).
51. See, e.g., *Thompson v. Capital Steel Co.*, No. CA-91-1619, La.Ct.App. (1st Cir. 1992).
52. National Research Council: Under the influence? Drugs and the American Workforce. Washington, DC, National Academy Press, 1994, pp 1–336.

DEAN HASHIMOTO, MD, JD, MOH

DEFINING THE ROLE OF MANAGED CARE IN WORKERS' COMPENSATION

From the Boston College School
of Law
Newton, Massachusetts

Reprint requests to:
Dean Hashimoto, MD, JD, MOH
Boston College School of Law
885 Centre Street
Newton, MA 02159

The workers' compensation system has been heavily criticized for its failure to provide sufficient positive incentives to reduce what legislatures and the public view as the high costs of accidents.[16] Because nearly half of all workers' compensation costs have been attributed to medical expenses, there has been a recent call for the implementation of managed care in workers' compensation systems.[15] Unlike other programs that finance health care, workers' compensation provides reasonably complete medical care for work-related injuries and diseases without requiring deductibles or co-payments. To limit medical costs, state regulators for many years have relied primarily on fee schedules. Compared to payments by other health financing systems, workers' compensation payments were substantially lower, thereby discouraging the participation of most health care providers. However, because managed care has lowered payments to its providers in "regular" or "mainstream" health care delivery, an increasing number of providers and medical organizations have expressed interest in treating workers' compensation patients. At the same time, an increasing number of states are considering ways to implement managed care in workers' compensation.

Many assume that managed care may be implemented in workers' compensation in the same way it has been implemented in the "regular" health care delivery system, i.e., by emphasizing a reduction in the amount of treatment given to injured workers. "Managed care," however, is an ambiguous term that has been used to describe the implementation of several different kinds of private regulatory systems. For example, the most common form of managed care in modern workers' compensation relies on treatment guidelines and utilization review. Under this approach, state regulators adopt treatment guidelines that insurers must use to determine whether treatment is necessary and proper, while utilization review agents require providers to obtain approval before treatment can be continued after the initial visit. A second major form of managed care relies on health maintenance organizations (HMOs) and preferred provider networks to provide care based on specific contracts with employers or insurers. Because reimbursement may be fixed and predetermined by the size and characteristics of the employee group, HMOs and preferred provider networks have financial incentives to decrease costs. A third important form of managed care involves capitation, which creates financial incentives for clinicians to minimize the costs of care. The individual clinician's income ultimately depends on the costs of treatment or referrals to specialists by the physician group to which he or she belongs. Thus, the term *managed care* may refer to one or all of these major mechanisms designed primarily to reduce health care costs.

This chapter analyzes the potential role of managed care in workers' compensation. It offers the hypothesis that managed care may not optimally decrease the total cost of workplace accidents if the dominant aim is simply to reduce the amount of care provided to injured workers. If managed care influences only treatment decisions, current neglect of preventive strategies will be perpetuated. Moreover, decreased treatment per injured worker most likely will accelerate the delivery of high-volume, low-quality services. Alternatively, however, managed care may provide an opportunity to improve quality and efficacy of treatment, encourage the prevention of workplace injuries, and discourage the inappropriate use of health services. This chapter concludes that the optimal implementation of managed care and capitation in workers' compensation requires a paradigmatic shift to a community commitment based on a public health imperative to ensure quality medical care. The optimal implementation of managed care in workers' compensation requires a focus not only on treatment but also on accident prevention and reasonable return-to-work programs. Thus, managed care programs may be optimally effective only if they can be linked to these programs.

The practice of occupational medicine can reduce the costs of accidents in workplaces by emphasizing—in addition to effective and efficient treatment—prevention and mitigation of effects of work-related injuries. Indeed, the practice of occupational medicine may be especially compatible with managed care because physicians in this specialty have developed pragmatic approaches to accommodate the tensions created by duties owed to both worker-patients and employers. Occupational medical expertise has not yet, however, been widely implemented.

THE LEGAL STRUCTURE OF WORKERS' COMPENSATION

Workers' compensation constitutes one of the first and most enduring of all tort reform measures. It was initiated by states at the turn of this century to provide an exclusive remedy for work-related injuries and diseases.[5] The remedy included indemnity and medical payments. Thus, a health care payment system was created within the legal structure of workers' compensation.

State legislatures established workers' compensation systems that hold employers strictly liable to their employees for injuries and diseases caused by the workplace.[4] To qualify for benefits, the employee must prove (1) that he or she has experienced injury or illness, (2) that the injury or illness arose out of and in the course of employment, and (3) that harm has resulted in the form of lost wages, disfigurement, medical costs, or rehabilitation costs.[3] (The employer is not liable under workers' compensation, however, if the worker intentionally self-inflicts an injury.) The amount of recovery depends on the degree of impairment and disability. The determination of impairment involves *medical* judgment on the functional limitations of the injured worker, whereas the determination of disability involves *legal* judgment about the effect of the impairment on the ability of the injured employee to work. Benefits under workers' compensation are typically less than those traditionally available under tort law. In general, only two thirds of lost income is recovered, indemnity payments for disability are often much less than lost income, and award for pain and suffering are not available.[3] (Data indicate a 60% wage replacement for occupational injury victims and a 40% replacement for those who are severely disabled from occupational disease.) Workers' compensation provides the sole remedy for workers who qualify; claimant-employees usually are not allowed to file tort actions against their employers.[9]

Workers' compensation systems rely primarily on an administrative judicial process to resolve disputes over claims. Prior to administrative adjudication, insurers in many states may ask independent medical examiners (IMEs) to evaluate claimants to determine whether payments should be initiated or continued. The IMEs, who are physicians paid by insurers, determine such issues as whether the claimant's injury or illness falls within the jurisdiction of workers' compensation, whether the claimant is presently impaired and disabled, and whether the medical treatment rendered has been necessary and appropriate. If an insurer decides to withhold or discontinue payment to the claimant based on an IME report, the claimant may still present the claim to an administrative tribunal for legal decision on the above issues. Although workers' compensation was designed to provide a faster and more efficient claims system, protracted litigation can still delay the ultimate disposition of a claim.

Workers' compensation shifts the costs of workplace injury from the employee to the employer by means of insurance, because the employer is required to obtain insurance insurance or to self-insure.[14] The employer's insurance premiums depend on the hazardous risks of the workplace and the employer's experience.[14] Thus, workers' compensation internalizes the costs of workplace accidents by passing the costs on consumers of the products and services provided by the employer. If the costs of workplace accidents exceeds the cost of prevention, a rational employer would invest in making the workplace safer.[4] The workers' compensation insurance policy also provides a "deep pocket" to compensate injured employees who may be unable to sustain economic losses on their own.[4]

FAILURE TO ENCOURAGE REDUCTION OF WORKPLACE ACCIDENT COSTS

Despite the rising costs of workers' compensation, there has been no corresponding reduction in workplace injuries and diseases. From 1985 to 1990, workers' compensation costs doubled to $70 billion per year nationwide.[15] These costs, which represent more than 2% of payroll, are predicted to exceed $140 billion by the year 2000.[15] While the rate of increase of workers' compensation costs has been moderate in the last few years, employers continue to seek ways to control these costs.[15] Meanwhile, injury rates in the workplace have not declined during this period of rising costs. Thus, workers' compensation does not appear to provide adequate incentives to reduce the costs of workplace accidents.[16] This phenomenon arises from the current relationship between the legal and medical components of the workers' compensation structure. First, the interdependence of legal and health issues encourages overutilization of the health care delivery system. Second, there are significant disincentives to the development of the organizational coordination required to prevent workplace injuries and to the implementation of reasonable return-to-work programs.

Incentives to Overutilize Treatment

For employees, the intertwining of legal claims and health care services does not create incentives to reduce the costs of workplace accidents when state laws permit an employee to seek a physician of his or her own choosing. In the absence of deductibles or co-payments, there is no direct incentive or opportunity for workers to act as prudent purchasers of health care.[2] Thus, workers do not have a financial incentive to choose the best managed medical care program. Because primary care physicians and allied health professionals may have little expertise in occupational medicine, workers may not be able to identify appropriate providers. Furthermore, because the opinions of health care professionals may influence compensation decisions, workers may engage in physician shopping, especially if a provider renders an opinion that may adversely affect their legal claims. Finally, the injured worker may have a financial incentive to choose health professionals who provide excessive medical services. The amount of medical care provided may be used as evidence of the severity of disability to justify benefit payments under the indemnity portion of workers' compensation.[2]

Incentives to Underutilize Preventive Programs

The lack of appropriate medical expertise within business organizations and among community physicians may lead to underreporting of work-related injuries and diseases. Underreporting reduces the economic incentive to devote resources to lowering the cost of workplace accidents. At one level, the causal connection between an injury or disease and the workplace may not be obvious to a worker or primary care physician.[12] For example, workers and physicians may not recognize that injuries due to repetitive motion are not due to a single work-related event but often insidiously develop over time. At another level, high workers' compensation premiums may constitute an incentive for the employer to underreport work-related injuries and illnesses.[16] This underreporting decreases the cost of premiums for indemnity and health care and thus externalizes these costs. This externalization of costs reduces the financial incentive to make the workplace safer.

In American business organizations, the expertise for handling the legal and medical components of workers' compensation is often scattered among different departments. For example, the departments responsible for administering the legal indemnity portion of workers' compensation typically include risk management and personnel benefits. Risk management evaluates and processes the legal administrative claims, while personnel benefits actually administers disability benefits. Other departments, such as health services and environmental health and safety, are responsible for injury prevention. The optimal prevention of workplace injuries, however, requires the coordination of all these departments (and their supervisors) because workplace safety must be monitored at the grassroots level of a business. Thus, successful accident prevention programs require a commitment from many departments within a business organization and depend on cooperation between departments that are otherwise insulated from each other. These separate departments and offices may operate on independent budgets and may lack incentive to cooperate unless mandated to do so. Furthermore, all of these departments must freely share information to optimally design, implement, and monitor workplace safety. Each supervisor must understand the importance of workplace safety and be able to implement effective return-to-work policies. Unfortunately, it has been much easier for corporate decision-makers to simply ask their environmental health and safety officers to monitor compliance with government regulations than to gather the information necessary to determine the best way to reduce workplace accidents and to implement company-wide programs based on this information.

Insurers are not likely to serve as coordinators of legal and medical issues under the current system. Insurers have mainly acted as financial institutions that charge appropriate premiums and pay out or deny claims. Beyond this function, insurers have limited their activities to implementing traditional managed health care directives such as utilization review of providers. Insurers have not typically undertaken the role of inspecting workplaces or requiring programs to reduce accident costs by adopting appropriate return-to-work programs.

Thus, the current medicolegal structure of workers' compensation creates disincentives to lower costs. The informational and organizational challenges faced by business bureaucracies dealing with workers' compensation do not encourage efficient, high-quality health care and do not encourage prevention of accidents. Despite these shortcomings, most reform proposals are narrowly focused on reduction of medical treatment costs. With this narrow perspective, state agencies and legislatures are developing regulatory schemes that encourage the implementation of managed care programs.

REGULATORY SCHEMES

The Conflicting Legal Paradigms

Current perceptions of the value of managed care in workers' compensation are heavily influenced by at least three characteristics of health care services. Workers are likely to characterize the provision of health care as a right and thus oppose the imposition of managed care. By contrast, employers are likely to characterize the provision of health care as a welfare benefit and thus contend that managed care is necessary to reduce costs. Most legislatures and courts are likely to side with employers and allow managed care to be implemented. However, the characterization of health care as a right or as a welfare benefit does not encourage optimal health care delivery. If managed care is inevitable, it should be implemented on the basis on a community commitment to improving public health. Such a community commitment would emphasize the importance of quality of care and also encourage the reduction and mitigation of workplace injuries. This public health characterization of medical care would be consistent with the implementation of occupational medicine principles through managed care.

The Rights Paradigm

Prior to the establishment of workers' compensation systems, workers could sue their employers for workplace injuries, alleging violations of tort law. Under workers' compensation reform, workers forfeited the right to bring tort actions against their employers in exchange for a guaranteed set of benefits, including complete coverage of medical costs.[18] Thus, workers perceive the health care financing provided by workers' compensation as a legal right even if there is no legal "right to health care" recognized for the general population.[6]

In addition, injured workers have not been required to pay deductibles or co-payments. Thus, workers may view the imposition of managed care as an abandonment by employers of their agreement to provide health care coverage unfettered by cost controls.

The rights legal paradigm not only rejects managed care of treatment but also the imposition of injury prevention and return-to-work programs. Under this paradigm, employers may assert an independent right to prevent access to the workplace by health care providers. Thus, employers may seek to exclude providers from their workplaces and reject advice suggesting improvements in work practices. Similarly, both employers and workers may object to return-to-work programs. Again, such programs may be viewed as an intrusion on workplaces owned and controlled by employers. Also, workers may resist the notion that they should be required to return to work while they are still suffering from their injuries. Thus, the rights legal paradigm rejects the application of managed care to workers' compensation in all respects.

The problem with insisting that health care be administered under this rights paradigm is that ultimately the debate must focus on what constitutes adequate health care. Employers surely are not responsible for guaranteeing health care coverage for medical treatments that are unnecessary or excessive. However, the adequacy of health care is difficult to define objectively.[7] Because subjective factors such as the quality of the physician-patient relationship and the expected degree of therapeutic effectiveness strongly influence perceptions of adequacy, the preservation of patient choice of health care providers may be an important way to resolve the tension.

Because mainstream health care delivery has begun to rely on managed care to contain costs, it is increasingly difficult to defend the proposition that medical care received through workers' compensation should be totally unfettered by cost concerns. Historically, cost controls have been imposed on health care provided through workers' compensation. States have long relied on setting fee schedules that limit the amounts of payments made for medical services. Indeed, many providers in the past refused to treat injured workers because reimbursement rates were so low.

As a practical matter, experts expect that managed care will soon dominate health care delivery in workers' compensation in nearly all states.[6] Thus, realistically, the important issue is not whether managed care will be imposed on workers' compensation but rather what substantive form it will take. Workers should focus, perhaps, on the more important matter of preserving their choice of providers. Most states will allow some realistic choice of providers either initially or for a second opinion.[6] Preserving this choice is consistent with ensuring quality of care as well as providing a necessary outlet if physician/patient relations seriously deteriorate. Because the vast majority of claimants stay with the provider to whom they are first referred, maintaining the right of choice should not unduly interfere with effective implementation of managed care programs.

The Welfare Benefit Paradigm

Employers may contend that the imposition of managed care on workers' compensation is consistent with other welfare reform movements, such as cutbacks in Medicare and Medicaid. Under this vision, workers' compensation is considered a humanitarian gesture or a social welfare system that provides minimal support to keep injured workers from destitution.[14] Under the "welfare benefit" legal paradigm, managed care that focuses only on treatment (and reduces the quality of treatment) can nevertheless be justified as a reasonable approach to cost containment.

Unlike general welfare programs, however, workers' compensation arose from the relationship between employers and workers. Employers bear social responsibility for injuries that arise in the workplace.[16] This explains why employees who pay into social welfare programs such as Social Security do not have to make direct payments to be covered by workers' compensation. A further problem with the welfare benefit paradigm is that it may be used to justify any and all cutbacks in health care. Realistically, however, employers and workers share some common interests with respect to health care. A high quality system of health care that focuses on treatment, prevention, and mitigation of injuries may provide benefits to both groups.

The Public Health Paradigm

The current public debate is framed as a choice between the rights paradigm and the welfare benefit paradigm. Neither choice, however, leads to the goal of reducing overall costs of accidents in workplaces. This chapter advocates consideration of a third paradigm, one that emphasizes a community commitment to public health.[8] Such a paradigm recognizes the importance of cost containment but does not lose sight of human concerns. If the public health paradigm were adopted, occupational medicine principles emphasizing both quality and efficiency of treatment could be pursued. Workplace safety viewed from the public health perspective must be understood as a collective responsibility of employers, workers, health care providers, insurers, and government to integrate their efforts in practical ways to reduce the social and economic costs of accidents. Thus, accident prevention and injury mitigation become just as important as monitoring treatment. Workplace safety becomes a community commitment rather than a matter of choosing between the interests of the employer and the worker.

IMPLEMENTING OCCUPATIONAL MEDICINE PRINCIPLES THROUGH MANAGED CARE

Implementing occupational medicine principles through managed care systems would be consistent with the public health paradigm. Occupational medicine physicians (OMPs) are trained to identify work-related diseases and injuries by taking an occupational history, performing a physical examination, and applying the principles and knowledge of epidemiology, toxicology, and public health. Occupational medicine also involves the study and application of ergonomics, a discipline that examines the effects of physical and emotional stress on workplace performance. Some ergonomics programs have been shown to improve both health and workplace productivity by preventing back and repetitive trauma injuries. Additional prevention-oriented activities in occupational medicine include preplacement physical examination, drug testing, and compliance with health and safety regulations. Finally, OMPs routinely walk through workplaces to familiarize themselves with job functions and to identify hazardous exposures.

While occupational medicine principles are well-established, they are not yet systematically used. In a nation with relatively few board-certified specialists in occupational medicine, most patients are treated by primary care physicians who often have little or no training in occupational medicine principles. The advent of managed care in workers' compensation provides a significant opportunity to implement these principles widely. Occupational medicine physicians should participate vigorously in developing and implementing managed care programs. OMPs can educate and supervise other providers, encourage the utilization of programs aimed at prevention and mitigation of injuries, discourage overutilization of provider services, and improve the quality of care.

Discouraging Overutilization of Treatment

A system of managed care that relies on occupational medicine principles would discourage overutilization of health care and encourage the prevention and mitigation of injuries. Such an approach would discourage overutilization by encouraging treatment that is both efficient and of high quality. If managed care only emphasizes the minimization of treatment costs, these savings may be counterbalanced by indemnity costs associated with longer absences from work. To accommodate both efficiency and public health concerns, treatment costs and quality deserve equal emphasis. Thus, high quality health care that returns workers to productive employment sooner and at reasonable cost should be favored over an approach merely emphasizing the minimization of treatment costs. A growing medical literature advocates treatments that quickly return patients to the workplace. For example, workers with low back strains are returned to work as soon is it medically reasonable because early return improves prognosis and prevents physical deconditioning associated with isolation from regular activity.

Regulators should encourage both efficiency and quality of care in various managed care systems. OMPs should assist regulators in developing and vigorously applying treatment guidelines that encourage efficiency and quality of care. Also, regulators should require that HMOs and providers incorporate oversight that utilizes occupational medicine expertise. Treatment guidelines and utilization review should identify the most effective diagnostic tests and treatments; high quality care that may be more expensive should not be characterized as overutilization if it returns patients to work sooner.

To remedy the lack of empirical information about the effectiveness of managed care in workers' compensation, government agencies should initiate studies of outcomes to determine what kinds of evaluation and treatment are most effective and efficient.

Consistent with the traditional occupational medicine approach, the patient's choice of a treating physician should be preserved, especially if patients are primarily directed to providers with legitimate expertise in occupational medicine. Importantly, preservation of patient choice of providers has not been shown to prevent effective implementation of managed care. Indeed, choice may serve as a check on the quality of care provided.[13]

Encouraging Programs Aimed at Prevention and Mitigation of Injuries

As previously noted, the discipline of occupational medicine represents an integration of medical, administrative, and legal knowledge concerning workplace injuries and diseases. This multidisciplinary expertise facilitates provision of a number of different services to various departments within a single business organization. OMPs routinely interact with workers, employers, industrial hygienists, and other safety specialists, benefits administrators, supervisors, attorneys, insurers, and others to prevent, treat, and mitigate workplace injuries. The role of an in-house OMP may also include tracking the recovery of employees treated by physicians practicing in the community. OMPs collaborate with (1) administrators and personnel managers to establish return-to-work programs, (2) environmental health and safety officers to establish practices and programs to prevent future injuries, and (3) risk management professionals to determine the etiology of work-related injuries and to assist in evaluating prognoses, impairments, and disabilities of injured workers. Thus, the appropriately trained OMP is uniquely qualified to facilitate effective integration of various efforts to improve workplace health ad safety.

State regulators may encourage return-to-work and accident-prevention programs through restructuring fee schedules and by offering a reduction in workers' compensation premiums to employers who establish them. Managed care programs should implement these programs, and utilization review agents should be able to describe program features to both patients and providers.

As one example of prevention and mitigation of injuries, restricted duty positions are designed to allow employees to return to work activities that will not interfere with recovery. Restricted duty assignments may actually benefit a recovering worker because they tend to prevent physical deconditioning associated with isolation from regular activity. Prolonged work absence due to, for example, back injury is associated with poor prognosis. A restricted duty job, however, allows an injured worker to develop and maintain physical strength to return to regular duty and may serve as a useful gauge of recovery.

The consolidation of workers' compensation and regular health care delivery within HMOs and prepaid group practices would remove the incentive to shift costs by failing to identify work-related injuries. Instead, this approach would internalize the costs of workplace accidents, thereby encouraging employers to invest more in workplace safety. The success of this approach depends, however, on the ability of HMOs and group practices to implement occupational medicine principles within their organizations. This could be accomplished by engaging OMPs to develop protocols and supervise primary care providers.

It is not clear that capitation programs in workers' compensation will be more effective than reliance on treatment guidelines and utilization review in discouraging overutilization. In workers' compensation, providers already have strong financial incentives to rely on efficient treatments so as to maintain their contractual relationships with employers. (A dissatisfied employer can simply direct injured workers to more effective managed care providers.) Capitation, however, may increase patient distrust of physicians in workers' compensation compared to regular health care systems due to the explicit nature of the direct payments made by employers through their insurers. Physicians' treatment decisions in workers' compensation influence not only the amount of treatment provided but also the indemnity payments made to patients. Thus, it is important to preserve patient choice of providers in workers' compensation to minimize physician conflict of interest that may eviscerate the physician-patient relationship.

Capitated programs are more likely to thrive if managed care not only discourages overutilization but also encourages prevention and mitigation of the effects of workplace injuries. If regulatory systems encourage physician access to workplaces to establish injury prevention and return-to-work programs, capitation may produce incentives for providers to reduce the costs of workplace accidents through these means. If the sole focus of capitation is minimizing treatment, this may actually increase the costs of accidents in the workplace because of larger indemnity payments associated with increased absences from work if the treatments are less effective.

Managed care programs, including capitation, should encourage prevention and mitigation of the effects of workplace injuries because this enhances cost containment. Such an approach would also make managed care more acceptable to workers and is consistent with a community commitment to public health. Thus, the implementation of managed care could provide a meaningful opportunity to advance occupational medicine principles in workers' compensation.

The Threat of Managed Care to Physicians

The practice of medicine in the age of managed care presents a severe challenge to the traditional identity of the medical profession. The problem is that physicians may be perceived, or even see themselves, as brokers of competing financial interests, thereby losing their traditional identity as advocates for patients. In the case of workers' compensation, the most serious danger to the medical profession may arise when patients feel that physicians are minimizing treatments not due to professional standards but based on what an insurer or employer is willing to reimburse. This difficult situation is potentially aggravated when patients perceive that their physicians, through capitated systems, are financially rewarded for minimizing treatments and impairment assessments at the expense of potential indemnity awards to patients.

The challenge to physicians is to shape managed care programs in ways that preserve professional integrity. Long before the advent of of modern managed care, occupational medicine physicians coped with conflicts of interest and developed pragmatic approaches that preserved the physician-patient relationship and yet remained faithful to the calling of this public health profession. Thus, the practice of occupational medicine may provide useful lessons on how physicians may cope with conflicts of interest created by managed care systems.

The OMP must serve at least two masters. He or she owes legal and ethical duties to both the worker-patient and employer, and the financial incentive to satisfy the employer's wishes further complicates the dual duties. The OMP accommodates these conflicts in several pragmatic ways. The traditional core of the physician-patient relationship is largely preserved. This core relationship is maintained through communication with patients and adherence to confidentiality whenever feasible. The physician maintains confidentiality of information that the employer does not need to decide work-related issues. For example, a physician should not divulge unnecessary information such as diagnosis or specific medical information. Instead, the physician may indicate what physical impairments the worker has so that the employer can decide if reasonable accommodations can be made for continued employment. Furthermore, the physician must communicate relevant medical information to the patient even if the medical finding is only incidental to the objective of the testing. While the physician may be required to fulfill tasks ordered by the employer, the patient should be informed about findings relevant to his health. Moreover, the ethical physician informs the patient of her business relationship to the employer. Thus, communication and adherence to confidentiality are essential to maintaining the core physician-patient relationship.

Ideally, the OMP's treatment reflects both high quality and efficient care. This is not only an ethical ideal but also one that is economically justifiable. The employer must not only pay for medical treatments but also for a broader benefits package that includes indemnity for lost wages. Therefore, effective but more expensive treatments that accelerate recovery and return to work may be economically justified.[3] Furthermore, OMPs who monitor treatment by other providers should address not only overutilization of health care services but also the quality of those services.

Much of the potential conflict associated with dual duties has been further decreased by the occupational medicine focus on an objective shared by employers, workers, and the community-at-large: improving the health and safety of workplaces.

The commitment to certain public values is a defining feature of professionalism. Thus, in addition to a commitment to assisting others in their pursuit of self-interests, the professional also has a social obligation to pursue certain public health objectives. The code of ethical conduct for physicians providing occupational medical services accords "highest priority to the health and safety of the individual in a workplace."[1] This is a public health interest based on the profession's belief that high-quality occupational medical services serve the interests of the community-at-large. Occupational medicine grew out of an older discipline of "industrial medicine," which focused only on the treatment of work-related injuries.[11] Company doctors who practiced industrial medicine were perceived as biased in protecting the employers' interests. The modern discipline of occupational medicine recognizes the importance of treating work-related injuries, but it also emphasizes prevention of injuries and the mitigation of the effects of injuries on work. Focusing on this broader interest avoids forcing the physician to choose between potentially conflicting interests of employers and workers.

Inevitably, the potential conflict of interest confronting the occupational medicine physician leads to particularly difficult situations where either the employer (or its insurer) or the employee questions what the physician has done. In these situations, it is helpful to have alternatives such as second medical opinions or the selection of other providers. In some states, employers and their insurers may rely on independent medical evaluations by physicians of their choice as a check on the health care provider. Indeed, the treating physician may recommend to an insurer that an IME would be helpful, particularly if he or she feels that such an evaluation might confirm previous reports that have been challenged, denied, or rejected by a patient. In some states, the patient may be allowed to seek a second medical opinion or continue treatment with a different physician if the patient is not satisfied with his relationship with the initial treating physician. When the patient no longer trusts his physician, these alternatives can help to alleviate tensions or disputes. However, the fact that 80–90% of workers' compensation patients stay with their initial treating physician demonstrates overall patient satisfaction despite the existence of potential conflicts of interest.

Physicians should seek common ground among competing interests and yet maintain the physician-patient trust that is essential to the practice of medicine. Thus, the professional identity of health providers within workers' compensation ought to be shaped not by the side physicians take but by the public values they support. Physicians should shape managed care systems to serve public health ideals. They should not allow these systems to shape their identity as professionals.

REFERENCES

1. American Occupational Medical Association: Code of ethical conduct for physicians providing occupational medical services. In Levy BS, Wegman DH (eds): Occupational Health: Recognizing and Preventing Work-Related Disease. Boston, Little, Brown & Co., 1988, p 185.
2. Ballen DT: The sleeper issue in health care reform: The threat to workers' compensation. Cornell Law Rev 79:1291–1302, 1994.
3. Boden L: Workers' compensation. In Ashford NA, Caldart CC: Technology, Law, and the Working Environment. New York, Van Nostrand Reinhold, 1991, pp 455–461.
4. Calabresi G: Primary accident cost avoidance: The specific deterrence approach. In Calabresi G: The Costs of Accidents. New Haven, CT, Yale University Press, 1977, pp 95–130.
5. Caldart C: Are workers adequately compensated for injury resulting from exposure to toxic substances? An overview of worker compensation and suits in tort. In Ashford NA, Caldart CC (eds): Technology, Law, and the Working Environment. New York, Van Nostrand Reinhold, 1991, pp 453–460.

6. Doherty K: It's high noon for workers' comp. Business & Health 36–38, 1989.
7. Elhauge E: Allocating health care morally. Calif Law Rev 82:1449–1544, 1994.
8. Glendon MA: The land of rights. In Glendon MA: Rights Talk: The Impoverishment of Political Discourse. New York, The Free Press, 1991, pp 1–17
9. Keeton WP, Dobbs DB, Keeton RE, Owen DG: Employers' liability. In Keeton WP, Dobbs DB, Keeton RE, Owen DG: Prosser and Keeton on Torts. St. Paul, West Publishing Co., 1984, pp 572–576.
10. Levy BS, Wegman DH: Recognizing occupational disease. In Levy BS, Wegman DH (eds): Occupational Health: Recognizing and Preventing Work-Related Disease. Boston, Little, Brown & Co., 1988, pp 29–43.
11. McCunney RJ, Welter ES: Occupational medical services. In McCunney RJ (ed): Handbook of Occupational Medicine. Boston, Little, Brown & Co., 1988, pp 3–20.
12. Newman LS: Occupational illness. N Engl J Med 333:1128–1134, 1995.
13. Resnick R: Managed care comes to workers' compensation. Business & Health 32, 38–39, 1992.
14. Scarzafava GA, Herrera F Jr: Workplace safety—the prophylactic and compensatory rights of the employee. St Mary's Law J 13:911, 942–955, 1982.
15. Solomon B: Using managed care to control workers' compensation costs. Compensation & Benefits Rev 25:59–65, 1993.
16. Spieler EA: Perpetuating risk? Workers' compensation and the persistence of occupational injuries. Houston Law Rev 31:119–264, 1994.
17. U.S. Department of Labor: An interim report to Congress on occupational diseases. In Ashford NA, Caldart CC (eds): Technology, Law, and the Working Environment. New York, Van Nostrand Reinhold, 1991, pp 461–463.
18. Watson TA, Valen MJ: A historic review of workers' compensation reform in Florida. Florida State U Law Rev 21:501–527, 1993.
19. Wegman DH, Eisen EA: Epidemiology. In Levy BS, Wegman DH (eds): Occupational Health: Recognizing and Preventing Work-Related Disease. Boston, Little, Brown & Co., 1988, pp 55–73.

WILLIAM B. BUNN III, MD, JD, MPH
CLARION E. JOHNSON, MD

CAUSATION IN WORKERS' COMPENSATION

From Navistar International
Chicago, Illinois (WBB)
and
Mobil Corporation
Fairfax, Virginia (CEJ)

Reprint requests to:
William B. Bunn III, MD, JD, MPH
Director, Health Worker's
   Compensation Disability and
   Safety
Navistar International
455 City Front Plaza Drive
12th Floor
Chicago, IL 60611

With hundreds of thousands of occupational illnesses occurring each year, general practitioners, occupational physicians, and other subspecialists must decide if injuries or illnesses are work-related. Their decisions not only influence medical diagnosis and treatment but also help to establish causation for any future legal proceedings. Therefore, it is imperative that every decision be carefully considered. In addition, the physician must state the diagnosis in a form that will aid the legal disposition of the case. A basic understanding of legal systems and medicolegal analysis is essential for physicians involved in the decision-making process and also for those called on to present expert testimony.

For an occupational disease, i.e., one that is proven to be or may be related to work, there are several modes of obtaining compensation. Claims may be paid by the employer out of pocket. Such payment occurs in paternalistic situations and when both the employer and employee agree to avoid adjudication or third-party analysis of the causal event. Alternatively, the medical costs of illness or injury may be covered by an individual health insurance policy, as may any injury or illness not related to work. Most often, an insurance company is asked to pay when the cause of the event is unclear and/or the employee or employer resists the use of the compensation system. Typically, these claims for payment receive only a cursory review of their work-relatedness; however, if the treating physician states that the illness is work-related, the insurance carrier may contest the claim.

A third method of obtaining compensation involves filing a workers' compensation claim. The claim may be filed by the employee, employer, or physician in most jurisdictions. Because workers' compensation is an exclusive remedy, further litigation is precluded unless special circumstances exist. That is, in filing under workers' compensation coverage, the worker-claimant agrees to forego any litigation related to his employer's fault in causing the injury. By contrast, a tort claim for damages provides a fourth mechanism through which compensation may be obtained. In general, tort actions may be filed by the employee against the employer or third parties if a workers' compensation claim has not been filed. Workers' compensation laws typically exclude tort claims when an illness or injury is work-related. Exceptions to this exclusion may encompass intentional or reckless acts and some third-party claims.

The provider of medical care should help the employee decide which mode of reimbursement to seek. Any of the above four mechanisms may lead to an equitable settlement; the first two may produce faster resolution with less stress for both employee and employer. A civil action in tort may be appropriate and more financially advantageous than a workers' compensation claim, but the greater likelihood of predictable reimbursement makes a workers' compensation claim more attractive to many injured workers.

THE ROLE OF THE OCCUPATIONAL PHYSICIAN

The Plant Physician

The first physician to examine the claimant may be the plant physician or a physician designated by the employer. The plant's medical report of injury is often the first such report in the workers' compensation system. This report is reviewed closely—especially the notations regarding the claimant's medical and occupational history and the facts and circumstances surrounding the injury. Although the plant physician may provide no treatment beyond the initial contact with the claimant, his or her report is often the first medical statement and, therefore, among the most important documents on the issue of compensability.

The Treating Physician

If the claim is work-related, the claimant will be authorized to seek a treating physician who will provide reasonable and necessary medical treatment for the claimant's injury. The treating physician's report should emphasize the history, the nature and extent of the injury (including any pre-existing conditions), the treatment plan, an opinion on the claimant's ability to work, and a recommendation on the need for referral to a specialist. If the treating physician makes a referral, he or she must ensure that all relevant information concerning the claimant's condition is communicated to the referral physician, who often becomes the treating physician.

The Referral Physician

It is common for the referral physician to be an expert in a medical or surgical subspecialty, or in toxicology, epidemiology, or occupational medicine. The referral physician will evaluate the medical records and decide if further testing is necessary. Occasionally, a statement of justification will be required if the costs of the more expensive special tests are to be reimbursed.

When appropriate data have been accumulated, the referral physician will summarize the major findings and reach a medical decision, with legal consequences, in a final report. The report will often address causation ("arising out of employment") and document the impairment suffered by the individual. This written opinion will be relayed to the referring physician, the referring attorney, or directly to the compensation commission. Later, the referral physician may be called on to give oral or written expert opinion.

The Examining Physician

An examining physician will usually see the claimant at the request of the payor (generally an insurance company) or by order of the workers' compensation commissioner. The examining physician most frequently sees the claimant to give a second opinion regarding causation, the treatment plan, ability to work, or permanency of the disability. The scope of the examining physician's report may be more limited than that of the referring or referral physicians. For the examiner's opinion to be given maximum consideration, it is extremely important that he or she review all relevant information. If the information on which the examiner's opinion is based is incomplete or inaccurate, the examiner's opinion will typically be given little or no weight.

Analysis of Causation

Typically, the physician comes in contact with the workers' compensation system when filing a workers' compensation claim at the time of treatment. The typical form establishes a return-to-work date, restrictions, or period of impairment. However, the physician also may be asked to provide a more detailed written analysis, to serve as an expert witness, or to provide statements that may be used by the workers' compensation commission or in appellate proceedings. In oral testimony, the physician may assess the degree of impairment or describe the causal link between the workplace and the injury.

In workers' compensation proceedings, it is the "finder of fact" (commissioner, judge, jury) who must decide if the illness "arose out of" and "in the course of" employment—and, in some states, "by accident." The role of the physician-expert is to provide the "finder of fact" with the information necessary to make a legal determination. The physician must be able to clearly explain both the analytical process and the facts used to reach his or her medical opinion. Furthermore, the physician must be able to render that opinion with a degree of confidence that will satisfy the standard of proof necessary for adjudication of the case. The physician's opinion might be, for example, that there is a "reasonable probability" that the disorder is causally linked to an agent in the workplace. A clearly structured analysis incorporating all the required facts makes adjudication easier and aids in the equitable disposition of claims. Moreover, the proof of *medical* causation provides information critical to the proof of *legal* causation.

To establish that a disorder arose "in the course of employment," it must be distinguished from diseases that are common to mankind and not distinctively associated with employment. The goal is to identify disorders that might as easily be contracted in other occupations. In jurisdictions where compensable diseases are listed in statutes, there is a strong presumption that these diseases are related to occupational exposure. If a disorder is not covered by statute, fact finders in most states will consider the disease under general causation requirements. A nonstatutory disorder has been described as an ailment that does not become an occupational disease simply because it is contracted on the employer's premises. Indeed, the disorder must be one that is constantly regarded as natural to, inherent in, incident to, and concomitant with the work in question. There must be a recognizable link with the claimant's job and some distinctive feature of the claimant's job, common to all jobs of that sort.

The concept of "dual causation" has created a formidable analytic challenge for those who must interpret workers' compensation or occupational disease statutes. Dual causation arises when a personal element, such as smoking, combines with an employment element, such as asbestos or textile fibers, noxious fumes, acrid smoke, or irritating dust, to produce disease. Not surprisingly, the relative quantitative or percentage contribution of each causal element has often been difficult to prove.

A RATIONAL APPROACH TO WORK-RELATED DISEASES

In any rational approach to occupational disease, experimental studies must be located and evaluated, epidemiologic and clinical case series and reports must be located and evaluated, the worker-patient must be clinically evaluated and special clinical testing performed as indicated, and the exposure and/or exposure levels must be determined and related to the clinical presentation.

Evaluation of experimental evidence should include both in vitro and animal studies. This often requires an extensive literature search and review. Both negative and positive studies and their quality must be assessed before an opinion is offered. The review should also address analogues of toxic substances and other disorders with similar pathophysiologic mechanisms.

Epidemiologic (human) data include case reports and series as well as retrospective and prospective studies. Unfortunately, human studies typically are not carried out under circumstances that can be manipulated or adequately controlled. Therefore, the quality of both negative and positive studies deserves especially close scrutiny.

A general clinical evaluation of the worker—with special attention to common etiologic agents—is particularly important if the clinical presentation is unusual for exposure to the suspected agent. After a complete history, physical, and laboratory examination, an exposure-specific evaluation must be performed that includes an occupational and environmental history, a target-organ-specific physical examination, and specialized testing such as measurement of body-fluid or tissue concentrations of the suspect substance or its metabolites, or sensitive analyses for injury that may not be detected by common screening tests. For example, sensitive lung, neurologic, or liver function tests or specialized muscle testing may be indicated. The clinician should always remember that multiple causal, aggravating, and exacerbating factors may substantially contribute to a worker's medical condition.

The actual exposure of the worker to the specific etiologic agent in the workplace must be evaluated. The following should be considered: (1) the agent's physical and chemical properties, routes of entry, and exposure levels of the substance on entry to the body, and (2) for musculoskeletal processes, the amount and type of muscle stress, repetitive trauma, or vibration. For instance, to assess occupational lung disease, air levels may be available for common agents, although the quantity of those samples and the time and place of testing must be scrutinized. To assess musculoskeletal processes, job description, ergonomic job analysis, caloric requirements, and/or enzyme measurements could be considered. It is important to determine if the worker was exposed to an agent in a situation where he or she could have contracted the disease.

The duration and intensity of exposure must be correlated with the disease process or alleged injury and its clinical course. Exposure to agents at low concentrations typically does not cause clinically or quantitatively significant damage.

TABLE 1. Systematic Analysis of Causation/Compensability of Illnesses
Potentially Related to Occupation

Experimental evidence
Epidemiologic evidence
Clinical evidence
Evidence of environmental correlation with clinical data

Moreover, if disability predates exposure or the latency period is very short or very long, a cause-and-effect relationship may be difficult to prove. Finally, work-related disorders in coworkers and evidence of use of protective measures may influence the causation analysis.

After these four types of evidence have been accumulated and systemically evaluated, the clinician can offer an opinion on the causation of the disease. If appropriate information is not available to support an opinion on causation, the clinician should indicate this.

Table 1 outlines a systematic approach that incorporates all four components of the analysis of causation in occupational disease. The experimental and epidemiologic evidence are considered first. If either type of evidence suggests an association of exposure with disease, there is some support for a causal relationship. The clinical evaluation of the patient comes next. If the clinical evidence is consistent with the experimental and/or epidemiologic evidence, further analysis may not be required, especially if a signature disorder or pathognomonic sign is documented.

If the data are not so consistent, however, the clinician must correlate environmental exposure data with the clinical, epidemiologic, and experimental evidence. If the experimental or epidemiologic evidence, the clinical evaluation, and the environmental correlation are consistent and supportive, causation is operationally established.

If the data from any one or more of the four evaluations are inconsistent, further scrutiny must be given to that portion of the analysis. For example, it is possible that adequate experimental or epidemiologic studies have not been performed. If the clinical picture is not supportive, more detailed clinical evaluation may be required and special consideration should be given to competing diagnoses. Furthermore, the environmental evaluation may be supplemented with additional retrospective estimates of exposure duration and intensity. If a proposed causal connection is supported only by the experimental and/or epidemiologic data, or only by the clinical picture or only by the exposure history, an opinion supporting the causal connection should not be offered. In summary, the use or a structured approach in determining medical causation should enhance the ability of the physician to clearly outline his or her thought processes.

Causation Analysis in Selected Pulmonary and Musculoskeletal Occupational Illnesses

The above analytical system can be applied to selected occupational lung and musculoskeletal conditions (Table 2).

For example, the epidemiologic literature on asbestos is extensive. Asbestos has characteristic clinical symptoms, radiographic changes, and pulmonary function abnormalities. Sputum cytology and postmortem counts of asbestos bodies or documentation of pulmonary pathologic change also may confirm asbestos exposure and the probability of a causal relationship between exposure and disease. Finally, concentrations of airborne particles may have been measured or estimated by industrial

TABLE 2. Contrasting Analytic Issues

	Asbestos-Related Disease	Musculoskeletal Disease Related to Cumulative or Repetitive Trauma
Epidemiologic/toxicologic data	Confirmatory data present	Conflicting studies
Clinical picture: initiation	Distinct clinical picture or disease with objective evidence of exposure in many cases	No distinct clinical picture; many other competing etiologies
Clinical picture: exacerbation/aggravation	Usually not an issue	Exacerbation/aggravation commonly a medical and legal issue
Exposure and correlation with disease	Exposure either occupational or environmental	Exposure common in ordinary life
Exposure: quantification	Multiple environmental and clinical methods to verify and quantitate exposure	Indices of qualitative exposure not relevant; quantitative exposure methods not well established

hygienists. Thus, for asbestosis it is often possible to evaluate all four components of the analytical process to determine medical causation.

Mesothelioma, by contrast, is a rare cancer that is frequently associated with asbestos exposure in the United States. Because the epidemiologic studies provide strong support and the clinical and radiographic presentation is distinctive, mesothelioma can be causally related to asbestos exposure in the absence of detailed exposure data.

The clinical picture of bronchogenic carcinoma does not by itself implicate an industrial hazard. However, concurrent asbestos-related changes (parenchymal, pleural, and skin changes) increase the probability of a causal connection between bronchogenic cancer and exposure to asbestos. Furthermore, the actual or predicted fiber concentrations and fiber types may have been documented in the workplace. Therefore, objective evidence of exposure may be available in cases of asbestos-related carcinomas, and this evidence may be used to establish the probability of occupational causation.

For some types of musculoskeletal disorders, comparable analyses can be made. For example, a vinyl-chloride–exposed worker who cleans reaction vessels and develops acro-osteolysis, acrosclerosis, or hepatic angiosarcoma, probably has a disease of occupational origin. Fluorosis, caisson disease, infectious tendinitis, and Caplan's syndrome are also well-documented, frequently work-related disorders where only the clinical presentation and exposure correlation need to be evaluated to establish causation. In fluorosis, the distinctive clinical syndrome and documentation of significant occupational exposure to fluorides can be used to determine causation; in caisson disease, the occupational history is combined with the clinical presentation and radiographic picture. In infectious musculoskeletal diseases, contact with the suspect agent and clinical infection by that agent must be documented.

The characteristic radiographic changes and occupational history in a patient with rheumatoid arthritis are required for the diagnosis of Caplan's syndrome. By contrast, exposure assessment data are less critical for causation analysis if the current immunologic hypotheses for the pathogenesis of the syndrome is eventually confirmed.

Carpal tunnel syndrome, tendinitis, and back pain are musculoskeletal processes that have been causally related to repetitive or cumulative physical trauma. However, there is no consensus on the precise role of the workplace in the development of these disorders. The clinical syndromes that arise at work are not associated with pathognomonic signs that distinguish them from similar syndromes that occur in other settings. Exposure to trauma is difficult to measure quantitatively. Thus, because these disorders are those of ordinary life, the clinical presentation may not substantially contribute to the causation analysis. However, careful evaluation of the past medical history, history of present illness, review of systems, and occupational history can help to rule out nonoccupational etiologies and risk factors for musculoskeletal disorders. The history may indeed suggest a causal connection to the workplace owing to the time of onset of the symptoms, their occurrence or exacerbation with time spent at work, or the appearance of the problem in several workers.

A common issue in repetitive or cumulative use disorders is aggravation, exacerbation, or progression of an underlying disease. Because exacerbations are typically compensable under workers' compensation laws, occupational health professionals must consider work-related factors that may aggravate preexisting illness. This aggravation is more likely to occur with musculoskeletal disease than it is with pulmonary or other conditions in which multiple agents combine to cause a single disease process or in which multiple, distinct disease processes (each linked to different exposures) combine to cause impairment. Thus, the clinical history and course must be carefully scrutinized in workers with musculoskeletal disorders. If a nonoccupational cause is present or the sequential history of the disease process suggests an occupational origin, this information should be presented to the finder of fact.

As noted, the identification and quantification of exposure remain problematic. Although special or repetitive movements can be measured, the actual movements may be indistinguishable from those made in ordinary life. Consequently, the actual work-related exposure variable is extremely difficult to assess accurately.

Despite these difficulties, the medical expert should nevertheless assist the finder of fact. Discussing competing etiologies, defining temporality or latency of the disease process, quantifying the duration and intensity of exposure, and commenting on unique aspects of the disease process can be useful to decision-makers. The purpose of testimony is to provide evidence and not to make a definitive medical decision. However, a unique legal situation exists in which neither the disease process nor the agent of exposure suggests a specific etiologic event resulting in musculoskeletal impairment. To remedy the issue, specific statutes (e.g., statutes relevant to the back) have been passed in some states, and other statutes are under consideration.

Public Health Considerations

Although the physician who treats a patient with a potential occupational injury or illness typically considers only the disorder under treatment, there are other implications and obligations when health problems are alleged to be work-related. To protect the public health, systems designed to prevent recurrent injury or illness in the workplace and community are administered by the Occupational Safety and Health Administration, the Environmental Protection Agency, and other regulatory agencies. These systems depend on accurate medical and employment records. The failure to accurately diagnose or to establish a causal relationship between injury or disease and work may result in misclassification and under- or overreporting of the condition. Consequently, a potentially hazardous worksite or work practice may go unscrutinized, and industries that are aware of health and safety issues may be frustrated by inappropriate diagnoses or by the failure of the reporting system to document the positive effects of health and safety programs. In addition, the workers' compensation system is designed to equitably distribute the expense of work-related injuries and illnesses. Therefore, inaccurate diagnoses will increase the likelihood of failure of the system to allocate costs to employers according to their safety records ("experience rating").

A second matter of public health is that the failure to properly categorize the cause of injuries and illnesses potentially related to occupation results in the inability of clinicians, epidemiologists, and toxicologists to study underreported diseases. This may inappropriately increase the scrutiny of disorders that are routinely reported or overreported. For example, several occupational illnesses related to exposure to carcinogens and other chemicals have been recognized only after periods of underreporting. Conversely, injuries and musculoskeletal disorders are almost universally scrutinized and their work-relatedness evaluated. It deserves emphasis that the study of occupational health by governmental, academic, industrial, and labor groups cannot be more accurate than the diagnostic evaluation of the physician.

CONCLUSION

The medical evaluation of a worker-patient for occupational disease requires a consistent approach to medical causation and an understanding of legal systems. Physicians must analyze each case systematically to determine the medical cause and to assist in the determination of the legal cause of impairment.

Consistency of approach will reduce frustration with the diagnosis and treatment of patients potentially involved in litigation. When the issue of causation arises during the adversarial process, physicians who adopt a systematic approach can more effectively communicate their opinions to the finder of fact. The ability of employers, insurance evaluators, commissioners, judges, juries, and legislatures to integrate medical decisions into the existing legal framework will be enhanced. Systematic determination of causation will lead to more rapid, equitable, and reasonable allocation of compensation for atraumatic occupational illness.

REFERENCES

1. Blair EH: A Reference Guide to Workmen's Compensation. West St. Louis, Thomas Law Book, 1968.
2. Hadler NM (ed): Clinical Issues in Regional Musculoskeletal Illness. Orlando, Grune & Stratton, 1987.
3. Hadler NM: Medical Management of the Regional Musculoskeletal Diseases. Orlando, Grune & Stratton, 1984.
4. Hadler NM: Occupational Musculoskeletal Disorders. New York, Raven Press, 1993.
5. Hadler NM, Gillings DB (eds): Arthritis and Society. London, Butterworth, 1985.
6. Harris PG, et al: Radiologic survey of man exposed to asbestos in naval dockyards. Br J Intern Med 29:274, 1970.
7. Larson AB: Larson's Worker's Compensation Law. New York, Matthew Bender Corp, 1994.
8. Merchant JA: Byssinosis: Progress in prevention. Am J Public Health 73:137–138, 1983.
9. Meurman LO: Pleural fibrocalcific plaques and asbestos exposure. Environ Res 2:30, 1968.
10. Pratt PC, Vollner RT, Miller JA: Epidemiology of pulmonary lesions in non textile and cotton workers: A retrospective autopsy analysis. Arch Environ Health 25:133–138, 1980.
11. Richman SI: Why change? A look at the current system of disability determination and workers compensation for occupational lung disease. Ann Intern Med 97:908, 1982.
12. Selikoff IJ: Asbestos and Research. New York, Academic Press, 1978.
13. Sheers G, Templeton AR: Effects of asbestos in dockyard workers. Br Med J 3:574, 1968.

D. GARY RISCHITELLI, MD, JD, MPH

LICENSING, PRACTICE, AND MALPRACTICE IN OCCUPATIONAL MEDICINE

From the Division of Occupational
Health
The Johns Hopkins University
School of Hygiene and Public
Health
Baltimore, Maryland

Reprint requests to:
D. Gary Rischitelli, MD, JD, MPH
Clinical Fellow
Division of Occupational Health
The Johns Hopkins University
School of Hygiene and Public
Health
615 North Wolfe Street
Room 7041
Baltimore, MD 21205

In a particular jurisdiction, the practice of occupational medicine is generally subject to the same laws that govern the practice of medicine in other specialties. Occupational physicians, however, often interact with people in ways that challenge traditional legal views of the physician-patient relationship. For example, the rights and responsibilities associated with the interpretation of employment-related drug tests, the performance of preplacement and medical surveillance exams, and the fulfillment of corporate administrative responsibilities have few parallels in other medical specialties. This creates a legal bramble bush for occupational physicians, who often do not fully appreciate the peculiar legal aspects of their professional activities.

In some situations, the typical evaluation of an individual by an occupational physician does not create the usual physician-patient relationship. Rather, the physician provides services for the benefit of a third party, usually a business or government entity. The physician may be a salaried employee of this third party or may act as a private contractor, creating additional layers of legal complexity. The absence of a legally recognized physician-patient relationship has a profound influence on the nature and extent of the physician's responsibilities to examinees and third parties. For example, the absence of a physician-patient relationship has traditionally been a complete bar to a claim of malpractice. The importance of the physician-patient relationship and medical malpractice is discussed below.

Because the law pertaining to licensing, practice, and malpractice varies by state, this chapter addresses the unique legal challenges of occupational medicine from a general perspective, pointing out specific issues where pertinent. Citations to general references predominate; citations to specific cases or statutes are used for illustration. Physicians must be familiar with the laws and regulations of all the states in which they practice. When questions arise, the physician must seek advice from an attorney with competence in health law. The old adage regarding regarding an ounce of prevention applies equally well to legal matters.

LICENSING

Legal Basis

In the traditional sense, a physician is anyone who attempts to treat the ill or infirm and who holds himself out as possessing specialized knowledge or skills in this regard. A physician in the modern or legal sense, however, is one who holds a medical or osteopathic degree and a license or certificate of competency from the state that authorizes the prescription of medication and the performance of surgical procedures.[1]

Because the power to regulate the practice of medicine and other learned professions is not an enumerated federal power in the United States Constitution, it has been reserved to the states provided that other important federal rights are not abridged. Moreover, the right to practice medicine does not fall within the privileges and immunities of national citizenship.[2] States clearly have the right to regulate the practice of medicine and to license physicians.[3] To survive a constitutional challenge, regulation by the state need only be reasonable and bear a rational relationship to the legislature's stated goals.[4]

Duly qualified practitioners have a valuable interest in their ability to practice medicine. Some courts have elevated this interest to the status of a constitutionally protected property right deserving full due process of law.[5] This right, however, is not unlimited or unqualified. Although the state may not prohibit the practice of medicine, it can regulate the conduct of individuals under its police powers when it can demonstrate a risk to the public health, safety, or morals. The state may therefore proscribe the practice of medicine within its boundaries by those who do not possess a valid license.[6]

State Medical Practice Acts

Licensing is typically implemented by administrative boards or agencies under the authority of a state medical practice act. These acts typically authorize the creation of an agency or board with responsibility for regulating the practice of medicine and licensing individuals within the state. Like other administrative enabling acts, medical practice statutes describe the number and composition of the board or agency, its powers and jurisdiction, and a legislative purpose by which courts may review agency performance. The board may have both quasi-legislative powers, i.e., rulemaking authority, and quasijudicial powers, i.e., investigative and adjudicative authority. The board typically has provisions for hearings and appeals, with ultimate judicial review after all administrative procedures have been exhausted. Most state courts defer to the expert findings of the board except where bias, violation of law or procedure, or acts in excess of jurisdiction can be demonstrated.[7]

Occupational Medicine and Interstate Practice

Because states have the power to prohibit the practice of itinerant physicians, states may require that all physicians rendering service within the state hold a valid license granted by that jurisdiction. This may pose a problem for the occupational medicine consultant or corporate physician providing services in more than one state. The critical issue is the definition of "the practice of medicine" in the jurisdiction of interest. This all-important definition creates boundaries for civil or criminal liability for unlicensed practice. Unfortunately, most statutes governing "the practice of medicine" do not define that term specifically.[8] As with many legal terms, the definition may be fact-dependent and subject to interpretation. In some states, accepting payment for any professional service while holding oneself out as a physician is sufficient to constitute medical practice. In other states, merely appending the title physician, doctor, or MD to one's name in a professional transaction is sufficient.[9] This broad definition of medical practice seems to encompass most of the professional activity of the occupational physician, including that which does not involve diagnosis or treatment. Therefore, reviews of drug test results, interpretations of screening tests or procedures (medical surveillance or health promotion), and contributions of professional advice (corporate consulting) may fall under the medical practice acts of some states. Restated simply, many states are likely to consider any work obtained or performed by virtue of holding a medical degree as the practice of medicine requiring licensure.

Physicians involved in interstate practice would be wise to contact the licensing board of any state in which they may have professional contacts to determine if temporary or permanent licensure is required. They should be licensed in any state where any of their activities could conceivably fall within that state's definition of the practice of medicine. When in doubt, if the physician anticipates significant or regular contacts or activities within a state, the prudent choice is to obtain a license.

PRACTICE

Liability Insurance

Attempts to define the practice of medicine raise another issue for occupational physicians. While states may attempt to broaden the scope of the definition to regulate all practitioners, liability insurers seek to constrict the definition as much as possible. The insurer may deny coverage or refuse to pay damages if the claim involves activity viewed as beyond the scope of the practice of medicine as defined in the terms of the policy. The standard professional insurance policy may not cover some of the activities of an occupational physician that fall outside the traditional physician-patient, diagnosis-and-treatment paradigm. Furthermore, most of these policies tend to exclude coverage for intentional torts, defamation, breach of confidence, invasion of privacy, and civil rights violations such as age or disability discrimination. Occupational physicians must carefully consider these risks and seek additional insurance or indemnification contracts to cover these non-malpractice liabilities.

Forms of Medical Practice

The business organizations in which physicians practice include sole proprietorships, partnerships, and professional corporations. During most of the 20th century, many physicians have practiced as sole proprietors contracting directly with patients or third parties.[10] This traditional form of medical practice has become less common in the increasingly complex health care environment. Many occupational medicine consultants and some independent contractors still practice alone, but the growth of managed care has made it increasingly difficult for independent clinicians to compete with group practices or integrated health care organizations.

In the last two decades, physicians have associated in single specialty and multispecialty group practices. Many of these groups were, and continue to be, partnerships. Although a partnership is a distinct legal entity, the partners remain individually responsible for the debts and liabilities of the partnership. Partners have a fiduciary duty to each other and must use their best efforts for the good of the partnership. They must account for any profits, typically sharing all assets and liabilities equally or according to a previously stated partnership agreement.[11] States typically have a partnership act that describes the duties and liabilities of partners.

Professional corporations are a relatively new form of business entity with powers granted by a state corporation act. Corporations are owned by shareholders whose legal liability is limited to the value of their shares. They were originally chartered in this country to encourage investment in risky but publicly beneficial enterprises such as transportation or shipping. Prior to the passage of professional corporation acts, most states prohibited doctors and lawyers from practicing in the corporate form. State legislatures did not wish to extend the prospect of limited liability to physicians and attorneys for fear that the public would be left without compensation in cases of legal or medical malpractice. Changes in tax laws, however, gave significant benefits to incorporated businesses. Professional associations lobbied legislatures for the means to enjoy the same pension, profit-sharing, and delayed compensation opportunities available to corporate entities. In response, legislatures passed professional corporation acts that allow physicians to practice for profit as a corporation but that also mandate personal liability of shareholders for any professional malpractice. Therefore, only licensed members of the particular profession can be shareholders, and the corporation can only render services through its individual shareholders.[12]

In contrast, nonprofit health service corporations typically enjoy more freedom under state licensure and insurance laws. Originally organized for benevolent purposes, these entities can contract with licensed physicians for the provision of medical care. Because courts and legislatures recognized the need for medical services in specified locales and populations, they relaxed prohibitions on corporate practice for these entities. The determining factors in early decisions were the lack of profit motive and the need for assurances that medical services would be provided only by appropriately licensed practitioners.[13]

Legal restrictions on the creation of for-profit corporations by nonphysician stockholders for the purpose of medical practice are often referred to as the "corporate practice of medicine doctrine." This legal doctrine remains valid in many states but is rarely enforced or discussed. The doctrine grew out of concerns that the personal relationship between physicians and patients would be adversely affected by the introduction of corporate business practices.[14] Lawmakers feared that corporate practices would harm the personal accountability, trust, and integrity of the medical profession, an idea that some may find anachronistic in the modern world of managed care and giant health care corporations. However, the basic core concept remains: a corporation, although legally treated as a "person," cannot receive a license to practice medicine; nor can nonphysicians use the corporate form to practice vicariously through employment of licensed practitioners.

Today many states have limited or repealed corporate practice statutes, or they have created legislative exceptions to the common law doctrine. A few states, however, still have viable corporate practice doctrines that remain enforceable.

Obviously, the corporate practice doctrine seems to raise questions about the practice of occupational medicine in a corporate medical department. The questions are more apparent than real, however, because courts have recognized exceptions for corporations whose primary business purpose is not the practice of medicine and who employ physicians to care primarily for their own employees. Corporate medical departments, then, are viewed no differently than other staff departments that assist in the primary mission of the business enterprise, as long as those services are provided by licensed practitioners only within the scope of their authority under the state's medical practice act. Real questions arise, however, if for-profit stock corporations are formed by nonphysicians for the purpose of providing occupational medical services. In the absence of specific state legislation authorizing this type of corporate purpose, these organizations could run afoul of the common law prohibition of the corporate practice of medicine.

Of late, little has been written about the corporate practice prohibition, and few enforcement activities have been reported. Recently, however, an employment contract between a physician and a hospital was deemed illegal and unenforceable under the corporate practice doctrine, allowing the physician to avoid the contract and its noncompetition clause.[15] Although the corporate practice doctrine may be moribund in some jurisdictions, it remains a legal doctrine that cannot be completely ignored in the organization and delivery of occupational health services.

Noncompetition Agreements

Medical practitioners continue to enjoy the freedom to contract their services as they see fit. Just as a state cannot restrict the practice of medicine by a qualified and licensed physician without cause, it cannot prevent the physician from limiting his or her scope of practice. Physicians are free to refuse new patients or to refuse to practice at all (subject to laws prohibiting abandonment), and they may likewise enter into contracts with other providers limiting the geographic or temporal scope of their practice.[16]

Commonly known as noncompetition clauses or agreements, these contractual restrictions on a physician's right to practice are valid. Courts typically enforce the terms as long as they are reasonable in scope and duration.[17] Reasonableness is judged by many factors, including the geographic distances involved, the duration of restriction, and the availability of other qualified practitioners in the area. Longer distances are probably acceptable in rural areas where patients are accustomed to longer travel times, unless the agreement creates a shortage of qualified specialists in that region. Conversely, agreements may be expansive in areas where an oversupply of equivalently trained and qualified physicians exists and competition is high. Courts will balance the needs of the party seeking to prevent competition against the public need for access to qualified medical personnel.

Given the shortage of board-certified occupational physicians, would a court reviewing a noncompetition clause find board certification significant when the ratio of certified to noncertified practitioners is low in most communities? Would a court extend the same public need consideration to an occupational physician that it would to a neurosurgeon or obstetrician? These are interesting questions with little or no guidance from the courts. Occupational physicians should therefore exercise great care in executing a noncompetition agreement. It is better to address this issue during contract formation, with the advice of competent counsel familiar with local law, than to challenge the validity of the noncompetition provision at some later date.

MALPRACTICE AND OTHER LIABILITIES

Physicians are potential defendants under numerous legal theories. Professional negligence or malpractice is the most common basis for liability, but physicians also may be sued for battery, failure to obtain informed consent, abandonment, breach of confidence, or breach of contract or warranty of cure.[18] Note that battery, which arises from the unconsented touching of another, is one of the *intentional* torts, which are frequently excluded from coverage under modern malpractice insurance policies. Failure to obtain informed consent significantly increases the risk of tort liability for occupational physicians. Intentional failure to provide informed consent may be considered fraud. Lack of consent accompanied by physical contact may be battery. Where consent is negligently withheld, damages based on professional negligence or malpractice may be sought. Informed consent is not merely a form signed by the patient or examinee. Courts will look beyond a piece of paper to see if the individual had in fact given consent after a meaningful attempt by the physician to describe the procedure, alternatives, and risks. The requirements of informed consent may be defined by court decisions or statute; adequacy of consent may be judged by various standards, including what a reasonable physician would say, what a reasonable or particular patient would want to know, or whether the information meets the requirements of a statute.

Physicians should take the issue of informed consent seriously. Mere production of a form signed by the patient or a chart note indicating "procedure discussed" may be insufficient to properly defend a suit alleging the physician has ignored his duty to inform the patient fully and adequately.

For occupational physicians, the issue of informed consent encompasses more than the purely medical aspects of an examination, test, or procedure. Occupational physicians have an ethical and perhaps a legal duty to adequately inform the patient or examinee of the purposes and potential consequences of an evaluation performed on behalf of a third party. Even where no legal duty exists, full disclosure may avoid future conflicts or protect the physician in subsequent legal action.[19] For example, when examining a person to evaluate his or her fitness to work, the physician should inform the examinee that no physician-patient relationship exists and that the physician's opinion is requested by the employer to determine that person's ability to safely perform the job.

Medical Malpractice in General

Medical malpractice is but one type of professional negligence. Attorneys, accountants, insurance agents, real estate agents, and other professionals also can be sued for malpractice. Professional negligence is a specific application of the general tort theory of negligence to any person with a heightened duty of care arising from his or her professional status. The tort of negligence has four elements that the plaintiff must demonstrate by sufficient evidence to establish a prima facie case: (1) the presence of a duty and (2) a breach of that duty, (3) which has proximately caused (4) some foreseeable injury to the plaintiff. Once the plaintiff has produced sufficient evidence to make his prima facie case, the defendant assumes a burden to produce either evidence that refutes the plaintiff's evidence or a defense that negates the plaintiff's lawsuit. Ultimately, the plaintiff in most civil actions retains the burden of persuading the judge or jury by a preponderance of the evidence.

Duty

Although physicians have an undisputed ethical duty to provide diligent and compassionate attention to those under their care, the law views the physician-patient relationship in rather mercantile terms. Although some courts have held that the ethical principles of medicine are enforceable through licensing statutes or common law, most courts view the physician-patient relationship simply as an expressed or implied contract between the parties. The essential terms of the contract are that the physician will treat the patient with professional skill and attention and the patient will pay the physician for this service. The formation of this contract most often depends on what the court believes occurred in the mind of the examinee, not the physician. The question for the fact-finder becomes: Would a reasonable person in the position of this individual believe that a legally enforceable exchange of promises has occurred? Because few individuals outside of law and business appreciate the full contractual significance of their actions, courts often relegate this threshold issue to a relatively low standard of proof. Courts consider a number of factors in determining whether the physician-patient contract was formed, including issues of volition, consensus, reliance, and third-party involvement.[20] Once this physician-patient relationship creates an express or implied contract, it fixes certain professional and fiduciary duties on the physician. The physician must diligently and faithfully exercise his or her best efforts, knowledge, skill, and attention for the benefit of the patient. The physician is not an insurer of outcome and is not required to act infallibly.

There is a common misperception that a mistake or bad outcome per se constitutes malpractice. Occupational physicians should understand, however, that malpractice occurs only when a mistake is judged unreasonable or the physician has failed to behave in an acceptably skillful or diligent manner. Malpractice should not be confused with incompetence because competent physicians may act negligently. It is the commission of an unreasonable act, or the omission of an act reasonably required, that constitutes malpractice. The operative act of the tort of negligence is a failure to behave as a reasonably prudent person would under similar circumstances. In cases involving professional negligence, the reasonably prudent person standard is replaced with the reasonably prudent professional standard. Restated in the context of medical malpractice, the question posed to the jury becomes: "Did this physician diligently exercise the same degree of knowledge, skill, and care that a reasonably prudent physician would exercise under similar circumstances?"

Standard of Care

Determining how a reasonably prudent physician would act under similar circumstances is an essential step in determining liability for malpractice. Evidence of the applicable standard of care is offered by both parties through expert witnesses, who often testify to causation and damage issues as well. After the presentation of evidence, it is the judge or jury who must discern the applicable standard of care and decide if the defendant has acted in conformity with that standard. The standard of care has traditionally been defined by local custom or practice, geographic location, and available resources. Modern courts, however, have embraced national standards of care that can be supported by offering into evidence practice guidelines or consensus documents of professional associations.[21] Specialists will be held to a higher standard of care commensurate with their training and experience. Moreover, generalists offering specialty care also may be held to the higher specialist standard. To clarify another common misperception, the standard of care does not represent what *most* physicians would do. A physician may choose among several alternatives and will not be held liable even if the choice was in error, as long as the choice was reasonable. When judging the reasonableness of the chosen alternative, physicians are held to a "respectable minority" standard. That is, would a respectable minority of physicians exercise the same option even if the majority would not?

Causation

Even if the plaintiff can prove that the physician failed in his duty to act in a reasonably prudent manner, the plaintiff must still prove that this failure caused some injury to him or her. Legal causation is an elusive concept due to the infinite combinations of factual possibilities leading to a legally significant event. Legal causation has two elements, proximate causation and foreseeability. Proximate causation assumes actual causation. Proof of actual causation, or "causation in fact," requires evidence that the act or omission by the defendant contributed in some essential way to the plaintiff's alleged harm. The test for causation is often described as the sine qua none or "but-for" test, i.e., *but for* the defendant's act, would the harm have occurred?

Proof of proximate causation further requires evidence that the defendant's act was sufficiently close in time and space that it reasonably can be viewed as a substantial factor in the plaintiff's harm. In other words, *actual* causation requires that the act is one of the links in the chain of events leading to the harm, and *proximate* causation requires that the link be reasonably close to the end of that chain. Proof of foreseeability, by contrast, requires evidence that the plaintiff's harm is of a type reasonably anticipated to occur as a result of the defendant's negligent behavior. The plaintiff's burden to prove proximate causation and foreseeability becomes, in essence, a protection against unlimited retrospective and prospective liability for the defendant's negligent act. The defendant is only responsible for harm to plaintiffs in a foreseeable "zone of danger" created by the negligent act.

The causation element is an indispensable element of the plaintiff's prima facie case. Thus, even if the plaintiff can prove that the defendant acted unreasonably and that the plaintiff has suffered some injury, there will be no recovery if the plaintiff cannot establish the causal relationship between the defendant's breach of duty and the plaintiff's harm. Likewise, the causation element can be critical to a physician's malpractice defense. For example, a failure to diagnose or refer may not have altered the patient's opportunity for treatment or cure.

Damages

Legal damages are often classified as compensatory or punitive. Compensatory damages may include general and special damages. General damages provide compensation for injuries that are typical and expected results of the defendant's action or inaction. Special damages are unique to the particular plaintiff and may include loss of future income or opportunities, worsening of preexisting conditions, or future medical or custodial costs.[22] Punitive damages serve to punish the defendant and deter others from similar behavior. Punitive damages are typically associated with intentional torts and are not usually awarded in negligence suits unless the defendant's actions have been particularly wanton or reckless (gross negligence).

MALPRACTICE LIABILITIES IN OCCUPATIONAL MEDICINE

Doctor to Patient

The duty of care in malpractice suits most often arises out of the professional relationship between the parties. For occupational physicians, the common threshold question has been, "Was a physician-patient relationship created?" Where the occupational physician offers treatment of diagnosis, a physician-patient relationship is typically formed.

Traditionally, however, a physician-patient relationship did not exist when the physician examined the patient for the benefit of an employer or insurer. In this situation, the physician's only duty to the patient was not to injure him during the examination. In the past, this gave some "company doctors" a shield against liability for clearly egregious conduct. For example, courts have held that no cause of action for malpractice existed even where a physician informed an employee with x-ray evidence of active pulmonary tuberculosis that there was nothing seriously wrong with him[23] or where a physician "willfully and deliberately concealed" a diagnosis of silicosis from an employee after consultation with a specialist.[24] In the latter case, however, the court did find that the plaintiff could recover damages in tort outside the physician-patient relationship because one who acts gratuitously and without obligation nevertheless must act in a reasonably careful manner.[25] The court noted that although his professional duty of care ran only to the corporation that employed him, the physician, by affirmatively representing to the employee that his condition was not serious, became liable to the employee under the general duty of due care.[26]

Recent cases suggest that this view of "no physician-patient relationship" still persists in some jurisdictions. In *Felton v. Schaeffer*,[26] an applicant presented for a preplacement examination at a clinic offering occupational medicine services. During the examination, the physician noted an increased blood pressure and asked the applicant whether he had taken his medication. The applicant, who had been instructed not to take anything by mouth in preparation for laboratory testing, said no. The physician recorded this response as indicating that the examinee was noncompliant with his medications, even though he routinely took them. The clinic's director, on reviewing the examining physician's notes, told the employer that the applicant was not medically qualified for the position. The applicant had, meanwhile, resigned his former position. When the error was discovered, the new position had already been filled and the applicant was forced to return to his lower-paying former job. The applicant sued the physician for the damages arising from the negligent reporting of inaccurate information that cost him the better-paying position. The California court held that there could be no liability for professional negligence without a physician-patient relationship, except for injuries arising from the examination itself. The court held that any duty of care of the physician was owed to the employer and not to the examinee.[28]

Occupational physicians should not rely on this traditional bar to malpractice actions against physicians performing examinations for employers and insurers. Although courts are nearly unanimous in holding that the absence of a physician-patient relationship limits the physician's professional duty, they have differed substantially on the extent of any duty that remains. Most courts have held that the physician has a duty not to injury the person during the examination, and others have held that the physician is subject to a general duty of reasonable care as previously discussed.[29] Significantly, there appears to be a trend toward eroding this historical bar to malpractice actions. As a first step, a few cases have held that when a physician undertakes to *advise or treat* the examinee during the examination, some duty of reasonable care attaches.[30]

Similarly, although the majority of courts continue to hold that the examining physician is not liable for failing to diagnose or report a serious medical condition to the examinee where no physician-patient relationship exists,[31] some recent decisions have held otherwise.[32] These cases seem to emphasize the examinee's reliance on the results of the examination, the nature of the injury suffered from the missed diagnosis, and for whose benefit the examination was performed.[33] One court has even held that an occupational physician does have a physician-patient relationship with an examinee, at least to the extent of the tests conducted. In *Green v. Walker*,[34] the court ruled that under the Louisiana Civil Code:

> ... when an individual is required, as a condition of future or continued employment, to submit to medical examination, that examination creates a relationship between examining physician and the examinee, at least to the extent of tests conducted. This relationship imposes on the examining physician a duty to conduct the requested tests and diagnose the results thereof, exercising the level of care consistent with the doctor's professional training and expertise, and to take reasonable steps to make information available timely to the examinee of any findings that pose an imminent danger to the examinee's physical or mental well-being.[35]

It is clear then, that occupational physicians walk a fine line during an examination performed for the benefit of an employer or insurer. If they fail to notify the examinee of abnormal findings or test results, they run a significant risk of malpractice liability if the examinee later suffers some injury from the lack of notification. On the other hand, if the physician's communications with the patient are construed as advice, diagnosis, or treatment, the physician may lose a valuable defense to a claim of malpractice. This is particularly important in the high-risk encounter where the occupational physician may have only one contact with the examinee, and that examinee has no sense of loyalty and may even be hostile to a company- or insurer-selected doctor.

Company to Patient

On occasion, companies have been held vicariously liable for the malpractice of their physician. In *Mangrum v. Union Pacific R. Co.*,[36] the widow of a railroad employee sued the railroad for the alleged negligence of a physician who examined her husband at the employer's request. The physician diagnosed bronchitis but the employee died later that day from pneumonia. The District Court of Appeal of California found that the physician was an agent of a railroad, even though the railroad could exercise no control over the physician as an independent professional. The court reasoned that the physician was an agent because his services contributed to the overall operational activities of the railroad, the railroad derived an economic benefit by supplying his services, and the railroad had a customary duty to care for employees who were ill while on duty. Finding that the physician was an agent, the railroad could then be found vicariously liable for the negligence of its physician through the doctrine of *respondeat superior*.[36]

Courts have traditionally held that where an employer supplies medical care to its employees gratuitously, the doctrine of respondeat superior does not apply. The employer is liable to the employee only where it has negligently or knowingly selected an incompetent practitioner. The employer may be vicariously liable, however, where it derives some direct financial or economic gain by providing medical services[38] or where the employer has expressly undertaken a contractual duty to provide medical care to the employee.[39]

Early cases tended to reject the vicarious liability of employers for malpractice, ruling that physicians were independent contractors or that medical care was provided as a benevolent and gratuitous act. The modern trend, however, is to hold employers liable by finding physicians to be agents or employees or by simply identifying the indirect economic benefit to employers who provide medical care to their workforce.[40]

This trend toward a more liberal application of the doctrine of respondeat superior parallels historically and probably reflects the expansion of other labor and employment rights, including workers' compensation. Note, however, that even if respondeat superior were applicable, the exclusive remedy doctrine of workers' compensation could limit the employee's legal right to sue the physician or employer for medical malpractice, particularly where the injury or illness would be otherwise compensable.

Workers' Compensation and the Dual Capacity Doctrine

Occupational physicians are clearly subject to liability for malpractice when treating injured workers under a state's workers' compensation act. Because diagnosis and treatment are provided, a physician-patient relationship is formed. Company-employed or company-retained physicians, however, may sometimes avoid malpractice liability by invoking the exclusive remedy doctrine of workers' compensation.

Workers' compensation is a system of social insurance created by the states to compensate workers and their families for injuries arising out of employment. The workers' compensation system provides a form of "no fault" insurance for employees who give up their right to sue in tort in return for guaranteed benefits.

Among the defenses used by employers in the 19th century was the "fellow servant doctrine," which held that a master was not liable to his servant where the injury arose from the actions of a fellow servant. Employers could often cite the negligence of a co-employee as the cause of injury and therefore escape liability. The injured worker could sue his co-employee but was unlikely to do so, and even if successful, the co-employee was usually unable to satisfy a judgment. One of the legislative compromises in drafting workers' compensation acts in the early 20th century was the elimination of the fellow servant doctrine and the granting of co-employee civil immunity.

Another major employee-employer compromise in the workers' compensation exchange was an agreement that workers' compensation was the sole remedy available to the injured employee. This allowed employers to avoid potentially unlimited tort liability by fixing workers' compensation as the exclusive remedy between the parties.

Companies and the physicians they employed could assert both the co-employee immunity and exclusive remedy provisions of workers' compensation to escape malpractice liability. Eventually, however, some courts found a way to circumvent the exclusive remedy provision where it acted to deny employees compensation for malpractice-related injuries. This exception to the exclusive remedy doctrine was called the "dual capacity doctrine," which held that whenever employers acted in a role other than that traditionally associated with an employer, they could be sued in tort for those activities. The dual capacity doctrine allowed the court to nullify the exclusive remedy defense of company physicians.

The California Supreme Court was the first to identify the dual capacity of medical provider and co-employee in *Duprey v. Shane*.[41] *Duprey* involved an employee of a chiropractic clinic who injured her shoulder while on the job. She was treated for her injury by her employer and a co-employee, both chiropractors. Ms. Duprey alleged that the treatment aggravated her injury and led to permanent disability. The California Court held that Duprey should not lose her right to sue in malpractice merely because the physician was also her employer. The court noted that Dr. Shane stood in a position of attending physician separate from his role as employer and had all the same legal responsibilities that attached to the treatment of any other private patient. Applying this precedent, a later court extended dual capacity liability to company physicians, holding that the co-employee immunity provision of the Workers' Compensation Act was not a bar to a medical malpractice suit for aggravation of a work-related injury.[42]

In *Ducote v. Albert*,[43] an employee filed a malpractice suit against the company doctor, alleging negligent misdiagnosis and treatment of a scapholunate dislocation that led to permanent disability. The physician was dismissed as a party by the trial court under the exclusive remedy and co-employee immunity provisions of the Louisiana Worker's Compensation statute. The Court of Appeals reversed, holding that the independent professional status of the physician made him more akin to an independent contractor without the benefit of co-employee immunity from liability. The Supreme Court of Louisiana affirmed the Court of Appeals but on different grounds. Rejecting the independent contractor analysis, the Supreme Court based its holding on the dual capacity doctrine. Citing *Duprey v. Shane*,[44] and *Wright v. District Ct. In & For City of Jefferson*,[45] the court held that the physician could be liable because he stood in a physician-patient relationship separate from the co-employee relationship. This created a different set of legal obligations under general tort law, where the physician could be held liable for medical malpractice. By separating the legal effects of these two relationships, the court found him liable as a medical professional notwithstanding his co-employee status.

In applying this doctrine to company physicians, courts have found that underlying principles of exclusive remedy and coworker immunity did not comport with the physician's status as an independent professional providing a service removed from the risks and circumstances of the workplace. Because the physician "does not participate in the mutual compromise of rights which is the essence of the worker's compensation scheme,"[46] he should not enjoy the benefits of civil immunity as a co-employee. It deserves emphasis, however, that most courts have not adopted this reasoning. The dual capacity doctrine represents a minority view and a number of states have legislatively limited or abolished its application.[47]

Doctor to Company

If a physician performs a physical examination for the benefit of a third party, the physician may be liable to that party if he or she conducts the exam or reports the result negligently. One court has even held the physician could be liable to the third party for contribution or indemnity if the third party is required to pay damages arising from its reliance on the physician's report. In *Wharton Transport Corp. v Bridges*,[48] a physician certified an interstate truck driver as medically qualified despite visual and other impairments that should have disqualified him under the Federal Motor Carrier Safety Regulations.[49] The driver was involved in a deadly accident, and Wharton Transport subsequently entered into a settlement with the victim's family. The company then sought indemnification from Dr. Bridges, alleging that he had been negligent in conducting and reporting the examination. Despite findings by the trial and appellate courts that the alleged negligence of Dr. Bridges was not the proximate cause of the accident, the Tennessee Supreme Court held that sufficient evidence existed to allow the questions of negligence and proximate cause to go to the jury. The court also held that there was an implied right of indemnity or contribution if negligence and proximate cause were found.

Wharton suggests that, even if an occupational physician has no liability to an examinee because of the absence of a physician-patient relationship, the physician may still be liable to the company if it suffers an identifiable harm as a result of the physician's negligence. Wharton's implied right of indemnity or contribution arose from the contractual relationship between Dr. Bridges and the company. The court noted that this right arises in both employer-employee and independent contractor relationships. Occupational physicians must not forget this source of potential liability when providing contracted services to third parties.

The *Wharton* court also noted the possibility that a physician's liability could extend to unrelated third parties if the physician's actions create a foreseeable risk to those parties. The court cited *Kaiser v. Suburban Transportation System*,[50] which held that a physician would be liable to passengers injured when a bus driver lost control while impaired by the sedating effects of a drug if the doctor failed to provide the driver with adequate warning of the side effects. It therefore seems plausible that an occupational physician could be found liable to employees injured by a coworker following a negligently performed fitness-for-duty evaluation. This is a sobering realization given the countervailing need to return individuals to the workplace to control workers' compensation costs and prevent disability discrimination. Occupational physicians should carefully tailor recommended work accommodations and restrictions with this in mind.

One last pearl can be gleaned from the *Wharton* case. The court noted that a large portion of Dr. Bridges' practice was devoted to industrial medicine and that he performed U.S. Department of Transportation certification exams for more than 20 companies. The court inferred that this was relevant to the standard of care to which Dr. Bridges should be held. The nature of his practice created a presumption that he was familiar with the applicable DOT medical standards. Therefore, injury to the victim arising from his failure to adhere to those standards was foreseeable.[51]

The occupational physician should never underestimate the sophistication of the bench. Courts can determine the appropriate standard of care through expert testimony provided by the parties or through court-appointed experts. The physician who provides occupational medical services may be held to a standard of care that assumes all the skills and knowledge of a specialist in the field. Familiarity with the laws and regulations governing the practice of occupational medicine is an important aspect of those skills.

CONCLUSION

This chapter has examined a number of legal issues pertaining to the practice of medicine, and it has identified some unique legal considerations in the practice of occupational medicine. Although occupational medicine is not usually considered a high-risk specialty, this may be due to factors other than a lack of legal risk. The perception of low risk is most likely due to the small number of practitioners relative to other specialties, the application of the physician-patient relationship defense in older cases, and a lack of recognition of occupational physicians as potential defendants by plaintiff's attorneys.

Courts are likely to expand occupational physician liability in the future. There is a trend in the courts to enlarge the physician-patient relationship in occupational medicine encounters. Imagining worst case scenarios is not difficult based on current decisional law. Consider the primary care physician in private practice who also serves as a contract medical director at a local plant. He or she is held to the same standard of care as a board-certified occupational physician. What happens when the physician fails to recognize and investigate a significant trend in medical surveillance data indicating that some workplace exposure has caused a large number of employees to develop a disabling occupational illness? If a court finds that a physician-patient relationship existed, at least with regard to the medical surveillance tests provided, the physician may be liable to a large number of plaintiffs, with damages quickly exceeding the limits of his malpractice insurance policy.

Occupational physicians should therefore seek adequate insurance. All aspects of practice should be discussed with the insurer, and covered activities should be confirmed in writing. Some practitioners may wish to consider errors-and-omissions or general business liability coverage, if available. Practitioners should seek an indemnification agreement from corporate clients but do not agree to bilateral (mutual) indemnification.

Occupational medicine invariably involves the participation of relevant third parties. Legal duties and liabilities are often created outside the traditional physician-patient transaction. These third party or nonpatient relationships may result in liability that is not covered under the terms of a standard medical malpractice policy.

Physicians should never agree to provide services for which they lack adequate training or experience. They must avoid all illegal activity, including corporate activities that may result in breach of confidentiality or discrimination. At least one court has held that corporate officials can be sued personally under the Americans with Disabilities Act. Conceivably, the company medical director could be that person. One must always practice within the standard of care expected and never rely on the absence of a physician-patient relationship as a defense.

Occupational physicians practice in various roles and perform a multitude of tasks. Legal risk varies significantly with the role, the task, and the relationship of the parties involved. It is this array of roles, tasks, and relationships that makes the law surrounding the practice of occupational medicine so complex and arcane.

Fortunately, the model of recognition, evaluation, and control can be applied to legal risks as well as to chemical, physical, and biologic risks. The occupational physician can successfully introduce policies and procedures that minimize risk, but only after carefully identifying and evaluating the risks. Because the practice of occupational medicine is so diverse, physicians must undertake this analysis individually, familiarizing themselves with relevant laws and regulations in their jurisdiction.

REFERENCES

1. 61 Am Jur 2d, Physicians, Surgeons, and Other Healers § 1; 70 CJS Physicians and Surgeons § 2.
2. 16 Am Jur 2d, Constitutional Law § 480.
3. 61 Am Jur 2d, Physicians, Surgeons, and Other Healers § 13; 70 CJS Physicians and Surgeons § 6.
4. 70 CJS Physicians and Surgeons § 7.
5. *Id.*, § 6.
6. 61 Am Jur 2d, Physicians, Surgeons, and Other Healers §§ 13, 27; 70 CJS Physicians and Surgeons § 11.
7. 61 Am Jur 2d, Physicians, Surgeons, and Other Healers § 30.
8. *Id.*, § 36.
9. *Id.*
10. *Id.*, § 150.
11. *Id.*, § 151.
12. *Id.*, § 152.
13. *Id.*, § 153.
14. Attorneys-Doctors-Corporate Practice 4 ALR3d 383-392.
15. *Berlin v. Sarah Bush Lincoln Health Center*, No. 95-MR-7, 6-15-95 (Ill. Cir. Ct.).
16. 61 Am Jur 2d, Physicians, Surgeons, and Other Healers § 14.
17. *Id.*, §§ 24, 25.
18. Flamm MB: Medical malpractice: Physician as defendant. In American College of Legal Medicine: Legal Medicine: Legal Dynamics of Medical Encounters. St. Louis, Mosby, 1991, pp 525–534.

19. Rischitelli DG: The confidentiality of medical information in the workplace. J Occup Environ Med 37:583–593, 1995.
20. *Id.*
21. Some states have adopted malpractice reform statutes that legislatively recognize conformity with parameters as conclusive evidence of practice within the standard of care.
22. Flamm MB. *Supra*, note 18.
23. *Riste v. General Electric Company*, 289 P.2d 338 (1955).
24. *Hoover v. Williamson*, 203 A.2d 861, 10 ALR3d 1064 (1964).
25. Restatement (Second) of Torts, §325.
26. *Hoover v. Williamson, supra* note 24.
27. 279 Cal.Rptr. 713 (Cal.App. 1991).
28. *Id.*
29. *Felton v. Schaeffer*, 279 Cal.Rptr. 713 (Cal.App. 1991); *Lee v. New York*, 560 NYS2d 700 (1990); *Violandi v. New York*, 584 NYS2d 842 (1992).
30. 10 ALR3d 1071, 1074 (1964).
31. *Lotspeich v. Chance Vought Aircraft*, 369 S.W.2d 705 (Tex.Civ.App. 1963); *LoDico v. Caputi*, 517 N.Y.S.2d 640 (A.D.4 Dept. 1987); *Lee v. New York, supra* note 29.
32. *Coffee v. McDonnell Douglas Corp.*, 503 P.2d 1366 (Ca. 1972); *James v. United States*, 483 F.Supp. 581 (N.D.Cal. 1980); *Green v. Walker*, 910 F.2d 291 (5th Cir. 1990); *McKinney v. Bellevue Hospital*, 584 NYS2d 538 (1992).
33. *Felton v. Schaeffer, supra* note 29, at 717.
34. 910 F.2d 291 (5th Cir. 1990).
35. *Id.*
36. 41 Cal Rptr 536, 16 ALR 3rd 543 (Cal. 1965).
37. The doctrine of respondeat superior holds that a master is liable in tort for the actions of his servant performed in the course of employment.
38. Employer's liability to employee for malpractice of physician supplied by employer. 16 ALR3d 564, 573.
39. *Id.*, at 576.
40. *Id.*, at 577.
41. 39 Cal 2d 781, 249 P.2d 8 (1952).
42. *Hoffman v. Rogers*, 22 Cal App 3d 655, 99 Cal Rptr 455 (1972).
43. 521 So 2d 399, 73 ALR4th 101.
44. 39 Cal 2d 781, 249 P.2d 8 (1952).
45. 661 P.2d 1167 (Colo. 1983).
46. *Wright v. District Ct. In & For City of Jefferson*, 661 P.2d 1167, 1170-71; see also: "Dual capacity doctrine" as basis for employee's recovery for medical malpractice from company medical personnel. 73 ALR4th 115, 123.
47. See, for example, *Siva v. General Tire & Rubber Co.*, 146 Cal App 3d 152, 194 Cal Rptr 51, noting that *Duprey* was legislatively overruled. See Cal. Lab. Code § 3602(a).
48. 606 SW2d 521 (Tenn 1980), 24 ALR 4th 1310.
49. 49 CFR §§ 391.41-391.49.
50. 398 P.2d 14 (Wash. 1965).
51. Evidence at the trial demonstrated that the driver had been found 100% disabled and unemployable five years before the accident. He was 95% blind in his left eye and had a substantial visual impairment in his right. He also had significant musculoskeletal and emotional impairments.

ROY S. KENNON, MD, JD, FCLM

FEDERAL SECTOR ISSUES REGARDING WORKPLACE LAW

From the Departments of
  Occupational Medicine and
  Clinical Investigation
Navy Medical Center
San Diego, California

Reprint requests to:
Roy S. Kennon, MD, JD
Clinical Investigation Department
Naval Medical Center
San Diego, CA 92134-5000

The Chief, Navy Bureau of Medicine and Surgery, Clinical Investigation Program, Washington, DC, sponsored this report 84-16-1968-550, as required by HSETC 6000.41A. The views expressed in this chapter are those of the author and do not reflect the official policy or position of the Department of the Navy, Department of Defense, or the U.S. government.

The perspective of this chapter is that of federal health care providers. The primary goal is to identify issues and principles controlling significant legal vulnerabilities that federal officers and employees may personally face. To avoid duplication of material presented elsewhere in this issue, the specifics of state standards and the basic principles of professional negligence law are not reviewed here.

EARLY LAW AND THE FERES DOCTRINE

A principle known as sovereign immunity became well established in 16th century English common law. It served the interests of royalty for the existence and exercise of their authority to be considered the will of God. One expression of this was the adage, "The King can do no wrong." This perspective served as the basis for the immunity of the "sovereign" government from claims based on negligence. The agents of the government, acting under the king's "infallible" directions, also were protected. This established an effective shield against liability and against civil legal actions unless they were permitted by consent of the king. Over the centuries, laws and rules also have developed to establish the circumstances under which the sovereign agreed to be sued. In the United States, a major development along this line occurred in 1946 with the passage of the Federal Tort Claims Act (FTCA).[28] This legislation permitted lawsuits *against the federal government*, which were based on wrongful or negligent conduct by federal officers or employees acting within their "scope of employment."

A decision by the United States Supreme Court in 1950[8] provided important historical perspective and guidance in interpreting the new statute. It established an important principle, the *Feres* doctrine, which restricted the right of active duty members to sue the United States. The *Feres* case arose after a barracks fire killed a soldier, and compensation for his death was sought under the provisions of the FTCA.

The Supreme Court offered its perspective on the historical immunity of the king and its application in the United States:[8] "While the political theory that the King could do no wrong was repudiated in America, a legal doctrine derived from it that the Crown is immune from any suit to which it had not consented was invoked on behalf of the Republic and applied by our courts as vigorously as it had been on behalf of the Crown."

In applying the relatively new FTCA, the Supreme Court held to this underlying principle of immunity. The court ruled that Congress had not opened the door to the courthouse wide enough to active duty members or their survivors to sue the government for wrongful death during active duty. The *Feres* doctrine has subsequently served to bar liability suits against the government based on the death or injury of active duty members arising out of, or in the course of, activity incident to active duty service. Of special importance as precedent for the liability of federal physicians was a companion case to *Feres*, also filed under the provisions of the FTCA. The suit was on behalf of a soldier who discovered, after some significant complications, that a towel measuring 18×30 inches had been left in his abdominal cavity during surgery. Denial of damages in that case was based on the same rationale as in *Feres*.

SEMANTICS AND SCOPE OF UNDERSTANDING

To understand legal issues and outcomes, occupational physicians should not assume that the dictionary definition or common meaning of a word necessarily applies to its use in a legal context. Also, the same word or phrase used by different administrative or judicial authorities may reflect or produce quite different interpretations. Physicians must recognize the limitations of language, the checks and balances of power inherent in our form of government, and the fact that reasonable people often have different interpretations of the same facts. Furthermore, physicians must realize that compromise and negotiation leading to federal legislation often produces unique statutory definitions of words. In addition, judges must routinely apply novel words and standards to unique situations in the context of complicated judicial rules and precedents.

The phrase "scope of employment"[9] illustrates many of these points. Varying interpretations of this phrase have profoundly influenced the course of federal negligence claims, litigation, and resulting liabilities. A brief review of the history of federal liability law may enhance understanding of scope of employment issues.

The Westfall Case

In the Westfall case,[37] a civilian federal employee sued his supervisors, all of whom had been employed at an Army depot where he sustained chemical burns. Mr. Westfall claimed that his injuries resulted from the negligent acts and omissions of his supervisors. A federal district judge in Alabama ruled that the supervisors had acted within their scope of employment and were therefore immune from suit.

On appeal, the United States Supreme Court returned the case to the lower court for consideration of additional factors. In doing so, the Supreme Court stated: "We are also of the view, however, that Congress is in the best position to provide guidance for the complex and often highly empirical inquiry into whether absolute immunity is warranted in a particular context. Legislated standards governing the immunity of federal employees involved in state-law tort actions would be helpful."

Congress rapidly responded to this message by passing the Federal Employees Liability Reform and Tort Compensation Act (FELRTCA) of 1988.[34] This statute supplemented prior laws and produced a clear overall policy: that FTCA would be the exclusive remedy "for injury or loss of property, or personal injury of death arising or resulting from the negligent or wrongful act or omission of any employee of the government while acting within the scope of his office or employment."[34] Importantly, this 1988 revision did not immunize federal employees from civil actions based on alleged violations of either the U.S. Constitution or U.S. statutes that specifically authorize actions against an individual. Implementation of FELRTCA by the United States Department of Justice was swift and comprehensive.[1] The Attorney General was given discretion to apply FELRTCA to protect federal officers and employees who had been named as defendants in either federal or state court. The act provided that such suits would proceed with the federal government as the substituted defendant "upon certification by the Attorney General that the defendant employee was acting within the scope of his office or employment at the time of the incident out of which the claim arose."

The requirement for the Attorney General to certify the employee's scope of office or employment (before the government would be substituted as defendant in place of the individual) emphasizes the extreme importance of how this phrase is interpreted. In drafting FELRTCA, Congress realized that the interpretation of "scope of employment" by the U.S. Attorney's Office might result in an unfavorable decision for federal employees. The statute therefore defines a right of the defendant employee to challenge in federal court an unfavorable ruling by the U.S. Attorney's Office. This adds yet another dimension to interpretation of the phrase "scope of office or employment."

As might be expected, differences of opinion are inevitable and further complicated by variations among the states in definitions and standards to be used in deciding the question. The government sometimes contends that the incident did not occur at all, adding further uncertainty as to how the case will be processed and what role, if any, the U.S. Attorney's Office will have in representing an individual defendant.[17]

These "negligence…in the scope of employment" cases are tried in federal district court by a judge without a jury. The federal judge typically determines the liability of the federal government using the law of the state in which the claim arose.[15]

Forms of Liability

Even if the individual officer, employee, or physician has been replaced by the federal government as the target of financial liability in a lawsuit for alleged negligence, the physician may still be reported, under the Health Care Quality Improvement Act,[33] to the National Practitioner Data Bank.[20] Although the HCQIA does not mandate malpractice reporting by the federal government, it does require the Department of Health and Human Services to develop data-gathering and reporting procedures. Malpractice data processing agreements have since been developed for federal agencies.[10]

The Department of Legal Medicine of the Armed Forces Institute of Pathology has been actively involved in data collection, analysis, and evaluation of federal malpractice claims, including those originating in the Department of Veterans Affairs. A 1993 review[11] of the outcomes of 3,796 cases in the VA database indicated that 30%

of the cases were unresolved, 27% were settled by denial, 16% were settled by VA counsel, and 22% proceeded to litigation; about half of the 22% that proceeded to litigation (12% of the whole) were settled by offices of the U.S. Attorney. Of the 5% that were actually tried, the United States won 3% and the plaintiff won 2%.

The Department of Defense and the Department of Veterans Affairs have developed an overall policy and procedure for the submission of malpractice reports to the National Practitioner Data Bank. Such reports are generally made regarding "paid malpractice claims in which the standard of care was not met."[12] The standard of care is determined by a process that includes peer review.

Federal Contractors and Their Employees

Neither the *Feres* doctrine nor the FELRTCA of 1988 provided immunity from personal civil liability, or for government legal representation, of independent government contractors or their employees. There are situations, however, where the federal government has assumed, or may agree to assume in the future, the responsibility of civil liabilities of a contractor. As a matter of precedent and practicality, it is expected that such situations would be limited to matters of research, development, weaponry, nuclear energy, or other similar issues related to national defense or security. Contractors and their employees must therefore be alert to the specific terms of their contract and to the provisions of any specifically relevant legislation or federal regulation. In general, they must expect that they will not be legally represented, insured for civil liability or reimbursed for legal expenses or civil liability damages, or represented in the event of criminal charges by the federal government. In fact, contractors may find that agencies of the federal or state government are vigorously acting or cooperating to attach civil or criminal liability to the acts of the contractor or their agents or employees.

Legal Counsel

Analysis of VA malpractice claims indicates that the offices of the United States Attorney are rather selective in their choice of cases to be tried. These offices must process cases within specified time limits, and they do not have an excess of trial attorneys. Consequently, the pressure and inclination to negotiate and settle are extremely high. Because the U.S. Attorney is the attorney for the United States, the interests of the United States are given first priority. The interests of the government and the employee may not coincide completely, and they may even be in direct conflict. If employee and governmental interests are critically different, the U.S. Attorney may legitimately decline to represent the employee.

It is therefore prudent for an allegedly negligent federal officer, employee, or physician to consult early with an experienced personal attorney who can identify and provide guidance regarding the individual's interests. Occupational physicians should not expect the government to pay for services obtained from a private attorney.[18]

Criminal Charges

Unless indigent, a civilian occupational physician must retain a personal attorney when charged with criminal conduct.[13] In contrast, military defendants have a right to military defense counsel in military courts regardless of personal finances.[26]

Reports in the media[18] and the fine print in routine forms[25] provide constant reminders of the possibility of criminal liability in day-to-day professional activities. The possibilities range from mishandling routine paperwork to ignoring the requirements of environmental protection laws such as the Resource Conservation and Recovery Act.[13]

Limitations on political activities imposed by the Hatch Act and traditional bans on honoraria for speakers recently have been modified by Congress[22] and the Supreme Court,[2] respectively. With such changes, confusion and variable interpretation are predictable. Prudent federal physicians should ask locally designated ethics officers to clarify the rules about such activities.

Third Party Liabilities

In occupational medicine, numerous statutory and regulatory reporting requirements are designed to protect the public health[3] and specific categories of workers.[4] Failure to comply can lead to civil and criminal liability. Occupational physicians also may be liable for failure to consider and/or prevent harm that results from an examinee's mental, intoxicated, infectious, or physical condition.[6] In California, failure to warn a specific third party of the possibility of injury by a violence-prone patient may provide a unique basis for liability.[23] Finally, many jurisdictions have complex and not always consistent rules governing the improper release of, or failure to release, information concerning serostatus of the human immunodeficiency virus.[14] Rapid changes in laws regarding HIV require physicians to regularly update their knowledge and procedures.

Military Health Care Providers

The scope of military criminal law is extremely broad under the Uniform Code of Military Justice.[26,29] The procedural rights of a criminal defendant under military law are impressively comprehensive and rigorous. These rights, however, must be exercised in an environment that makes a wide range of both minor and major infractions potentially criminal. Being late to work, wearing a uniform improperly, working in an off-duty job without proper permission, performing a job poorly, committing conduct "unbecoming" an officer, and an extensive array of other offenses are subject to criminal sanctions often unique to military jurisprudence. Typical and routine offenses generally punishable as misdemeanors and felonies also are covered.

The Occupational Safety and Health Administration

Federal physicians who implement the requirements of the Occupational Safety and Health Administration assume a risk of personal civil or criminal liability. For example, making a false statement in any record or document that OSHA requires, giving advance notice to the target of an unannounced inspection, causing the death of an employee, and assaulting an OSHA compliance officer are punishable events.[24] Reports of prosecutions for such offenses have been rare. Reformers of OSHA have proposed significant increases in the potential frequency and resulting penalties of criminal violations. The outcome of such proposals is uncertain.

Confidentiality and Jurisdiction

The confidentiality of patient medical information has been an issue since the time of Hippocrates. Federal criminal penalties can be assessed for violations of confidentiality.[32] More severe civil and criminal penalties may arise under individual state laws, particularly those enacted to protect information related to AIDS.[14] Occupational physicians should learn the scope and severity of potential liability in the local jurisdiction (see the preceding chapter).

Determining the application of state law to a federal worksite can be a complex task. A state may have jurisdiction inside one federal facility but not another. State jurisdiction also may vary from one location to another within the same federal installation. Federal standards sometimes preempt state control; at other times, the stricter of two standards controls. Specific inquiry is typically required to learn the local rules. The federal government occasionally adopts and enforces a state standard as part of its own rules, especially in a military setting. Commanders, facilities managers, and safety or security officers are typically aware of the important jurisdictional boundaries in their installations.

FEDERAL WORKERS' COMPENSATION

Workers' compensation benefits for civilian employees have been established primarily by the Federal Employees' Compensation Act.[30] Other statutes define benefits for specified employee categories or occupations, including harbor workers, longshoremen, and employees of base exchanges. By implementing orders and regulations included and cited in Title 20 of the Code of Federal Regulations,[19] the Office of Workers' Compensation was established under the Secretary of Labor, and a director was designated to administer the program.

To assess its effects and effectiveness, the workers' compensation program is best understood as an employee benefits program. It was established not only with charitable sentiments but also as a compromise to avoid burdensome and incessant litigation. An employee filing a claim must carry the burden of proving that his or her medical condition was caused, aggravated, or adversely affected by their federal employment. Approval of benefits by the Department of Labor provides compensation to employees for impairment and lost wages. A period of continuation of pay for lost work time may be allowed. Payment for medical care and appropriate rehabilitation expenses is included, as is a death benefit for survivors of the deceased.

Benefits for occupational disease or illness are less generous and less likely to be approved. This is due, in part, to a greater difficulty in showing that these conditions are work-related, particularly when a claim involves a locally endemic infection.

Criminal issues can arise in federal workers' compensation cases. Anyone who knowingly makes a false statement or misrepresents or conceals facts in a claim is subject to criminal penalties, including a fine of up to $10,000 and/or imprisonment for no more than 5 years. If a conspiracy is proved, the potential length of imprisonment doubles. Likewise, a person who is responsible for inducing an injured employee to forego filing a claim also faces possible fine and imprisonment.[19]

An unusually detailed and sophisticated analysis[7] of federal workers' compensation cases was reported in 1993 using cost data from the United States Navy. The purpose of the study was to develop a realistic estimate of the cost of a case under the Federal Employees' Compensation Act. Using retrospective data and actuarial projections, the study estimated the average cost of such a case to be $18,632. It also pointed out that the total costs for administration of the program by the Department of Labor are charged back to the employing agencies of the workers receiving benefits.

It must be emphasized that most federal employee occupational illnesses and injuries are minor, do not result in financial claims or significant time lost from work, and are not included in the above database.

Medical Qualification for Employment

Because the statutory benefits also cover occupational recurrence or aggravation of preexisting medical conditions, some supervisors or personnel officers may exert inappropriate pressure on a medical office to "medically disqualify" an applicant or employee considered likely to submit a claim for workers' compensation benefits in the future.

In the private sector, the Americans with Disabilities Act protects individuals against disability discrimination. Using its power to define and limit the meaning of words, Congress initially excluded most of the federal government from coverage by the ADA. However, recent legislation[36] applies the act to Congress itself.

Protection against disability discrimination in the federal sector has long been available through the Rehabilitation Act of 1973,[31] as amended. The ADA is patterned after this earlier statute, and in substantial ways it has adopted the same or similar principles, protections, and penalties. A case-by-case assessment is required to determine the appropriate effects of either of these laws. Their protections and benefits may not be as broad or as absolute as commonly believed. The requirement for accommodation of a qualified employee is a "reasonable" one, and assessment of the "hardship" it would impose on the employer is a legitimate consideration.

Practical difficulties often arise in providing a competent medical evaluation of applicants or employees who have impairments. The foremost problem for employers is the lack of an adequate assessment of the "essential functions" of the position. This is typically exacerbated by the lack of an accurate, current position, description. Assuming these potential barriers have been overcome, assessment of the "reasonableness" of the requested accommodation, in light of the degree of hardship it would impose on the employer, may present occupational health providers with an opportunity to facilitate a resolution satisfactory to both sides.

CONCLUSIONS

The practice of federal health care providers is immersed in rules and regulations, most of which have attached civil or criminal penalties for noncompliance. Such harsh results are uncommon, but adverse effects through administrative reporting and disciplinary actions are much more common.

Procedural devices to protect federal practitioners from civil liability for their professional actions are rather extensive, but those charged with criminal offenses outside the military justice system are typically on their own. Violation of a mandatory federal regulation also may put federal physicians at risk for civil liability.[27] Even if a physician is tried and found not guilty of a crime, the government probably will not provide legal assistance for related civil litigation, where standards of proof are much less demanding.

Prudent occupational practitioners seek to understand not only the contents but also the effects of the documents and forms they sign as well as the records they are responsible for updating or maintaining. Physicians must learn about existing laws and regulations that apply to a specific duty location and must establish contacts and policies that will alert personnel to changes. Anticipation of the effects of such changes on both old and new programs and services is necessary to avoid perpetual noncompliance.

REFERENCES

1. Bolton J: Memorandum, Civil Division, United States Department of Justice, November 22, 1988.
2. Brand S, Ethics and professionalism—The Supreme Court approves speech for pay by federal employees: Is there a Herman Melville in the house? Federal Lawyer 7:1995.
3. Cal. Health and Safety Code, Ch.3, Section 3125.
4. Cal. Health and Safety Code, Ch.9, Section 2950.
5. Chinski A: Medical surveillance in the workplace—Legal issues. Occup Med State Art Rev 5:457–468, 1990.

6. Derrick v. Ontario Community Hospital, App., 120 al. Rptr. 556 (1975).

7. Doyle E, Shepherd S, LaFleur B: Costs for Department of the Navy civilians due to the Federal Employees' Compensation Act: How much does a case cost? San Diego, Naval Health Research Center, 1993, report 93-6.

8. Feres v. United States, 71 S. Ct. 153 (1950).

9. Glanz v. Vernick, 750 F. Supp. 39 (D. Mass. 1990).

10. Granville R, Mawn S: A threshold question: How do payment amounts in medical malpractice claims relate to medical care rendered? Legal Medicine Open File 1:5–10, 1994.

11. Granville R, Greenblatt M, Bradshaw D, et al: Department of Veterans Affairs—Analysis of medical malpractice claims—An initial report. Legal Medicine Open File 1:1–9, 1993.

12. Granville R: Some characteristics of Department of Defense medical malpractice claims: An initial report. Legal Medicine Open File 1:7, 1992.

13. Grossman L: The liabilities of government work. Government Executive 23:30–33, December 1991.

14. HIV testing—Occupational exposure. California Physician 12:28–30, February 1995.

15. Kimbro v Velten, Department of Veterans Affairs, 30 F3d 1501 (D.C.Cir. 1994).

16. Malpractice settlements and awards dropped last year. American Medical News 38:5, February 13, 1995.

17. McHugh v University of Vermont, 966 F2d 67 (2d Cir. 1992).

18. Navy Justice—Updating a tragic story. US News & World Report. 8, March 6, 1995.

19. Office of the Federal Register, Employees' Benefits. 20 CFR, Parts 1 to 25, as revised.

20. Office of the Federal Register, National Practitioners Data Bank. 45 CFR Part 60.

21. Postol L: Suing the doctor: Lawsuits by injured workers against the occupational physician. J Occup Med 31:891–896, 1989.

22. Splitting Hatch Act Hairs. Government Executive 26:8, November 1994.

23. Tarasoff v. Regents of the University of California, 131 Cal. Rptr. 14 (1976).

24. US Department of Labor, Occupational Safety and Health Administration: All About OSHA, OSHA 2056, 1994 (revised).

25. US Office of Personnel Management: Optional Application for Federal EMployment—OF612.

26. US v Billig, 26 MJ 744 (NMCMR 1988).

27. US v Gaubert, 111 S. Ct. 1267 (1991).

28. US Congress: Federal Tort Claims Act of 1946, 28 USC Sections 1346, 2671 et seq., as amended.

29. US Congress: Uniform Code of Military Justice, 10 USC Section 801 et seq., as amended.

30. US Congress: Federal Employees' Compensation Act of 1966, 5 USC Section 8101, et seq., as amended.

31. US Congress: Rehabilitation Act of 1973, 29 USC Section 794, 42 USC 1988, as amended.

32. US Congress: Privacy Act of 1974, 5 USC Section 552, et seq.

33. US Congress: Health Care Quality Improvement Act of 1986, 42 USC 11101 et seq.

34. US Congress: Federal Employees' Liability Reform and Tort Compensation ct of 1988, 28 USC Section 2679.

35. US Congress: Public Law 101-336, 104 Stat 337, Americans with Disabilities Act of 1990.

36. US Congress: Public Law 104-1, 109 Stat 3, Congressional Accountability Act of 1995.

37. Westfall v. Erwin, 108 S.Ct. 580 (1988).

JAY A. GOLD, MD, JD, MPH

THE OCCUPATIONAL PHYSICIAN AS EXPERT WITNESS

From the Wisconsin Peer Review
  Organization
Madison, Wisconsin

Reprint requests to:
Jay A. Gold, MD, JD, MPH
Principal Clinical Coordinator
Wisconsin Peer Review
  Organization
2909 Landmark Place
Madison, WI 53713

More than any other specialty except the forensic subspecialties of pathology and psychiatry, occupational medicine requires its practitioners to function as experts in judicial and quasijudicial proceedings. This chapter deals with the law of expert testimony as it applies to physicians in general and to occupational physicians in particular.

WHY EXPERT TESTIMONY?

Most witnesses in court are laypeople who offer lay testimony. A traditional rule of evidence, the nonopinion rule, circumscribes such testimony. This rule states that a witness may testify to the facts the witness observed but may not offer an opinion based on those facts. For example, a witness in a case involving a motor vehicle accident may testify as to the location of the accident, the identification and movements of the vehicles involved, but may not testify that one of the vehicles was or was not being driven in a negligent manner.

The nonopinion rule in fact binds lay witnesses in progressively fewer jurisdictions. "Facts" that typically are admissible can themselves be viewed as conclusions drawn from more fundamental sense data. Furthermore, lay witnesses generally are permitted to draw common sense conclusions that are not thought to require expertise (for example, that a person was drunk or sick). Nevertheless, the basic rule excluding lay witness opinion testimony remains one of the hallmarks of the law of evidence in many jurisdictions.

However, there are many situations in which a court will be unable to reach conclusions without obtaining the opinions of specially trained experts. Virtually all professions deal with matters that are not a part of common experience, and a judge or jury that must decide facts about such matters needs the help of professionals. This is true especially when scientific principles are concerned: science by its very nature is based on studies that go beyond common experience, and many scientifically verified facts violate the superficial conclusions of common sense. For this reason, in cases that turn on medical issues, duly qualified medical experts may testify without the constraints of the nonopinion rule.

When issues beyond common experience arise, courts will permit—and may require—that opinions be offered by experts. In personal injury cases, issues requiring expert testimony typically fall into two categories. The first is causation: is the plaintiff's ailment the direct result of the accident that took place? The second category is damages: how incapacitated is the plaintiff? In malpractice cases, experts also are needed to establish both the standard of care that is customary among reasonable, competent practitioners and whether that standard of care was violated.

An expert witness sometimes has personal knowledge of the facts at issue. This may be true if the witness is a physician who treated the patient after an accident, or is an occupational physician who has performed an independent medical examination of the plaintiff. When physicians testify on the basis of personal knowledge, they are not treated differently from other witnesses. Once qualified as experts, however, they may testify to their opinions as well as to the facts they have observed.

Examination of Witnesses

Lawsuits typically follow a definite structure and order. The plaintiff presents his case, followed by the defendant. The party proffering a particular expert calls that expert for direct examination. After the witness takes the oath, the proffering attorney questions the witness regarding the witness's conclusions about the case. When the direct examination is completed, the attorney for the opposing party may conduct a cross-examination. When that is finished, the original attorney may undertake redirect examination, attempting to explain issues and to correct misinterpretations that may have arisen during cross-examination. Legal proceedings outside the courtroom often have a similar structure. For example, prior to a court hearing, experts frequently testify at a deposition, which usually takes place in a lawyer's or an expert's office. This enables both sides to know in advance the content of an expert's testimony. In addition, occupational physicians frequently testify in administrative hearings before an administrative law judge or workers' compensation tribunal. Procedures during such hearings are similar to those in courts, although the rules of evidence are somewhat more relaxed.

The Burden of Proof

In noncriminal cases, the plaintiff has the burden of proving all elements of his case by a preponderance of the evidence. That is, he must show that it is more likely than not that he has sustained certain damages and that those damages were the result of certain acts, omissions, or conditions. If there is any particular element that the plaintiff does not prove by a preponderance of the evidence, the plaintiff loses the case. In other words, the defendant need not prove his own case; if the plaintiff fails to prove his own, the case fails.

Who Is an Expert?

The general rule in America is that any physician may give testimony as an expert on any medical issue. It is not necessary for the expert to be a specialist in the area under consideration or to have had any personal experience regarding the particular issue. Such matters are likely to influence the weight that a jury or other trier of fact will give to the expert's opinion, but not the admissibility of the testimony.

Before rendering expert testimony, a physician must be qualified as an expert by the court—that is, the physician must answer a series of questions that establish his or her medical training and experience. The technical term for these questions is the examination voir dire, which typically focuses on medical school and postgraduate training, specialty certification, experience in the area under consideration, medical society memberships, and published works.

Obligations of Truth-Telling and Objectivity

An expert's testimony must be as accurate and objective as possible. First and foremost, expert witnesses must not exaggerate their qualifications. Cross-examiners are free to challenge misstatements of qualifications, and such misstatements have led clients to sue their own experts for malpractice or fraud.

Second, the expert should offer a genuine, objective opinion about the issues that should not be biased in any way by the interests of the client on whose behalf the expert is testifying. Everyone understands that if the expert's opinion does not support the client's case, the client would not be calling the expert to testify. The expert, however, always must attempt to strike a golden mean: the opinion must not sound more certain or less certain than it is. At least one expert has been convicted of perjury for giving a false opinion.[11] Finally, the expert should not make statements that could not be defended before his or her colleagues.

Grounds for an Expert Opinion

There can be many bases for an expert's conclusions. Most jurisdictions are in accord with Rule 705 of the Federal Rules of Evidence, which states the following:

> The expert may testify in terms of opinion or inference and give his reasons therefor without prior disclosure of the underlying facts or data, unless the court requires otherwise. The expert may in any event be required to disclose the underlying facts or data on cross-examination.

By contrast, a few jurisdictions hold that the witness must state all the facts or data upon which the medical opinion is based. Even when the majority rule applies, however, experts will typically be asked on direct examination to disclose the underlying facts that ground their opinions, as this makes those opinions more persuasive to the trier of fact. Facts may be based on the following elements.

Personal Observation. A medical opinion may be based on the personal experience of the testifying expert, either as the treating physician or as an independent examiner.

Professional Literature. Most courts will admit opinions even if the testifying expert has had no personal experience with the kind of case at issue but has formed an opinion based in part upon a reading of the literature. The prevailing view is that enunciated by Justice Oliver Wendell Holmes in a leading Massachusetts Supreme Judicial Court case:

> [W]hen one who is competent on the general subject accepts from his experience as probably true a matter of detail which he has not verified, the fact gains an authority it would not have had from the printed page alone, and, subject perhaps to the exercise of some discretion, may be admitted.[5]

This is not to say that a book or an article upon which the witness has relied in forming an opinion may be introduced into evidence or that the witness may quote from it. This is not permitted, because it would violate the hearsay rule, an important part of the law of evidence that provides that a witness may not testify to assertions made by others in order to prove the truth of what is asserted. By this rule, statements in the literature cannot be offered to prove the truth of the matters contained therein. Furthermore, most experts presumably base their testimony on general knowledge and experience as well as on what they have read. The literature often is used to confront witnesses on cross-examination; this is discussed below.

Statements of Patients during Examination. Justice Holmes's pronouncement would seem to apply equally well to statements of patients. In general, a physician is permitted to testify as to what a patient told him or her about present symptoms. In contrast, courts are divided concerning cases in which the patient discussed a medical condition that existed in the past; some would accept such testimony, and others would exclude it as hearsay.

In states that have enacted statutes creating a physician-patient privilege (many states have not), a treating physician may not testify as to facts that were learned as a result of the physician-patient relationship unless the physician has the permission of the patient. The scope of the privilege varies among the states. In general, however, such privilege does not bind the expert who has never examined the patient, nor does it bind the expert who has conducted an independent examination, since in neither case has a physician-patient relationship been formed for legal purposes.

The Hypothetical Question

Traditionally, expert witnesses have been examined through the use of the hypothetical question. While many jurisdictions no longer require this technique, others do, and it is worth understanding.

When a hypothetical question is posed, the attorney asks the witness to assume certain relevant facts about the case. He then asks the witness for an opinion about causality, permanency of damage, or other medical issues. The theory behind the use of the hypothetical question is that when an expert lacks first-hand knowledge of the facts but has learned them from records, reports, and discussions, the expert can testify only on the assumption that the facts are as he or she has been led to believe.

The use of hypothetical questions may seem to violate the hearsay rule, but when there is conflict, an expert witness typically is not bound by the hearsay rule. When hypothetical questions are not required, the witness simply will be asked on what information his or her opinion is based and what the opinion is.

The Degree of Certainty

Medicine, for the most part, is not an exact science. Even the best physicians may be surprised on occasion by a particular diagnosis or outcome. Thus, medical witnesses may tend to discount their confidence in their own testimony. However, to the degree an expert witness is uncertain of his or her conclusions, that witness is of little use to the legal process.

The law has developed various formulas regarding the degree of certainty required of a medical expert. Perhaps most frequently today, an expert must testify "to a reasonable degree of medical certainty." Other such formulas include "reasonably certain based on prevailing standards," "reasonably probable," or "most likely." Such formulas are imprecise, but they do embody the basic standard that the testimony should meet: given the uncertainties inherent in medicine, is the opinion one that the expert believes is true and is prepared to defend?

The required degree of certainty may differ from one issue to the next. In general, because testimony as to prognosis is more uncertain, it may require a greater degree of probability than testimony about diagnosis or appropriate care.

Novel Scientific Testimony

In American law, judges must decide whether newly discovered scientific tests, techniques, or principles will be admitted for consideration by the jury. State laws continue to differ on the appropriate standard a judge should use in making these decisions. For 70 years, the most influential federal standard was that of *Frye v. United States*,[6] where the court held that new discoveries are admissible only when they are sufficiently established to have gained general acceptance in the particular field. In contrast, a handful of courts allowed judges to admit all scientific testimony they deemed relevant to a case. In the 1970s, Rule 702 of the new Federal Rules of Evidence authorized scientific testimony where it will assist the trier of fact to understand the evidence or to determine a fact in issue.

In 1993, in the case of *Daubert v. Merrell Dow Pharmaceuticals*,[4] the United States Supreme Court issued an interpretation of Rule 702. Seven of the nine justices ruled that judges must serve as gatekeepers who determine whether proffered ·evidence is scientifically valid and relevant. The courts suggested several factors for judges to consider in determining whether to admit a particular theory or technique:

- Is it testable, and has it been tested?
- Has it been subjected to peer review and publication?
- For a particular scientific technique, what is the known or potential rate of error?
- What (if any) are the standards that control the technique's operation?
- To what extent is the theory or technique accepted in the scientific community?

Because *Daubert* involved an interpretation of the Federal Rules of Evidence, the decision binds only the federal courts. However, *Daubert* already has influenced state courts as they grapple with new techniques such as DNA identification. Experts who wish to testify about scientific matters that are novel or are not generally accepted should be prepared to address each of the concerns articulated by the Supreme Court.

Causation

One of the key issues requiring medical testimony is causation—that is, whether and to what extent a patient's or a worker's condition resulted from particular acts, omissions, or conditions. The analysis of "cause and effect" in the legal context must be distinguished from the analysis of cause and effect typically undertaken by physicians.

In medicine, proof that two events (for example, tobacco use and lung cancer) are causally related initially requires demonstration of a statistical association between the two. The causation criteria enunciated by Austin Bradford Hill are then applied.[8] For example, are the two events temporarily related? Is there a biologically plausible explanation? Have confounding factors been considered?

By contrast, most courts want to know if there is a reasonable degree of medical certainty that a patient would not have suffered particular damage but for a particular act, omission, or condition. As explained above, the plaintiff must prove this element of his case, like all elements, by a preponderance of the evidence. A jury may have considerable doubt, but if the jurors feel that the act, omission, or condition at issue more likely than not caused the plaintiff's condition, that is all that is required by law to render a verdict on the plaintiff's behalf. Thus, the jury may find causation where the source of a condition may be medically uncertain. Note, however, that a jury typically will not be permitted to find causation unless a medical expert has testified that such causation exists.

Occupational physicians often confront causation issues. The establishment of work-relatedness under Workers' Compensation—that a specific injury arose "out of and in the course of employment"—is a causation issue highlighted in chapter 11.

Another issue that occupational physicians frequently confront is aggravation. For example, a musculoskeletal injury sustained by a worker is often complicated by degenerative changes or by previous injuries. If a claimant's condition clearly preceded the work-related trauma, there is no causation and hence no liability. By contrast, if the trauma is shown to have aggravated a preexisting condition, causation and liability may ensue, but only for the proportion of the condition attributable to the trauma. Physicians seldom have reasons to draw such distinctions in diagnosing and treating patients, but these distinctions are essential in calculating damages.

Damages

Medical testimony almost always is required for the determination of damages. In personal injury actions, damages may be awarded for loss of function, loss of earning ability, medical expenses, and pain and suffering. Expert testimony by occupational physicians is frequently sought to determine loss of ability to carry on one's occupation.

The physician who performs independent medical examinations must determine as precisely as possible the claimant's loss of function. It is axiomatic that the physician must understand the plaintiff's job to be able to provide an accurate assessment of his or her ability to perform that job satisfactorily. The physician also must be prepared to describe the types of jobs an impaired plaintiff *can* perform. On occasion, occupational physicians also testify as to a plaintiff's work-life expectancy—that is, if the plaintiff can perform a particular job, how long he or she can be expected to work absent unforeseen circumstances compared with how long he or she might have been expected to work if the trauma had not taken place.

In workers' compensation, various schedules fix the percentage of disability associated with specific permanent injuries.

Professional Literature in Cross-Examination

The most popular method for undermining the testimony of an expert is to proffer another expert with opposing views. As mentioned, however, a cross-examining attorney also may use books or articles to impeach or contradict an expert's testimony.

To impeach with books or articles, the attorney must first establish the text as authoritative. This is typically accomplished by asking the witness to enumerate the documents (if any) upon which he or she relied in forming an opinion or by asking the witness if a particular text is authoritative. The attorney then will offer the relevant text or portions of text into evidence.

In dealing with this technique, occupational medicine experts should keep certain policies in mind. First, do not agree that a text or paper is authoritative if it is not. Second, if a textbook is being cited, make sure it is the most recent edition. Third, once the statement is admitted, be sure that the statement has not been taken out of context. Fourth, do not be afraid to disagree with a statement in an "authoritative" text if there are well-substantiated grounds for the disagreement.

FURTHER READING

Physicians who wish to learn more about the issues discussed in this chapter should be directed, first and foremost, to the works of William J. Curran, to whom this chapter is dedicated. His edition of *Tracy's The Doctor as a Witness*,[3] while three decades old, has hardly aged. Also recommended are his chapters 17 and 56 on the courtroom presentation of evidence in *Modern Legal Medicine, Psychiatry, and Forensic Science*.[2] For a collection of cases and commentary, see chapter 4 of *Health Care Law, Forensic Science, and Public Policy*,[1] which Curran edited with Mark A. Hall and David H. Kaye.

Another excellent text for medical expert witnesses is *A Doctor's Guide to Court* by Keith Simpson.[10] For a scholarly discussion of the law of medical expert testimony, see Paul Rheingold's article, "The Basis of Medical Testimony,"[9] For the significance of the *Daubert* decision, see this author's comment in *JAMA*.[7]

ACKNOWLEDGMENT

This chapter is dedicated to William J. Curran, LLM, SMHyg, Frances Glessner Lee Professor Emeritus of Legal Medicine, Harvard University.

REFERENCES

1. Curran WJ, Hall MA, Kaye DH (eds): Health Care Law, Forensic Science, and Public Policy. 4th ed. Boston, Little, Brown, 1990.
2. Curran WJ, McGarry AL, Petty CS (eds): Modern Legal Medicine, Psychiatry, and Forensic Science. Philadelphia, FA Davis, 1980.
3. Curran WJ: Tracy's The Doctor as a Witness. Philadelphia, WB Saunders, 1965.
4. Daubert v. Merrell Dow, 61 U.S.L.W. 4805 (1993).
5. Finnegan v. Fall River Gas Works, 159 Mass. 311, 34 N.E. 523 (1893).
6. Frye v. United States, 293 F. 10103 (D.C. Cir. 1923).
7. Gold JA, Zaremski MJ, Lev ER, Shefrin DH: Daubert v. Merrell Dow: The Supreme Court tackles scientific evidence in the courtroom. JAMA 270:2964–2967, 1993.
8. Hill AB: The environment and disease: Association or causation? Proc R Soc Med 58:295–300, 1965.
9. Rheingold P: The basis of medical testimony. Vanderbilt Law Rev 15:473–510, 1962.
10. Simpson K: A Doctor's Guide to Court. 2nd ed. London, Butterworth, 1967.
11. State v. Sullivan, 24 N.J. 18, 130 A.2d 610 (1957).

JACK W. SNYDER, MD, JD, PhD
SUSAN G. McQUIGGAN, BSN, RN

REGULATORY ALPHABET SOUP

From Thomas Jefferson University
Philadelphia, Pennsylvania

Reprint requests to:
Jack W. Snyder, MD, JD, PhD
Associate Professor
Departments of Emergency
  Medicine and Laboratory
  Medicine
401 Pavilion
Thomas Jefferson University
  Hospital
125 South 11th Street
Philadelphia, PA 19107-4998

Alphabetized by acronym, this chapter describes an extensive array of regulatory agencies, medicolegal terms, governmental programs, and other common entities often encountered in the practice of occupational medicine.

ALJ   Administrative Law Judge

An administrative law judge presides at an administrative hearing—an oral proceeding before an administrative agency consisting of an argument, a trial, or both. The ALJ has the power to administer oaths, take testimony, rule on questions, regulate the course of the proceedings, and make determinations of fact. The ALJ may be called a hearing officer or a hearing examiner.

ANSI   American National Standards Institute

ANSI is responsible for developing consensus standards on a wide range of matters, including those related to occupational and environmental health and safety. ANSI has established standards for respiratory protection, exposure limits for chemicals and physical agents, and standards for safety harnesses, safety eyewear, hardhats, footwear, and other protective gear. Some of these standards have been incorporated into OSHA regulations.

ATSDR   Agency for Toxic Substances and Disease Registry

The ATSDR was established as an operating agency within the Public Health Service by the Secretary of Health and Human Services. Its mission is to carry out the health-related responsibilities of the Comprehensive Environmental

Response, Compensation and Liability Act (CERCLA). In cooperation with federal, state, and local agencies, ATSDR (1) collects, maintains, analyzes, and disseminates information relating to serious diseases, mortality, and human exposure to toxic or hazardous substances; (2) establishes appropriate registries necessary for long-term follow-up or specific scientific studies; and (3) establishes and maintains a complete listing of areas closed to the public or otherwise restricted in use because of toxic substance contamination.

BEI   Biologic Exposure Index

Biologic exposure indices are reference values intended as guidelines for evaluating potential health hazards in the practice of industrial hygiene. BEIs represent concentrations of determinants (either the parent substance or its metabolites) that are most likely to be found in biologic specimens collected from a healthy worker who has been exposed to chemicals at the threshold limit value-time weighted average. BEIs do not provide a sharp distinction between hazardous and nonhazardous exposures. Due to biologic variability, it is possible for an individual's measurements to exceed the BEI without incurring an increased health risk. If, however, measurements in specimens obtained from a worker on different days persistently exceed the BEI, or if a majority of measurements in specimens obtained from a group of workers at the same workplace exceed the BEI, the cause of the excessive values must be investigated and proper action taken to reduce the exposure. BEIs are not intended for use as a measure of adverse effects or for diagnosis of occupational illness.

CDC   Centers for Disease Control
and Prevention

The Centers for Disease Control was established as a federal agency within the Public Health Service by the Secretary of Health, Eduction, and Welfare on July 1, 1973. Although its name was changed to the Centers for Disease Control and Prevention in 1992, its acronym remains CDC. The CDC is charged with protecting the public health of the nation by providing leadership and direction in the prevention and control of diseases and other preventable conditions and responding to public health emergencies. The agency directs and enforces foreign quarantine activities and regulations; provides consultations and assistance in upgrading the performance of public health and clinical laboratories; and organizes and implements a National Health Promotion Program that includes a nationwide program of research, information, and education in the fields of smoking and health. The CDC also collects, maintains, analyzes, and disseminates national data on health status and health services.

CERCLA   Comprehensive Environmental Response,
Compensation and Liability Act

In 1980 Congress authorized the EPA to regulate current and future waste management and disposal practices through the Resource Conservation and Recovery Act. However, RCRA did not address the legacy of abandoned waste sites or emergencies created by spills or releases of hazardous substances. To deal with these situations, Congress enacted the CERCLA or "Superfund" law. Financed in part by a tax on chemical manufacturers, Superfund established a $1.6 billion trust fund and gave EPA the authority to respond to hazardous substance emergencies that threaten public health or the environment.

CFR   Code of Federal Regulations

The Code of Federal Regulations consists of the annual commutation of executive agency regulations published in the daily *Federal Register* plus any previous regulations that are still in effect. The CFR is an essential tool of practice and procedure in the federal administrative agencies.

A typical detailed process leading to publication of a regulation in the *Federal Register* can be outlined as follows:

1. Statute enacted
2. Designation of responsible agency
3. Development of a list of issues
4. Meetings and discussions
5. Resolution
6. Development of regulation specifications
7. Preparation of draft regulation language
8. Review of language by responsible component
9. Meetings, discussions, and resolutions
10. Revision
11. Circulation within agency
12. Preparation of written comments
13. Meetings, discussions, and resolutions
14. Revision
15. Head of responsible agency approves, signs, and sends to HHS
16. Circulation within HHS
17. Preparation of written comments
18. Meetings and discussions
19. Meetings and discussions
20. Meetings and discussions
21. Revision
22. Send to responsible agency for final clearance and signature
23. Send to secretary for signature
24. Send to Office of Management and Budget
25. Meetings and discussions
26. Meetings and discussions
27. Negotiation of provisions and reaching of agreement
28. Revision
29. Send to agency head for signature
30. Send to secretary for signature
31. Review by Office of Management and Budget
32. Send to *Federal Register* for publication

CHAMPUS   Civilian Health and Medical Program of the Uniformed Services

CHAMPUS pays for the health care services provided by nonmilitary health care institutions and physicians to the spouses and dependent children of active members of the armed forces and certain disabled veterans. In addition, the Department or Veterans Affairs may authorize eligible veterans to receive care, in certain circumstances, from nonfederal hospitals. General and special hospitals participate in Medicare or that are approved by the Joint Commission are not required to request formal approval to participate in CHAMPUS. Other facilities, however, are required to complete and submit CHAMPUS Form 200 to the Office of Civilian

Health and Medical Programs of the Uniformed Services (OCHAMPUS) and to provide such additional information as may be requested by that agency. OCHAMPUS may conduct an on-site survey and will render a final determination regarding approval to the facility in writing. Services provided to mentally or seriously physically disabled dependents of active-duty servicemen under the Program for the Handicapped are only covered by CHAMPUS if they are provided in a non-profit CHAMPUS-approved institution. Effective October 1, 1987, CHAMPUS adopted a prospective payment system for inpatient hospital care. Minor changes to conform the CHAMPUS rules to changes in the Medicare payment system were later adopted, with revised DRG weights, thresholds, and beneficiary cost-share per diem rates. The CHAMPUS-PPS closely resembles that of Medicare. Payment is based on federal-national rates, with capital and direct medical education costs being treated as pass-throughs if the hospital makes a written request for such payment. Payments for indirect medical education costs are calculated by a formula that differs from that of Medicare.

CIH   Certified Industrial Hygienist

A CIH is an individual certified for the practice of industrial hygiene by the American Board of Industrial Hygienists. To qualify for certification, a person must have at least 5 years of experience (or 4 years plus a Master of Science degree) and complete a two-day examination.

CLIA   Clinical Laboratory Improvement Act

CLIA 1988 is a federal statute that mandates the compliance of clinical laboratories with federal standards for laboratory testing. This act also requires all U.S. laboratories that examine human specimens to meet performance requirements in order to be certified by the Department of Health and Human Services.

CON   Certificate of Need

Certificate of need programs provide review and approval of health planning agencies of capital expenditures and service capacity expansion by hospitals and other health care facilities. The primary purpose of CON programs is to discourage unnecessary investment in health care facilities and to channel investment into socially desirable uses. A health care facility covered by a state CON program typically must submit a permit application to an official state health planning agency before undertaking specified capital expenditures and other projects subject to review. The review criteria include consideration of community need, financial feasibility, expected quality of care, less costly alternatives, and accessibility of the project to underserved and indigent populations.

CPSC   Consumer Product Safety Commission

The commission is an independent agency established by the Consumer Product Safety Act of 1972 following a recommendation of the National Commission on Product Safety. The commission protects the public against unreasonable risks of injury associated with consumer products; develops uniform safety standards for consumer products; and minimizes conflicting state and local regulations concerning these products. The CPSC is also charged with maintaining an Injury Information Clearing House to collect, analyze, and disseminate data relating to cause and prevention of accidents involving consumer products. Finally, the CPSC conducts and promotes research on product safety and safety testing methods.

DAWN   Drug Abuse Warning Network

The Drug Abuse Warning Network was started by the Bureau of Narcotics and Dangerous Drugs to provide information on medical and psychological problems associated with drug use. The network is designed to identify patterns and trends in drug use and to pinpoint drugs that are bringing users into emergency treatment facilities. DAWN provides quarterly reports describing drug emergencies and details trends in suicides, dependence, and drugs being used for psychic effects. Information for DAWN is obtained from at least 26 metropolitan areas.

DEA   Drug Enforcement Administration

DEA is one of the federal agencies that deals with drug abuse. The DEA is charged with enforcement of the federal laws on drug control and illicit drug traffic. The DEA manages the National Narcotics Intelligence System in cooperation with federal, state, and local officials. The agency also investigates violations and regulates legal trade in narcotics and dangerous drugs. The DEA also provides the public with information on drugs and drug abuse.

DOJ   Department of Justice (Antitrust Division)

The Antitrust Division of the Department of Justice is responsible for promoting and maintaining competitive markets by enforcing the federal antitrust laws. The DOJ investigates possible antitrust violations, conducts grand jury proceedings, prepares and tries antitrust cases, prosecutes appeals, and negotiates and enforces final judgments. The antitrust laws affect virtually all industries (baseball and insurance have been well-known exceptions) and apply to every phase of business, including manufacturing, transporting, distribution, and marketing. These laws prohibit various practices that restrain trade, such as price-fixing conspiracies, corporate mergers likely to reduce competitive markets, and predatory acts designed to achieve or maintain monopoly power. The Antitrust Division of DOJ also represents the United States in judicial proceedings to review certain orders of the Interstate Commerce Commission, the Federal Maritime Commission, the Federal Communications Commission, and the Nuclear Regulatory Commission and provides representation for the Secretary of the Treasury in some cases involving the Bureau of Tobacco, Alcohol and Firearms.

DOT   Department of Transportation

The Department of Transportation develops, coordinates, and reviews emergency preparedness programs for use in national disasters and in emergencies affecting national defense. DOT develops environmental policy and reviews and comments on the environmental impact of major transportation projects. DOT classifies hazardous material for transportation and is also concerned with emergency medical services. The basic hazard classes include compressed gases, flammables, oxidizers, corrosives, explosives, poisons, and radioactive materials. This classification guides the development of proper labels, placards, and shipping instructions. DOT also plays a major role in the regulation of forensic urine drug testing.

DRGs   Diagnosis Related Groups

Under Medicare's 13-year old payment system, hospitals are paid a fixed, prospectively determined amount for each Medicare discharge, using a classification system called diagnosis related groups. Medicare patients are categorized into fairly homogeneous groups based on resource consumption. The classification system was developed by researchers at Yale University and is based on a nation-wide sample of more than 1.4 million discharge records taken from 332 hospitals. The researchers classified the cases according to principal diagnosis, age, sex, procedures performed, discharge status, and any secondary diagnosis. This process resulted in the development of 470 DRG categories. Each Medicare discharge is assigned to one of these DRGs, and the hospital is reimbursed according to the applicable DRG-specific payment rate, adjusted to reflect cost differences between urban and rural hospitals and area wage variations. To calculate the DRG-specific rates, the Health Care Financing Administration (HCFA) established weighting factors for the 470 groups. These weights reflect the relative cost, across all hospitals, of treating patients within a particular DRG. For each discharged beneficiary the payment rate is the product of the applicable DRG weight and a standard amount.

EAP   Employee Assistance Program

The employee assistance program is an occupational health service program designed to help employees cope with substance abuse or physical or behavioral problems that affect job performance. The assistance may be provided within the organization or by referral to outside resources.

EEOC   Equal Employment Opportunity Commission

The EEOC was created under Title VII of the Civil Rights Act of 1964 (42 U.S.C. §2000e-2) to implement an equal opportunity policy by working with local agencies, paying the expenses of witnesses before the commission, affording persons subject to Title VII technical assistance to further compliance, helping to conciliate employers with employees or members refusing to cooperate, making technical studies, and intervening in civil actions on behalf of an aggrieved party. The commission has been composed of five members, appointed by the President and approved by the Senate. The commissioners serve five-year terms, and no more than three of the five may belong to the same political party.

EMTALA   Emergency Medical Treatment and Active Labor Act

The EMTALA provisions of the Consolidated Omnibus Reconciliation Act of 1986 state that if any individual (whether or not he or she is eligible for benefits under Medicare) comes to a hospital and the hospital determines that the individual is in active labor or has an emergency medical condition, the hospital must provide treatment for the labor or such medical examination and treatment as may be required to stabilize the medical condition. Alternatively, the hospital may transfer the person to another medical facility *if* specific criteria are met and the receiving facility (a) has available space and qualified personnel for the treatment of that person and (b) has agreed to accept transfer of the individual and to provide appropriate treatment.

EPA   Environmental Protection Agency

The EPA is a federal agency whose goal is to coordinate effective government action to protect the environment through systematic abatement and control of pollution. EPA is responsible for various research, monitoring, standard-setting, and enforcement activities controlling air pollution, water pollution, hazard waste disposal, and other threats to the environment.

During the 1970s the enactment of major new environmental laws and important amendments to older laws greatly expanded the EPA's responsibilities. The agency now administers nine comprehensive environmental protection laws: the

Clean Air Act (CAA); the Clean Water Act (CWA); the Safe Water Drinking Act (SDWA); the Comprehensive Environmental Response, Compensation and Liability Act (CERCLA, or Superfund); the Resource Conservation and Recovery Act (RCRA); the Federal Insecticide, Fungicide and Rodenticide Act (FIFRA); the Toxic Substances Control Act (TSCA); the Marine Protection, Research, and Sanctuaries Act (MPRSA); and the Uranium Mill Tailings Radiation Control Act (UMTRCA).

The EPA is directed by an administrator and a deputy administrator who are appointed by the President with the advice and consent of the Senate. Nine assistant administrators, who manage specific environmental programs or direct other agency functions, and the agency's general counsel are also named by the President and subject to Senate confirmation. Ten regional administrators across the country cooperate closely with state and local governments to ensure that regional needs are properly implemented. The agency's executive staff includes associate administrators for international activities and regional operations.

ERISA   Employee Retirement Income Security Act

The Employee Retirement Income Security Act of 1974 (ERISA) established uniform national standards for the funding, vesting, administration, and termination of employee benefit (private pension) plans. This act also established the Pension Benefit Guaranty Corporation. ERISA broadly preempted state regulation of these plans. 19 USCA § 1144(a) states that ERISA supercedes state laws to the extent that they "relate to any employee benefit plan" covered by ERISA. This preemption clause is qualified by 29 USCA § 1144(b)(2)(A), a "savings clause," which specifies that ERISA does not preempt state laws regulating insurance, banking, or securities. This clause is limited, however, by the "deemer clause," 29 USCA § 1144(b)(2)(B), which states that self-insured employee benefit plans or trusts will not be considered as engaging in the business of insurance for purposes of any state law "purporting to regulate insurance companies or insurance contracts." The interaction of these clauses with state malpractice laws as well as laws that attempt to regulate employee health insurance has caused substantial controversy and litigation.

ESA   Employment Standards Administration

The Employment Standards Administration is an agency of the U.S. Department of Labor that administers laws and regulations relating to employment, including those concerning the provision of compensation to workers injured on their jobs. One of its major divisions is the Office of Workers' Compensation.

ESRD   End Stage Renal Disease Program

The ESRD program focuses on kidney disease that is covered by Medicare, especially that stage of kidney impairment that appears irreversible and permanent and requires a regular course of dialysis treatment or transplantation to maintain life. The federal benefits are available regardless of age after 3 months on dialysis.

The objectives of the end stage renal disease program are (a) to assist beneficiaries who have been diagnosed as having ESRD to receive the care they need, (b) to encourage proper distribution and effective utilization of ESRD treatment while maintaining or improving the quality of care, (c) to provide the flexibility necessary for the efficient delivery of appropriate care by physicians and facilities, and (d) to encourage self-dialysis or transportation for the maximum practical number of patients who are medically, socially, and psychologically suitable candidates for such treatment.

FDA   Food and Drug Administration

As an administrative agency that regulates the safety and quality of foodstuffs, pharmaceuticals, cosmetics, and medical devices, the FDA is a part of the Department of Health and Human Services. Its activities include establishing mandatory standards of identity, quantity, and quality of food; regulating the safety of additives to food, drugs and cosmetics; and ensuring that drugs, food, cosmetics and devices are fairly packaged, labeled, and not adulterated or mishandled.

The Federal Food, Drug and Cosmetic Act covers products that are prepared for interstate commerce and applies until the ultimate sale to the consumer.

The *labeling* of drugs and devices provides an example of an important arena for FDA regulatory influence. The immediate container of all drugs and devices must include a label that includes the identification, directions for use, shelf life, and applicable warnings concerning the use of the drug or device. Any drug or device without a conforming label is deemed "misbranded" and is subject to seizure, and its manufacturer or distributor is subject to criminal penalties. Extensive disclosure through labeling is required on products sold directly to the public and products supplied to health care professionals, although an exemption is provided for physicians and pharmacists who dispense medications pursuant to a lawful prescription. The label on the container of a lawfully prescribed drug must contain:

- name and address of the dispenser,
- serial number and date on which the prescription was written or filler,
- name of the prescriber,
- name of the patient, and
- directions for use and cautionary statements contained in the prescription.

FTC   Federal Trade Commission

This federal agency was established in 1914 to protect consumers against unfair methods of competition and deceptive business practices, including sales fraud and violation of the antitrust laws. The Bureau of Consumer Protection protects consumers against sales fraud and any other unfair or deceptive business practices. The Bureau of Economics performs economic analysis both for informational purposes and for use in litigation by the trial staff. To accomplish its goals, the FTC has authority to issue "cease and desist" orders, which may be challenged in federal court.

FTCA   Federal Tort Claims Act

The statute essentially waives sovereign immunity and allows the United States government to be sued in tort. The act confers exclusive jurisdiction on U.S. district courts to hear claims against the U.S. for "money damages accruing on and after January 1, 1945, for injury or loss of property, or personal injury or death, caused by the negligent or wrongful act or omission of any employee of the government, under circumstances where the United States, if a private person, would be liable to the claimant in accordance with the law of the place where the act or omission occurred," 28 USC §1346(b). The FTCA provides for a number of specific exceptions to the general waiver of sovereign immunity. For example, injuries received by members of the armed services during war typically are not covered by the FTCA. In addition, claims may not be brought under the FTCA by (1) persons bearing a special relationship to the federal government or by (2) civil officers and employees of the federal government. For example, members of the armed services bear a special relationship with the federal government, and the U.S. is not liable under FTCA for injuries sustained while on active duty (not on furlough) that are caused by the negligence of others in the armed forces.

GAO   General Accounting Office

Supporting the Congress is GAO's fundamental responsibility. The GAO audits and evaluates government programs and activities and ensures that Congress has current, accurate, and complete financial management data available for its use. To do this, GAO prescribes accounting principles and standards for the executive branch, advises other federal agencies on fiscal and related policies and procedures, and prescribes standards for auditing and evaluating government programs. This independent congressional agency established in 1921 is directed by the Comptroller General of the United States, who is appointed by the President with the advice and consent of the Senate for a non-renewable 15-year term of office.

GPO   Government Printing Office

The Government Printing Office prints, binds, and distributes the publications of Congress as well as the executive departments of the federal government. The Congressional Joint Commission on Printing serves as an oversight committee for the GPO. The Public Printer, who serves as the head of the agency, is required by law to be a practical printer versed in the art of bookbinding and is appointed by the President with the advice and consent of the Senate.

HCFA   Health Care Finance Administration

Owing to wide variation in state Medicare program design, Medicare is governed by the Health Care Finance Administration within the Department of Health and Human Services. HCFA delegates much of the front-line, day-to-day work to "fiscal intermediaries," which are private insurance companies that contract with HCFA to handle Medicare claims administration. HCFA has also established different performance standards for all physician services, surgical services, and nonsurgical services, and has defined "surgical services" to mean services performed by a surgical specialist and previously classified in medicare payment records as either "surgery" or "assistant at surgery" services.

HHS   Department of Health and Human Services

The Department of Health and Human Services is the cabinet level department of the federal executive branch most concerned with people and most involved with the nation's human concerns. The secretary of HHS advises the President on health, welfare, and income security plans, policies, and programs of the federal government. The secretary administers these functions through the Office of the Secretary and the four Operating Divisions, which include the Social Security Administration, the Health Care Financing Administration, the Administration for Children and Families, and the Public Health Service.

HMO   Health Maintenance Organization

These organizations typically require a single subscription fee and, in return, offer members a comprehensive range of health care services including walk-in medical (sometimes dental and other) services and hospitalization. The primary advantages for subscribers are the comprehensiveness of the services offered under the plans and the single annual premium for all services rendered under the plan. In justifying the title of health maintenance, these programs stress outpatient services, ambulatory care, preventive care and consultation, and early diagnosis and treatment.

IARC   International Agency for Research on Cancer

The U.N. International Agency for Research on Cancer provides information on suspected environmental carcinogens. The literature is examined, and summaries of available data with appropriate references are presented in monographs. Included in these reviews are synonyms; information on physical and chemical properties, uses, and occurrences; and biologic data relevant to the evaluation of carcinogenic risk to humans. The nearly 50 monographs in the series contain an evaluation of approximately 900 materials. In general, the available evidence of carcinogenicity for a specific substance or class of substances is assessed by IARC and judged to fall into one of four groups defined as follows: (1) sufficient evidence; (2) limited evidence; (3) inadequate evidence; or (4) no evidence of carcinogenicity.

IND   Investigational New Drug

The FDA must approve all new drugs as being both safe and effective before they can be imported, transported in interstate commerce, or commercially marketed. Once a manufacturer has carried out preclinical investigations and studies on laboratory animals that have led to the conclusion that a certain drug shows a high degree of promise in treating a specific disease, it is reasonably safe to initiate clinical trials. The next step involves filing a Notice of Claimed Investigational Exemption for a New Drug (IND) with the FDA. Clinical studies on humans may not begin until 30 days after the date of receipt of the notice by the FDA. The purpose of the IND is to alert the FDA of the investigation and to provide protocol and procedure to assure the quality of the investigation and protect the rights of the patients or other investigational subjects. The IND is not to be interpreted as an endorsement of the investigation by the FDA.

IOC   Indirect Operating Costs

Indirect operating costs include those resulting from use of heat, lighting, office space and equipment, security, and other commodities. These costs cannot be identified directly with a particular activity, service, or product of the program experiencing the cost. IOCs are usually divided among the program's services in proportion to the direct cost share of a given service.

IOC   International Olympic Committee

Founded in 1894 and headquartered in Lausanne, Switzerland, the International Olympic Committee enlisted the aid of sports organizations and individuals of various countries to revive the Olympic Games in Athens in 1896. In recent years, the IOC has certified a select group of laboratories in the U.S. and abroad to analyze the urine of Olympic athletes for the presence of unapproved drugs.

IPA   Independent Practice Association

Some health maintenance organizations may contract on a capitation basis with an independent practice association that in turn contracts with a private practice physician who provides care to HMO members in his or her office. IPA doctors may continue to treat patients not associated with an integrated delivery system. IPAs often pay their doctors on a fee-for-service basis supplemented by a bonus system to reward doctors who have been economical. Often an IPA will withhold a portion of a physician's payment to offset any excessive hospitalizations attributed to that physician.

JCAHO   Joint Commission on Accreditation of Health Care Organizations

The Joint Commission is an independent, nonprofit, voluntary organization sponsored by the American College of Surgeons, the American College of Physicians, the American Hospital Association, the American Medical Association, and other medical, dental, and health care organizations. The JCAHO develops standards and provides accreditation surveys and certification to hospitals and other health care organizations. It also offers education programs, consultation, and publications. The JCAHO annually publishes the JCAHO Accreditation Manual for Hospitals.

MRO   Medical Review Officer (Medicare)

The Medical Review Officer for Medicare carries out certain surveillance functions with respect to hospital and physician performance and detection of fraud. The medical review includes assessment of (a) the care being provided in the facility, (b) the adequacy of services available in the facility to meet the current health needs and to promote the maximum physical well-being of patients, (c) the necessity and desirability of continued placement of a particular patient in the facility, and (d) needs that may be met through alternative institutions or noninstitutional services. A medical review differs from utilization review in that it requires an evaluation of each individual patient and analysis of the appropriateness of specific treatments in a given institution.

MRO   Medical Review Officer (Department of Transportation)

The Medical Review Officer for the Department of Transportation is defined by DOT as "any physician (MD or DO) with knowledge of the medical use of prescription drugs and the pharmacology and toxicology of illicit drugs." The MRO's role was created in an effort to maintain a safe workplace without sacrificing corporate responsibilities or an individual's privacy. Every employer who undertakes drug testing under federal regulations must use an MRO to review and interpret positive test results. The MRO also may determine when an employee is fit to return to duty following rehabilitation, and the MRO may be required to report to a designated corporate official safety issues that arise during physical examination of an employee donor regardless of the individual's laboratory results.

MSDS   Material Safety Data Sheet

The Occupational Safety and Health Administration mandates that upstream manufacturers and suppliers shall develop, and employers shall implement, a written hazard communication for each substance in the workplace. Each MSDS shall contain, at the minimum, the following information: (1) the identity of the substance, if not claimed confidential; if the chemical and common name are claimed confidential, a generic chemical name must be used; (2) the physical and chemical characteristics of the substance; (3) the physical hazards of the substance known to the employer; (4) the potential human and environmental hazards; (5) the signs and symptoms of exposure and any medical conditions expected to be aggravated by exposure; (6) primary routes of exposure to the substance; (7) precautionary measures to control worker exposure and/or environmental release; (8) any general applicable precautions for safe handling and use of the substance; (9) emergency first aid procedures; and (10) the date of preparation of the MSDS or of its last revision. If the manufacturer, supplier, or downstream employer becomes aware of any significant new information regarding the hazards of the substance or ways to protect against the hazards, this new information must be added to the MSDS within 3 months from the time the party becomes aware of the new information.

MSP   Medicare Secondary Payer

The Tax Equity and Fiscal Responsibility Act of 1982 defines how Medicare benefits are coordinated with other health insurance plans. This law states that Medicare pays the remaining portion of Medicare benefits only after the benefits from other medical insurance have been paid.

NDA   New Drug Application

Upon successful completion of the IND procedure, if the sponsor determines that the drug is safe and effective for the purpose intended, the next step is to file with the FDA a New Drug Application. This procedure has become the principal regulatory device for the control of drugs in the United States. The NDA submitted by the drug's sponsor contains an exhaustive review of virtually all the information the sponsor possesses about the drug. The NDA includes reference to any INDs affecting the drug, evaluations of safety and effectiveness, methods of manufacture, chemistry, a list of investigators and their full reports, proposed labeling of the drug, and proposed instructions such as limiting the drug to prescription sales only. The regulations specifying the requirements for an NDA cover several pages.

NFPA   National Fire Protection Association

The NFPA prepares, publishes, and periodically revises the Life Safety Code as a set of standards for the construction and operation of buildings. In addition, the NFPA issues codes as a part of a system designed to identify and rank the potential fire hazards of materials. The NFPA system has three principal categories of hazard: flammability, health, and reactivity. Within each category, hazards are ranked from four (4), indicating a severe hazard, to zero (0), indicating no special hazard. The NFPA health hazard category is based on both the intrinsic toxicity of a chemical and the toxicities of its combustion or breakdown products. The overall ranking is determined by the greater source of health hazard under fire or other emergency conditions. The common hazards from the ordinary combustion of materials are not considered in the NFPA rankings. The NFPA system is intended to provide basic information to firefighting and emergency response personnel. Conditions at the scene, such as the amount of material involved and its rate of release, wind characteristics, and the proximity to and health status of various populations may be as important as the intrinsic properties of a chemical in determining the magnitude of hazard.

NIH   National Institutes of Health

The National Institutes of Health is the principal biomedical research arm of the federal government. The mission of the NIH is to pursue knowledge to improve human health. The NIH seeks to expand fundamental knowledge about the nature and behavior of living systems, to apply that knowledge to improve the health of human lives, and to reduce the burdens resulting from disease and disability. The agency sponsors biomedical and behavioral research domestically and abroad, conducts research in its own laboratories and clinics, trains promising young researchers, and promotes the acquisition and distribution of medical knowledge. Focal points have been established to assist in developing NIH-wide goals for health research and research training programs related to women and minorities, coordinating program direction, and ensuring that research pertaining to women's and minority health is addressed through research activities conducted and supported by NIH.

NIOSH   National Institute for Occupational Safety and Health

The NIOSH serves as the research arm of OSHA. NIOSH publishes criteria documents and detailed research reports on topics such as hazardous chemicals, safety in the workplace, environmental studies, and other issues in the fields of occupational safety and health. The NIOSH also supports and conducts research on occupational safety and health issues; provides technical assistance and training; and develops recommendations for the Department of Labor. NIOSH also operates an occupational safety and health data base. All publications researched by NIOSH are available from the Government Printing Office.

NIST   National Institute of Standards and Technology

As a nonregulatory agency, the NIST aids U.S. industry through research and services, carries out selected programs in public health and safety and environmental improvement, and supports the U.S. scientific and engineering research communities through fundamental research. The NIST develops generic technology and measurement techniques and standards. NIST researchers work at the frontiers of science and technology in such areas as chemical science and technology, physics, materials science and engineering, electronics and electrical engineering, manufacturing, engineering, computer systems, building and fire research, and computing and applied mathematics.

NPDB   National Practitioner Data Bank

The NPDB is a clearinghouse for information on disciplinary and malpractice actions against physicians. The NPDB was created by the Health Care Quality Improvement Act of 1986, which requires that the following be reported to the NPDB: (1) any payment made by an insurance company on a malpractice claim, (2) a sanction imposed by a state board of medical examiners on a physician, and (3) any adverse decision made by a health care facility that affects a physician's privileges for more than 30 days.

NLRB   National Labor Relations Board

The NLRB, established by the National Labor Relations Act of 1935, as amended by the Taft-Hartley Act of 1947, is an independent agency of the federal government. The board was created by Congress to administer the National Labor Relations Act, the basic law governing relations between labor unions and the employers whose operations affect interstate commerce. The statute guarantees the right of employees to organize and bargain collectively with their employers or to refrain from all such activities. The act, which generally applies to all employers involved in interstate commerce (other than airlines, railroads, agriculture, and government), implements the national labor policy of assuring free choice and encouraging collective bargaining as a means of maintaining industrial peace. The NLRB has two principal functions: (1) to determine, through secret-ballot elections, the free democratic choice by employees as to whether they wish to be represented by a union in dealing with their employers and, if so, by which union; and (2) to prevent and remedy unlawful acts, called unfair labor practices, by either employers or unions. The board has no independent statutory enforcement power for its decisions and orders, but it may seek enforcement in the U.S. Court of Appeals and parties to NLRB cases may also seek judicial review.

NTP   National Toxicology Program

The National Toxicology Program is an effort to strengthen the activities of the Department of Health and Human Services regarding the testing of chemicals of public health concern. The NTP seeks to develop and validate new and better integrated testing methods. Specific goals of the NTP are to (1) broaden the spectrum of toxicologic information obtained on selected chemicals, (2) increase the numbers of chemicals studied, (3) develop and validate a series of tests and protocols responsive to regulatory needs, and (4) communicate program plans and results to government agencies, medical and scientific communities, and the public. The NTP coordinates toxicology activities of the National Institute of Environmental Health Sciences, the National Center for Toxicological Research, and NIOSH.

OIG   Office of the Inspector General

The Office of the Inspector General is a federal office that reports to Congress and heads of agencies on the activities of those agencies. The OIG was authorized in the Medicare and Medicaid Patient Program Protection Act to exclude a person or entity from participation in government health care programs if the party engaged in a prohibited remuneration scheme. This authority is intended to provide an alternative to criminal prosecution in the regulation of abusive business practices. Under Section 1001.101, payment will not be made under Medicare for items or services provided by a practitioners, provider, or other supplier that the OIG determines has (1) knowingly and willfully made or caused to be made any false statements or misrepresentations of material fact in a request for payment under Medicare or for use in determining the right to payment under Medicare, (2) furnished items or services that are substantially in excess of the beneficiary's needs or of a quality that does not meet professionally recognized standards of health care, or (3) submitted or caused to be submitted bills or requests for payment containing charges (or costs) that are substantially in excess of its customary charges (or costs).

OMB   Office of Management and Budget

The OMB evaluates, formulates, and coordinates management procedures and program objectives within and among federal departments and agencies. The OMB also controls the administration of the federal budget while routinely providing the President with recommendations regarding budget proposals and relevant legislative enactments. The office's primary functions are to assist the President in developing and maintaining effective government by reviewing the organizational structure and management procedures of the executive branch to ensure that the intended results are achieved and, also, to assist in developing efficient mechanisms to implement government activities and to expand interagency cooperation.

OSHA   Occupational Safety and Health Administration

OSHA is a component of the Department of Labor established by the Occupational Safety and Health Act of 1970 (OSHAct). OSHA develops and promulgates standards relating to occupational safety and health, develops and issues regulations in this area, conducts investigations and inspections to determine the status of compliance with safety and health standards and regulations, and issues citations and proposes penalties for noncompliance. In general, the coverage of OSHAct extends to all workplaces in the 50 states, the District of Columbia, Puerto Rico, and all other territories under federal government jurisdiction. Coverage is provided either directly by OSHA or through an OSHA-approved program. OSHAct also covers religious groups to the extent that they employ workers for secular purposes.

PEL   Permissible Exposure Limit

Permissible exposure limits refer to specific allowable levels established by OSHA for human exposure to airborne industrial chemicals and noise. PELs set by OSHA have the force of law and are closely analogous to the ACGIH TLV-TWAs. In 1971, OSHA formally adopted the 1969 ACGIH TLVs for most of its PELs. In 1988, OSHA updated the PELs by adopting the 1986 TLVs. In 1993, the 1988 PELs were voided in court and the earlier values were restored. However, these restored values cannot be reliably presumed to protect worker health. Moreover, these values are subject to change as a result of further administrative or legislative action.

PPO   Preferred Provider Organization

The term PPO encompasses organizations that use a wide variety of health care delivery arrangements, but most PPOs share certain characteristics. For example:

- Most PPOs are separate entities that have assembled a provider network, by agreement, to deliver health care; the PPO itself does not deliver health care as a provider;
- most PPO provider agreements include special arrangements for compensation (i.e., fee schedules);
- most PPOs establish or contract for a utilization management program that is available to payers, or the payers may use their own utilization management system;
- most PPO provider agreements bind providers to a utilization management program of the PPO or of a payer;
- most PPOs enter into agreements with health care payers whereby the latter are granted access to the provider network and to the fee schedules and other special arrangements; and
- many payers have a beneficiary group with free choice of provider, but the beneficiary group has financial and other incentives to use the PPO network.

There are three basic models of the PPO. The first is the open panel, where the beneficiary is not limited to use of PPO network providers. The second is the gatekeeper plan that requires the beneficiary upon enrollment to select a primary care provider (physician and hospital) from among a group of network providers. The third is the exclusive provider organization (EPO), which encompasses arrangements similar to that of PPOs. In EPOs, however, the beneficiary annually selects either the EPO network providers in exchange for greater benefits or lower premiums, or non-network providers with reduction of benefits or higher premiums.

PRO   Peer Review Organization (Medicare)

The structure chosen to monitor the impact of prospective payment is the peer review organization. Created by the Peer Review Improvement Act of 1982, PROs replaced an earlier system of federally mandated medical review, the professional standards review organizations (PSROs). The function of the PROs is to review the appropriateness of hospital admissions, discharges, transfers, and lengths of patient stays. In addition, each PRO is responsible for assessing the quality of hospital services and the validity of diagnostic and procedural data furnished by participating hospitals located within the PRO's review area.

ProPAC   Prospective Payment Assessment Commission

The Prospective Payment Assessment Commission (ProPAC) is an advisory body established by the Social Security Act Amendments of 1983 to advise the Secretary of Health and Human Services on recommended adjustments in the weights and classification of diagnosis related groups under Medicare and to review and recommend any percentage or amount needed to reflect increases in the cost or mix of goods and services. The commission is composed of 15 experts selected by the director of the Congressional Office of Technology Assessment.

PRRB   Provider Reimbursement Review Board

The Department of Health and Human Services reimburses Medicare providers, including hospitals, according to standard national rates for particular therapies. Congress permitted the Secretary of HHS to consider cost audits before approving hospital applications for Medicare reimbursement. The costs of providers' services vary from one provider to another, and the variations generally reflect differences in scope of services and intensity of care. The provisions in Title XVIII of the Social Security Act for payments of reasonable cost of services is intended to meet the actual costs, however widely they may vary from one institution to another. This is subject to a limitation when a particular institution's costs are found to be substantially out of line with other institutions in the same geographic area that are similar in size, scope of services, utilization, and other relevant factors. The Provider Reimbursement Review Board is appointed by the Secretary of Health and Human Services to provide an appeal mechanism for health care providers to whom Medicare fiscal intermediaries deny reimbursement for services under Medicare.

PSDA   Patient Self-Determination Act

The Omnibus Reconciliation Act of 1990 requires hospitals to provide written information to their adult patients at the time of admission, advising them of their rights under state law to make decisions concerning medical care. These rights include the right to accept or refuse medical or surgical treatment and the right to formulate an advance directive concerning the withholding or withdrawal of care when the patient becomes incapacitated or incapable of making health care decisions.

RBRVS   Resource-Based Relative Value Scale

On January 1, 1992, Medicare began a five-year phase-in of a fee schedule grounded on a resource-based relative value scale. Under the new payment system, the relative value of each service is determined by adding up the relative value units (RVUs) representing physician work, practice expenses net of malpractice insurance costs (overhead), and professional liability insurance (malpractice). Nationally uniform relative values are adjusted for each locality by a geographic adjustment factor. HCFA determines dollar amounts for RVUs by calculating what these would have been in 1991 if the same amounts of money were spent on physician services as was in fact expended during that year. During the phase-in period, old payment rates have been blended with the new ones.

RCRA   Resource Conservation and Recovery Act (1976)

In 1976, Congress enacted the Resource Conservation and Recovery Act, which authorized the EPA to regulate current and future waste management disposal practices. The major priority under the act has been the development of "cradle-to-grave" regulations governing the generation, storage, transport, treatment, and disposal of hazardous wastes. These wastes include toxic substances, caustics, pesticides, and other flammable, corrosive, or explosive materials. EPA has estimated that more than 75 billion gallons of such wastes are produced every year. Another major goal under the RCRA is to encourage states to develop comprehensive programs for managing nonhazardous solid wastes, and every state now has a solid waste management agency. The EPA has supported research and demonstration projects to stimulate promising new methods of waste disposal, resource/energy recovery, and innovative technology. The agency also has laid out guidelines for developing waste management plans, established criteria for classifying land disposal facilities according to their environmental acceptability, and published a national inventory of unacceptable facilities.

RICO   Racketeer Influenced and Corrupt Organizations Act

This federal statute can be found under Title IX of the Organized Crime Control Act of 1970 (18 USC §§1961–1968). Many states have adopted similar statutes. There are four basic racketeering offenses under the federal statutes:

- Directly or indirectly investing in income derived from a pattern of racketeering activity or through collection of an unlawful debt in any enterprise affecting trade or commerce.
- Acquiring or maintaining any interest in an enterprise through a pattern of racketeering activity or collection of an unlawful debt.
- Conducting or participating in the affairs of the enterprise through a pattern of racketeering activity or collection of an unlawful debt.
- Conspiring to violate the racketeering provisions.

The provisions of the acts are designed to be liberally construed to best effect the Congressional intent.

SAMHSA   Substance Abuse and Mental Health Services Administration

The SAMHSA provides national leadership to ensure that knowledge, based on science and state-of-the-art practice, is effectively used for the prevention and treatment of addictive and mental disorders. SAMHSA strives to improve access and reduce barriers to high-quality, effective programs and services for individuals who suffer from or are at risk for these disorders, as well as for their families and communities. The major components of the SAMHSA include the Center for Substance Abuse Prevention, the Center for Substance Abuse Treatment, the Center for Health Services, and the Office of Management, Planning and Communication.

SARA   Superfund Amendment and Reauthorization Act (1986)

The Superfund authorizes the EPA to respond immediately to situations or sites that pose a danger to public health or the environment. In emergency situations, SARA authorizes the EPA to take the following direct actions:

- Begin immediate removal in cases of imminent danger (oil spills, train derailments, leaking barrels, fires, explosions). The objective is to bring the situation under control by stabilizing or stopping the release of the hazardous substances. The law ordinarily limits immediate removal actions to 6 months and total costs to $1 million.

• Begin planned removal when a hazard is substantial, but does not necessarily require immediate removal. The objective is to minimize any increase in danger or exposure that might otherwise occur. Planned removals are considered complete when the situation is stabilized and the immediate threat is abated. They are subject to the same time and cost limitations as immediate removals.

SDWA   Safe Drinking Water Act (1974)

This act requires that each state set water quality standards and restrict pollution. To curb pollution from household and commercial sewage, the act requires that all publicly owned municipal sewage systems provide secondary treatment of waste water (a biochemical process) before it is discharged. Since few communities could afford the facilities needed to provide such treatment, Congress established a financial assistance program for construction as part of the law. Under this program, the EPA provides funds to the states, which in turn allocate the money to local communities to help finance new or improved treatment facilities.

STEL   Short-Term Exposure Limit

A short-term exposure limit is defined as a 15-minute time-weighted average exposure that should not be exceeded at any time during a work day even if the 8-hour time-weighted-average is within the TLV. Exposure at the STEL should not be longer than 15 minutes and should not be repeated more than four times per day. There should be at least 60 minutes between successive exposures at the STEL. An averaging period other than 15 minutes may be recommended when warranted by observed biologic effects.

TEFRA   Tax Equity and Fiscal Responsibility Act

TEFRA was a 1982 federal act that contained provisions that limited hospital costs relating to Medicare and Medicaid. TEFRA placed a maximum limit on Medicare reimbursement of hospital costs. This plan laid the foundation for the Medicare prospective payment system established by the Social Security Act Amendment of 1983. TEFRA repealed the PSRO and established the PRO to make determinations about medical necessity, quality of services, and the most economic provision of services.

TLV   Threshold Limit Value

TLVs are guidelines developed to assist in the control of health hazards. They are based on the best available information from industrial experience, experimental human and animal studies and, when possible, from a combination of all three. These values represent conditions under which it is believed that nearly all workers may be repeatedly exposed day after day without adverse health effects. The basis on which the values are established may differ from substance to substance; protection against impairment of health may be a guiding factor for some, whereas reasonable freedom from irritation, narcosis, nuisance, or other forms of stress may form the basis for others.

TRO   Temporary Restraining Order

A temporary restraining order is an order granted without notice or hearing, demanding the preservation of the status quo until a hearing can determine the propriety of any injunctive relief, temporary or permanent. A restraining order is always temporary, pending a hearing. The TRO is issued upon application of a plaintiff who requests the court to forbid an action or threatened action of a defendant; the restraining order generally shows cause why the injunctive relief the plaintiff seeks ought not to be granted. After a hearing, a preliminary or permanent injunction may issue.

ToSCA   Toxic Substances Control Act (1976)

This act of Congress in 1976 sought to provide a safeguard against the introduction of additional contaminants to the environment and to address the risks posed by existing chemicals. The ToSCA mandates identification and control of chemicals that pose an unreasonable risk to human health or the environment through their manufacture, processing, commercial distribution, use, or disposal. Eight chemical products are exempt from ToSCA because they are regulated under other laws: pesticides, tobacco, nuclear materials, firearms and ammunition, food, food additives, drugs, and cosmetics. The ToSCA also requires the EPA to develop and keep a current comprehensive chemical inventory. This inventory, which is based on information submitted by chemical manufacturers, processors, and importers, presents an overall picture of the chemicals used for commercial purposes in the United States.

TWA   Time-Weighted Average

The time-weighted average is the concentration of a substance to which nearly all workers may be repeatedly exposed for a normal 8-hour workday and 40-hour workweek without adverse effect. For the vast majority of substances with a TLV-TWA, there is not enough toxicologic data to warrant a STEL. Nevertheless, excursions above the TLV-TWA should be controlled even where the 8-hour TLV-TWA is within recommended limits. Excursions in worker exposure levels may exceed three times the TLV-TWA for no more than a total of 30 minutes during a workday, and under no circumstances should they exceed 5 times the TLV-TWA.

UAGA   Uniform Anatomical Gift Act

Under Section 2 of this model legislation, (a) any individual of sound mind and 18 years of age or more may give all or any part of his body for any purposes specified in Section 3, the gift to take effect upon death; and (b) any of the following persons, in order of priority stated, when persons in prior classes are not available at the time of death, and in the absence of actual notice of contrary indications by the decedent, or actual notice of opposition by a member of the same or prior class, may give all or any part of the decedent's body for any purpose specified in Section 3: (1) the spouse, (2) an adult son or daughter, (3) either parent, (4) an adult brother or sister, (5) a guardian of the person fo the decedent at the time of his death, (6) any other person authorized or under obligation to dispose of the body.

UBIT   Unrelated Business Income Tax

A tax on income recognized by an exempt organization that is generated from activities not related to the exempt purpose of the entity. An example would be a pharmacy located in a hospital.

URO   Utilization Review Organization

The URO is made up primarily of physicians, allied health professionals, and other personnel from outside of the hospital or nursing home who examine and evaluate the necessity, appropriateness, and efficiency of the use of health care services, procedures, and facilities. In a hospital this includes review of the appropriateness of admissions, services ordered and provided, length of stay, and discharge practices. This organization or committee is a requirement for participation in Medicare. The Utilization Review Accreditation Commission (URAC) is a body founded in 1990 that evaluates and accredits utilization review programs and organizations. It develops and promulgates minimum industry standards, which serve as a basis of a voluntary accreditation process. Its board of directors includes representatives from the American Medical Association, the American Hospital Association, the American Nurses Association, the American Psychiatric Association, the Washington Business Group on Health, the National Association of Insurance Commissioners, the International Union of United Auto Workers, The National Association of Manufacturers, the American Managed Care and Review Association, Blue Cross/Blue Shield Association, and the Health Insurance Association of America. Its goal is to continually improve the quality and efficiency of the interaction between providers, payers, and purchasers of health care.

USC   United States Code

The original United States Code was an extraction of the Revised Statutes of 1875 that had not been repealed and all the public and general laws from the Statutes at Large since 1873 that were still in force. These were arranged into 50 titles and published as the USC in four volumes. A new edition of the U.S. Code is published every 6 years, and cumulative supplements are issued during the intervening years.

REFERENCES

1. American Conference of Governmental and Industrial Hygienists: Documentation of the Threshold Limit Values and Biological Exposure Indices. 6th ed. Cincinnati, ACGIH, 1991.
2. Batten D (ed): Encyclopedia of Government Advisory Organizations. 8th ed. Detroit, Gale Research Inc., 1993.
3. Black HC: Black's Law Dictionary. 6th ed. St. Paul, MN, West Publishing Co., 1990.
4. Medicare: Statutes and Regulations: A Service of the Medicare and Medicaid Reporter. Washington, DC, LPR Publications, 1991.
5. Mossman J (ed): Acronyms, Initialisms and Abbreviations Dictionary. 19th ed., Vols. I–III. Detroit, Gale Research Inc., 1995.
6. O'Leary MR: Lexikon—A Dictionary of Health Care Terms, Organizations, and Acronyms for the Era of Reform. Oakbrook Terrace, IL, Joint Commission on Accreditation of Healthcare Organizations, 1994.
7. Southwick AF, Slee DA: The Law of Hospital and Health Care Administration. 2nd ed. Ann Arbor, Health Administration Press, 1988.
8. Office of the Federal Register: The United States Government Manual 1994/1995. Washington, DC, National Archives and Records Administration, 1995.
9. Younger PA: Hospital Law Manual: Attorney's Volume. Vols II, IIa, IIb, IIc. Gaithersburg, MD, Health Law Center, Aspen Publishers, 1983.
10. Younger PA: Hospital Law Manual: Administrator's Volume. Vols. II, IIa, IIb, IIc. Gaithersburg, MD, Health Law Center, Aspen Publishers, 1983.

ARIA A. KLEES, JD

THE INTERFACE OF ENVIRONMENTAL REGULATION AND PUBLIC HEALTH

From Unisys Corporation
Blue Bell, Pennsylvania

Reprint requests to:
Aria A. Klees, JD
Counsel, Environmental Safety and
  Health
Unisys Corporation
Township and Union Meeting
  Roads
C1SW19
Blue Bell, PA 19424-0001

The driving force behind United States environmental law and regulation is the clear and explicit intent of the government to protect human health and the environment. Although the primary avenue to accomplish this goal is through ecological pollution control and waste management, most environmental laws have stated their policy interest as the establishment of environmental standards at levels that protect human health. Public health concerns are addressed by including, within the regulatory process, standards mandating consideration of human health risks by the development of hazardous constituent characteristics data, health risk assessment data, potential and actual exposure data, and extensive exposure or release reporting and recordkeeping requirements. These regulatory requirements provide the health professional with an extensive database of industry chemical type and quantity usage and known health effects and exposure risk information from which correlation of exposure to disease may be concluded, and from which preventive or responsive health practices may be developed for occupational and environmental groups and the community. This chapter provides an overview of the major federal environmental laws and regulations that reach beyond ecological protection to contemplate public, environmental, and occupational health interests (Table 1).

THE RESOURCE CONSERVATION AND RECOVERY ACT

The Resource Conservation and Recovery Act of 1976 (RCRA)[1] was enacted to address

TABLE 1.   Environmental Statutes and Regulations of Interest

The Resource Conservation and Recovery Act	42 USC §§ 6901–6992
	40 CFR §§ 240–281
Hazardous wastes lists	40 CFR §§ 261.31–261.33
Basis for listing hazardous waste	40 CFR § 261, App. VII
Hazardous constituents list	40 CFR § 261, App. VIII
Excluded wastes list	40 CFR § 261, App. IX
Exposure information and health assessments	42 USC § 6936a
Toxic Substances Control Act	15 USC §§ 2601–2655
	40 CFR §§ 700–799
Health and safety data reporting requirements	40 CFR § 716
Health and safety data reporting substance list	40 CFR § 716.120
Federal Insecticide, Fungicide and Rodenticide Act	7 USC § 136–136y
	40 CFR §§ 152–186
Data requirements	40 CFR § 158
Worker protection standards	40 CFR § 170
Comprehensive Environment Response Compensation and Liability Act	42 USC §§ 9601–9675
	40 CFR §§ 300–311
Hazardous substances and reportable quantities list	40 CFR § 302.4
Reportable quantity determination	40 CFR § 302.5
Agency for Toxic Substances and Disease Registry	42 USC § 9604(i)
	40 CFR §§ 90.1–90.14
Emergency Planning and Community Right-to-Know Act	42 USC § 11001–11050
	40 CFR §§ 350, 355, 370, 372
Extremely hazardous substances reportable quantities and threshold planning quantities	40 CFR § 355, App. A
Specific toxic chemical listings	40 CFR § 372.65
Hazardous substance threshold quantity determination	40 CFR § 372.25
Trade secret disclosure to health professionals	40 CFR § 350.40
The Clean Air Act	42 USC § 7401 et seq.
	40 CFR §§ 50–99
National ambient air quality standards	40 CFR § 50
National emission standards for air pollutants	40 CFR § 61
Hazardous air pollutants	42 USC § 7412 (b)
Regulated toxic substances and threshold quantities for accidental release	40 CFR § 68.130
Clean Water Act	33 USC §§ 1251–1387
	33 CFR §§ 320–330, 335–338
	40 CFR §§ 104–140, 230–233, 401–471
Hazardous substance designations	40 CFR § 116.4
Hazardous substance reportable quantities list	40 CFR § 117.2
Effluent guidelines, pretreatment and performance standards for new and existing point sources	40 CFR §§ 401–471
Toxics pollutant effluent standards	40 CFR § 129
Toxics criteria for water quality standards	40 CFR § 131.36
The Safe Drinking Water Act	42 USC §§ 300f–300j-26
	40 CFR §§ 141–149
National primary drinking water standards, MCLs and MCLGs	40 CFR § 141
National secondary drinking water standards, SMCLs	40 CFR § 143

concerns regarding the effects of solid and hazardous wastes and disposal management on human health and the environment. The act gave specific attention to problems posed by the disposal of hazardous wastes that by virtue of their composition or longevity are harmful, toxic, or lethal, and to ending unregulated land disposal of discarded materials and hazardous wastes.[2] RCRA established a "cradle-to-grave" hazardous waste management system that first required EPA to identify and list hazardous wastes[3] and then to promulgate regulations governing management of hazardous waste from generation through disposal, to be applied to generators and transporters of hazardous waste and hazardous waste treatment storage and disposal facilities (TSDFs).[4] RCRA further established TSDF operating and permitting requirements and an approval process for state waste management programs.[5]

In 1980, RCRA was amended by the Solid Waste Disposal Act Amendments,[6] which reauthorized the existing program, strengthened RCRA enforcement provisions to include civil penalties and to define criminal status offenses,[7] provided for special regulatory consideration for certain categories of wastes (e.g., coal and fossil fuel combustion waste, mineral and ore mining wastes and oil, natural gas and geothermal energy activity wastes[8]), and expanded "interim status" facility eligibility, allowing TSDF operations pending permit application review for TSDFs operating between 1976 and 1980.[9] RCRA was further amended by the Hazardous and Solid Waste Amendments of 1984 to expand RCRA's regulatory reach to small quantity generators,[10] waste oils,[11] underground storage tanks,[12] the use of hazardous wastes for fuel,[13] and waste streams not yet identified.[14] The 1984 amendments also prohibited land disposal of hazardous wastes,[15] set minimum technologic requirements for land disposal units,[16] and required corrective action for all releases of hazardous wastes at interim-status and permitted facilities.[17]

RCRA requires that generators of hazardous waste deliver the waste to facilities approved for disposal of that particular waste.[18] If the waste must be transported offsite for disposal, the waste shipment must be documented by a manifest (describing the shipment) that is signed by the generator, transporter, and approved receiving facility.[19] If the waste is stored for more than 90 days or is treated or disposed of at a TSDF, the facility must obtain a permit and meet technologic, managerial, recordkeeping, and response regulatory standards promulgated by EPA to prevent release of wastes from the TSDF to the environment. Corrective action requirements ensure pollution prevention and clean-up upon release from a TSDF, and closure requirements ensure full and proper decommissioning and decontamination upon closure.[20]

Elements of the RCRA program provide information useful to health professionals in assessing the potential effects of exposure to regulated hazardous substances. RCRA mandates the characterization, identification, and listing of hazardous wastes.[21] EPA defines characteristic and listed hazardous wastes by their toxicity. Characteristic hazardous wastes are those that cause or significantly contribute to mortality or irreversible illness, and/or pose a substantial present or potential hazard to human health or the environment during waste management.[22] Listed hazardous wastes may also include those that are fatal to humans in low doses, meet specific lethal dose criteria in animals, or contain certain toxic constituents listed in the regulations at 40 CFR § 261, App. VIII—unless specific circumstances are reviewed by EPA and the agency finds that substantial risk is not present.[23] EPA has established four waste lists, the F, K, U and P lists.[24] The F list contains wastes from nonspecific sources, including wastewater treatment sludges, spent stripping and plating solutions, and spent solvents such as trichoroethylene, toluene, and methylene chloride. The K list contains hazardous wastes from specific sources, including petroleum refining, pigment manufacturing, and chemical production processes. The U list identifies discarded commercial and off-specification chemical products and all containers and spill residues of these products. The P list identifies "acutely" hazardous discarded commercial chemical products. Several hundred hazardous wastes are currently listed in EPA's hazardous waste lists found at 40 CFR § 261.31–261.33.

In addition to the listed wastes, EPA may designate hazardous wastes by the characteristics that make them harmful to human health or the environment. The four characteristics are degrees of ignitability, corrosivity, reactivity, and toxicity.[25] Mixtures of characteristic and solid wastes are hazardous only if the entire mixture exhibits one of the four characteristics.[26]

Pursuant to the RCRA permitting process, waste generators must be able to "characterize" their wastes in accordance with the definitions provided in 40 CFR part 261. When characterizing wastes, facility operators must first determine that the material generated is a waste by EPA definition or that it has served its original intended use and is discarded, intended to be abandoned, recycled, or is "inherently waste-like." Facility operators must then decide if the waste they generate is solid waste. Solid wastes may be liquid, contained gaseous, semisolid, or solid. "Solid waste" covers almost all wastes, including hazardous wastes and municipal garbage. Waste is considered hazardous if it is specifically listed within the regulations or exhibits the required degree of ignitability, corrosivity, reactivity, or toxicity.[27] Wastes that exhibit a hazardous waste characteristic when they are recycled are also subject to hazardous waste regulations.[28]

RCRA requires owners and operators of facilities treating, storing, or disposing of listed hazardous substances to obtain a permit.[29] As part of that permit process, hazardous waste volumes, usage, emergency contingency plans, facility design and layouts, and lists of on-site hazardous waste container operating procedures to prevent environmental contamination are submitted to EPA.[30] Facilities must fully document all manifested wastes, release events, and monitoring activities.[31] This information may provide a health professional with some indication of potential sources of exposure and exposure risks.

Limited health effects data may be available through the hazardous waste landfill and surface improvement unit permitting submission requirements. An owner or generator seeking a permit for such a unit must also submit to EPA any reasonably ascertainable information concerning the potential for the public to be exposed to hazardous wastes or hazardous constituents through releases related to that landfill or surface impoundment.[32] At a minimum, such information must address (a) reasonably foreseeable potential releases from both normal operations and accidents at the waste unit or associated with transportation to or from the unit; (b) the potential pathways of human exposure; and (c) the potential magnitude and nature of human exposure following such releases.[33] EPA must provide any health assessment and related information to the Agency for Toxic Substances and Disease Registry (ATSDR) (discussed below).[34] If EPA believes a landfill or surface impoundment unit poses a substantial potential risk to human health, the agency may request ATSDR to conduct a health assessment in connection with the unit facility and to take other appropriate action with respect to such risks.[35] Members of the public may also submit evidence of release of or exposure to hazardous constituents from such a facility, or information regarding the risks or health effects associated with such releases or exposure, to ATSDR, EPA, or the state.[36]

Information regarding the treatment, storage, disposal, or release of a specific chemical, as submitted through the RCRA permit process, is available at EPA regional offices or the implementing state agency office. Health exposure information or health assessment data is available through ATSDR.

THE TOXIC SUBSTANCES CONTROL ACT

In 1976, the passage of the Toxic Substances Control Act (ToSCA)[37] granted EPA the authority to regulate existing and newly developed chemical substances and mixtures. ToSCA was designed to bridge the gap left by preexisting federal environmental safety and health laws that did not provide the means for discovering adverse environmental and health effects prior to the manufacture, processing, distribution, use, or disposal of chemical substances.[38] Congress concluded that the manufacture, processing, use, etc. of many chemical substances or mixtures may present unreasonable risk of injury to health or the environment. Therefore, Congress directed that adequate health and environmental data regarding the effects of chemical substances and mixtures be developed by those who manufacture or process those substances and mixtures. Congress also mandated that the government be given adequate information and authority to regulate those substances and mixtures which present risk of injury and to take action when such substances and mixtures pose imminent hazards.[39] There are two principal prongs to the regulatory scheme of ToSCA: the first is to gather sufficient information to identify or regulate potentially hazardous chemical substances or mixtures through the compilation of information or data already available, testing where data is inadequate and screening for potentially hazardous substances and mixtures;[40] the second is to regulate the manufacture, processing, distribution, use and disposal of these substances and mixtures.[41]

ToSCA's primary information bank was established as the ToSCA Chemical Substances Inventory. The CSI is the inventory of hazardous chemical substances "manufactured, imported or processed for a commercial purpose."[44] The CSI has subsequently been revised and expanded by additional preliminary assessment submissions or Comprehensive Assessment Information Reporting submissions for listed substances, and by information provided in new substance manufacturing or processing notifications (discussed below).[45]

In June 1986, EPA issued inventory update rules[46] requiring any person who manufactures or imports reportable volumes of certain chemicals listed on the CSI to report current data regarding production processes, volume, plant site, and site-limited use.[47] The inventory update rules then required additional updates every four years thereafter.[48] Specific chemical reporting requirements, codified at 40 CFR § 712, dictate uniform submission requirements for specific CSI chemicals that require assessment and update. A list of regulated chemicals and reporting periods is found at 40 CFR § 712.30. The CSI is managed by the EPA Chemical Inventory Section, Information Management Division of the Office of Toxic Substances, TS-793 M Street, SW, Washington, DC.

New Substances' Premanufacture and Significant New Use Notification

Under Section 5 of ToSCA,[49] manufacturers or importers of new chemical substances, i.e., chemical substances not already listed in the ToSCA Chemical Substances Inventory,[50] must, unless otherwise exempted,[51] notify EPA 90 days before manufacture or import begins.[52] Notice must include chemical identification information such as chemical name, CAS registry number, molecular formula, molecular weight, structural diagram, trade name and known synonyms, chemical precursors and reactants, a description of byproducts resulting from manufacture, processing, use or disposal, estimated amounts to be manufactured or imported, a description of intended use and application, identification of the manufacturing processing or use location, process operation and point of potential release, worker exposure information including worker numbers, activities and activity duration, and environmental release and control technology information.[53] Notice must also contain all test data in the submitter's control, or reasonably ascertainable by the submitter, regarding health or environmental effects related to any manufacturer processing, distribution, commercial use, or disposal of the new chemical substance or mixture.[54] Test data includes health effects data, ecological effects data, physical and chemical properties data, environmental fate characteristics, human exposure or environmental release monitoring data, and health and safety study results.[55] Manufacturers, importers, or processors who intend to engage in a significant new use of specific chemical substances[56] and exporters of chemical substances or mixtures[57] are subject to these same data requirements.[58]

Health Studies and Health Effects Testing Data

Pursuant to ToSCA's health and safety data reporting requirements, any person manufacturing, importing or processing listed substances or mixtures must submit or provide a list of any available unpublished health and safety studies on each such listed substance or mixture, or each manufactured, imported or processed mixture known to contain listed substances or mixtures.[59] Health and safety studies include any studies or data that relate to the effects of a chemical substance on health or the environment, including long- and short-term tests of mutagenicity; carcinogenicity or teratogenicity; data on behavioral disorders; dermatoxicity; pharmacological effects; cumulative, additive and synergistic effects; acute, chronic and subchronic effects; assessments of human and environmental exposure; biological, photochemical, and chemical degradation; physical properties; and human or environmental exposure monitoring data.[60] Scientific publications and studies previously submitted to the EPA's Office of Pollution Prevention and Toxics (in premanufacture or significant new use notices) do not have to be reported.[61]

EPA requires the submission of copies of all completed studies. EPA will, however, accept the submission of a list of initiated or ongoing studies, known studies that are not in possession of the reporter, and unpublished studies previously sent to federal agencies without confidentiality claims.[62] EPA may, in addition, request underlying data such as medical or health records, individual files, lab notebooks and daily monitoring records, preliminary reports of ongoing studies, and copies of the reports listed as known but not available for initial submission.[63] The list of substances and mixtures that trigger health and safety data reporting requirements is codified at 40 CFR § 716.120.

If a substance or mixture presents an unreasonable risk of injury to health or the environment, if the quantities produced create significant potential for environmental or human exposure, and if the information submitted is not sufficient to permit a reasoned evaluation of potential effects, section 4 of ToSCA authorizes the EPA to require that testing be conducted to develop the necessary data.[64] The health and environmental effects for which testing standards may be prescribed include carcinogenesis, mutagenesis, teratogenesis, behavioral disorders, and any other effects that may present unreasonable risk to health or the environment.[65] Standards may also be prescribed for the conduct of persistent acute, subacute, and chronic toxicity testing.[66] The methodologies that may be prescribed include epidemiologic studies, serial or hierarchical tests, in vitro and whole animal tests, and, upon consultation with the Director of the National Institute for Occupational Safety and Health, epidemiologic studies of employees.[67]

Where EPA, affected manufacturers and/or processors, and interested members of the public reach consensus on the need for and scope of testing, the agency will negotiate a consent agreement with the manufacturer or processor governing testing requirements. In the absence of consensus, EPA will promulgate test rules for individual chemical substances or mixtures.[68] EPA has promulgated several specific chemical test rules which are codified at 40 CFR § 799. The agency also established good laboratory practice standards and guidelines for chemical fate, environmental effects, and health effects testing.[69]

Substantial Risk and Adverse Reaction
Reporting and Recordkeeping

Section 8 (e) of ToSCA[70] requires that manufacturers, processors and distributors of chemical substances report to EPA any information indicating that such substances present a substantial risk of injury to health or the environment.[71] The EPA has extended this provision to spills or other emergency incidents of environmental contamination involving substances that pose substantial risk and, because of the extent of contamination, may seriously threaten human and non-human populations.[72] Where EPA has already been notified of a release incident pursuant to release reporting requirements under other laws, duplicative reporting under ToSCA is not required.[73] "Substantial risk" notification should provide all available data that could otherwise be submitted under any ToSCA notification requirements, especially information regarding carcinogenicity, mutagenicity, teratogenicity, serious or prolonged incapacitation or impairment, patterns of effects, widespread and unsuspected distribution in environmental media, bioaccumulation, ecological changes in species relationships and population, and facile transformation or degradation to a chemical having unacceptable risk to health or the environment.[74]

Section 8 (c) of ToSCA[75] requires manufacturers, processors, and distributors of chemical substances and mixtures to keep records of significant adverse reactions alleged to have been caused by the substance or mixture, and to permit inspection and submission of copies of such records upon the request of any designated representative of the EPA.[76] Significant adverse reaction is defined by the regulations to encompass any reactions that may indicate a substantial impairment of normal activities or long-lasting or irreversible damage to health or the environment.[77] Significant adverse reactions that must be recorded include cancer, birth defects, reproductive disorders, neurologic disorders, blood disorders, and impairment of normal activities experienced with each episode of exposure. Recording is not required for significant adverse reactions that are known or commonly recognized human health effects.[78]

Allegations of significant adverse reactions made by employees, health providers, consumers, or plant area residents trigger recordkeeping and potential subsequent reporting requirements if those allegations (a) name a specific substance or mixture or an article that contains a specific substance or mixture; (b) name a company process in which substances are involved; or (c) identify an effluent, emission, or other discharge from a site of manufacturing, processing, or distribution of a substance.[79] A manufacturer, processor or distributor receiving an allegation must retain in its records the written report or the transcript prepared from an oral report, of the original allegation as received; an abstract that details the date and location of the allegation, the implicated substance, mixture, article, process, operation or discharge; a description of the alleger and any alleged health or environmental effects; the results of any self-initiated investigation; and copies of records required under

OSHA[80] workplace injury reporting requirements.[81] Upon request by the EPA, all records must be made available for inspection by the EPA and/or submitted to EPA's Office of Pollution Prevention and Toxics for review.[82]

Existing Chemical Regulation

If the EPA finds a reasonable basis to conclude that a substance or mixture poses unreasonable risk of injury to health or the environment, the agency may protect against such risk by prohibiting or limiting the amount, the use, or the concentrations of substance manufactured, processed, distributed, used, or disposed. The EPA may further impose testing, labeling, quality control, hazard communication, public notice, and recordkeeping requirements tailored to specific substances.[83] The EPA has 90 days from submission of premanufacture or significant new use notifications to review the information submitted and determine whether regulation is necessary.[84] If the EPA does not initiate regulatory action in this time frame, manufacture or new use may commence.[85] The EPA may, however, for certain cause obtain a review period extension,[86] or, upon a finding of insufficiency of information, prohibit or limit manufacture or use pending additional testing and development of information.[87]

Where imminent hazard exists, the EPA may immediately commence a civil action in federal court seeking the seizure of substances, mixtures or articles using the hazard, or relief in the form of risk notification, recall, or replacement of the substance, mixture, or article.[88] Where a substance or use of substance posing risk to health and the environment is regulated by federal laws administered by other agencies, section 9 of ToSCA[89] requires that the EPA submit a report describing the risks to that other agency so they may conduct a risk assessment determining whether additional regulation by the EPA is necessary.[90] The EPA may not take action if the other agency finds there is no unreasonable risk not already regulated or initiates corrective action in 90 days.[91]

Although the EPA has not made widespread use of its regulatory authority under section 6 of ToSCA, the agency has promulgated specific use requirements for metal working fluids and water treatment chemicals and has set forth detailed manufacturing, processing, distribution, use, and disposal requirements for polychlorinated biphenyls (PCBs), fully halogenated chlorofluoroalkanes, asbestos, and dibenzo-para-dioxins/dibenzoflurans.[92]

There may be no greater singular source of health and environmental effects data for commercially imported, manufactured, processed, or used hazardous chemical substances and mixtures than the records required and maintained by EPA pursuant to ToSCA. If a claim of confidentiality does not accompany information at the time it is submitted to EPA, that information is available to the general public. Where confidentiality has been asserted, information necessary to prevent imminent substantial risk to health and the environment will be released.[93]

FEDERAL INSECTICIDE, FUNGICIDE AND RODENTICIDE ACT

In 1971, Congress enacted legislation that altered pesticide regulation already established pursuant to prior enacted provisions of what is now the Federal Insecticide, Fungicide and Rodenticide Act (FIFRA).[94] The prior legislation, which had been administered by the Department of Agriculture[95] and oriented toward pesticide product quality assurance, was modified by the 1972 enactment and later amendments to place administrative authority squarely in the hands of EPA.[96] The focus of regulation was shifted to product and use registration with consideration of the impacts of such products and their uses on human health and the environment.

FIFRA mandates that, unless otherwise exempted, a pesticide product may not be distributed or sold if it has not been registered under the act, and the distribution, sale, and use may be limited by the EPA to the extent necessary to prevent unreasonable adverse effects on the environment.[97] The FIFRA registration process requires the submission of information regarding product constituents, product efficacy in its proposed use, and any adverse effect of its use on health or environment. A registration applicant must submit the product name; the complete product formula; the draft product label and product labeling information, including a statement of all claims regarding product efficacy and any directions for its use; a request for clarification for general or restricted use; a demonstration of satisfaction of data requirements, including a full description of product tests and results or other data or literature upon which the product claims are based; any other data supporting the anticipated extent and pattern of use; statement tolerances of residues of use; and the degree of potential exposure to and deleterious effect on man and the environment.[98] Applicable regulations require submission of completed toxicologic studies,[99] incomplete toxicologic studies where preliminary data analysis has been completed or where there are observed serious adverse effects that may reasonably be attributed to exposure to the substances tested,[100] any epidemiologic study (or portion thereof) involving correlation between exposure and adverse effects in humans,[101] studies of dietary or environmental pesticide residues[102] or residue exceedance incidents,[103] and any toxic or adverse effect incident reports concerning humans or other non-target organisms.[104] Specific data are required from flagging studies for adverse effects,[105] residue chemistry data; environmental fate data; degradation data; dissipation studies; accumulation studies; acute oral, dermal, and inhalation toxicity studies; acute, chronic, and subchronic toxicity studies; teratogenicity and reproduction studies; mutagenicity studies; metabolism studies; and pesticide spray drift evaluation.[106] Upon review of the submitted data and sufficiency of support for pesticide labeling, efficacy, and use claims, the EPA may approve registration of a pesticide for restricted or non-restricted use where the pesticide will perform its intended function without unreasonable adverse effects on the environment.[107]

The FIFRA registration process creates a voluminous data base that is maintained by the Department of Agriculture and is available to health care professionals when information is required to provide medical treatment or emergency medical care for pesticide exposure.[108] Where the pesticide registrant has asserted claims of confidentiality for such information, the health professional may still gain access subject to confidentiality limitations. The Department of Agriculture and EPA have also created comprehensive reports concerning pesticide use and a Pesticide Tolerance Commodity/Chemical Index. This index is reprinted at the end of 40 CFR Parts 150 to 189 or can be obtained by request from the Biological Analysis Branch (7503W), Office of Pesticide Programs, EPA; other inquiries regarding health effects data may be directed to the Health Effects Division of that same office.

In addition to registration criteria, FIFRA establishes worker protection standards designed to reduce the risks of illness or injury resulting from workers' and handlers' occupational exposure to pesticides on farms and in nurseries, greenhouses, and forests, and also from accidental exposure of workers and other persons to pesticides. FIFRA worker protection standards, codified at 40 CFR § 170, require use area entry restrictions, utilization of personal protective equipment, posting of warning signs and pesticide safety information, notification of pesticide application, pesticide safety training, decontamination procedures, and notification of pesticide labeling and site-specific information that are designed to reduce or eliminate exposure.

FIFRA's worker protection standards also establish procedures for responding to exposure-related emergencies.[109] In the event of poisoning or injury following the use or handling of pesticides, an employer shall provide prompt transportation to an appropriate emergency medical facility. The employer shall also provide to the victim or treating medical personnel any obtainable information regarding the pesticide, including product name, EPA registration number, active ingredients, antidote, treatment protocol, medical information from the product label, the circumstances of the application, use or handling of the pesticide, and the circumstances of exposure.[110] These regulations stand independent from the worker protection standards of other laws and require specific compliance and occupational health response preparedness.

COMPREHENSIVE ENVIRONMENTAL RESPONSE, COMPENSATION AND LIABILITY ACT

In 1980, Congress enacted the Comprehensive Response, Compensation and Liability Act[111] (CERCLA), better known as Superfund, in response to growing public concern over the impact of disposal of toxic and hazardous substances and wastes on human health and the environment. Congress sought to fill the gaps in the environmental regulatory scheme for management and disposal of hazardous substances and wastes.[112] Congress specifically targeted assessment of liability for and remediation of abandoned or dormant disposal sites which continue to present immediate or long-term threats to human health or the environment.[113] CERCLA grants EPA some of the enforcement powers necessary for prompt, adequate and appropriate response to releases of hazardous substances and wastes. Importantly, CERCLA shifts the costs of adequate response and cleanup to those persons who created or otherwise contributed to the improper disposal of hazardous substances or wastes.[114]

CERCLA affords the government several options for response to releases of hazardous substances: (a) the government may, through USEPA, use the monies in the Superfund, a multibillion dollar fund, to address contaminated sites[115] and then seek cost recovery from liable parties;[116] or (b) EPA can order, or seek injunctive relief compelling, all necessary and appropriate response actions to abate or remedy a release of hazardous substances.[117] Responsible parties are defined as current owners and operators of hazardous substance or waste disposal facilities, past owners or operators of disposal facilities during whose period of ownership or operation hazardous substances or wastes were disposed of, persons arranging for disposal, treatment or transport of wastes, including waste generators, and persons accepting wastes for transport to disposal or treatment facilities.[118] CERCLA holds responsible parties strictly, jointly, and severally liable[119] and applies such liability retroactively.[120]

In 1986, Congress passed the Superfund Amendments and Reauthorization Act (SARA),[121] which reauthorized, refunded, and substantially expanded CERCLA. In part, CERCLA was amended to provide cleanup standards that protect human health and the environment,[122] to further define hazardous substance release reporting requirements,[123] and to expand health studies conducted by the Agency for Toxic Substances and Disease Registry.[124] With these amendments, SARA buttressed several of CERCLA's existing provisions and created new requirements that drive the development of exposure values that, in turn, guide assessment of the impact of cleanup on human health and the environment.

Cleanup standards define "how clean is clean" for the purpose of selection of an appropriate site cleanup remedy that protects human health and the environment. Section 121 of CERCLA[125] prescribes performance standards for remedy selection that are applied on a site-specific basis.[126] These standards must, as a threshold matter, meet individual state standards and, where relevant and appropriate, attain maximum contaminant level goals (MCLs) proscribed by the federal Safe Drinking Water Act (SDWA)[127] and water quality criteria dictated by sections 303 and 304 of the federal Clean Water Act (CWA).[128,129]

CERCLA defines the term "hazardous substance" to include chemicals or compounds regulated as "hazardous substances" or "toxic pollutants" under the CWA,[130] "hazardous wastes" regulated by RCRA,[131] "hazardous air pollutants" listed under the federal Clean Air Act (CAA),[132] hazardous substances regulated under section 7 of the Toxic Substances Control Act,[133] and any substances covered by a reportable quantity threshold for notification of releases under CERCLA section 102.[134] These regulated substances or pollutants share the common characteristics of presenting an imminent and substantial threat to human health or the environment.

EPA has promulgated regulations that indicate the quantities of hazardous substances that must be released in order to be reportable. The list of hazardous substances for which reportable quantities have been developed may be found at 40 CFR § 302.4. Where a reportable quantity has not been developed and listed at 40 CFR § 302.4, the reportable quantity for a particular substance shall be that established under CWA section 311(b)(4).[135] Otherwise, the release of one pound in a 24-hour period is reportable.[136]

Health Studies

CERCLA section 104(i)[137] established the Agency for Toxic Substances and Disease Registry within the United States Public Health Service. ATSDR is required to implement the health-related provisions of CERCLA and to maintain a national registry of serious diseases and illnesses in persons exposed to toxic substances. ATSDR must also establish and maintain an inventory of literature, research and studies on the health effects of toxic substances; a complete listing of areas closed to the public or otherwise restricted in use because of toxic substance contamination; and in the case of public health emergencies caused by exposure, provide medical care and testing to exposed individuals that may include tissue sampling, chromosomal testing, or epidemiologic studies. ATSDR conducts periodic survey and screening programs to determine relationships between exposure to toxic substances and illness.[138] ATSDR's responsibilities require the preparation of a list, in order of priority, of at least 100 hazardous substances that are most commonly found at facilities on the National Priorities List of Superfund Sites and which pose the most significant potential threat to human health due to their known or suspected toxicity and the potential for human exposure to such substances.[139] ATSDR has a continuing obligation to further expand the list of the 275 hazardous substances most commonly found at Superfund sites and shall, no less than annually thereafter, revise the list to include additional hazardous substances that meet ATSDR evaluation criteria.[140]

The toxicologic profiles are prepared in accordance with ATSDR and EPA guidelines that mandate a review of available toxicologic information, an assessment of the adequacy of the available information, identification of additional research needed to determine health effects, and coordination of effort with the Intraagency Testing Committees established under section 4(e) of ToSCA.[141,142] If

ATSDR deems further study to be appropriate on the basis of a health assessment, ATSDR must conduct a pilot study of health effects for representative exposure groups to determine whether a full-scale epidemiologic or toxicologic study should be conducted.[143] Where health assessment indicates potential significant risk to human health, ATSDR shall consider whether to establish a registry of exposed persons, and/or, in the case of release from a facility, initiate a health surveillance program for the exposed population.[144] CERCLA further requires ATSDR to periodically report any increased incidence or prevalence of adverse health effects in humans; moreover, all studies and results of research are to be reported or adopted only after appropriate peer review.[145]

Upon request, ATSDR will assemble, develop and distribute to medical colleges, physicians, and other health professionals materials regarding medical surveillance, screening, and methods of diagnosis and treatment of injury or disease related to exposure to hazardous substances.[146] The release of other ATSDR records and information may be allowed upon submission of a request for documents and information to the ATSDR Freedom of Information Act Office.[147] Additionally, ATSDR hazardous substance data, medical management guidelines for acute chemical exposures, and toxicologic and public health statement profiles are readily available on the ATSDR Internet homepage located at http://atsdr1.atsdr.edc.gov:8080/atsdrhome html. The value of ATSDR data to the health practitioner is clear. Through this resource, a large body of information and data is available to assist in occupational health management, exposure risk minimization, and treatment.

THE EMERGENCY PLANNING AND COMMUNITY RIGHT TO KNOW ACT

EPCRA, or Title III of the 1986 SARA Amendments,[148] was enacted to establish and coordinate local government chemical hazard emergency response efforts and to provide local authorities and the public with information regarding chemical hazards in their community.[149] EPCRA's three major areas of consideration are chemical characteristic, usage and manufacture reporting; emergency release notification; and government emergency response planning. Regulation of the first two areas has led to the compilation of a publicly available reference service for identification of local chemical use, potential or realized chemical exposure, and health effects from any such exposure.

Under EPCRA's emergency planning requirements, an owner or operator of a facility where "extremely hazardous" substances in amounts exceeding "threshold quantities" are present must notify state and local emergency planning organizations and the fire department of the location, volume, and chemical properties of each extremely hazardous substance, and of the name and contact number of the on-site emergency response coordinator.[150] Under "community right-to-know" provisions a facility must also submit a chemical list or material safety data sheet for any "hazardous substance" present above threshold quantities for which the facility must otherwise prepare or have available an MSDS under OSHA's hazard communication standard.[151,152] Chemical inventory information must be submitted for all hazardous and extremely hazardous substances, disclosing the maximum and average amount of hazardous chemical used, the location of storage or use,[153] and the physical and health hazards associated with the chemical.[154] When reportable quantities of a hazardous or extremely hazardous substance are released, immediate notification must be made to local authorities, EPA and the National Response Center, disclosing the substance released, the quantity, time, and nature of the release, response actions taken, the facility contact person, and any health risks associated with the release.[155] Specific toxic chemicals covered by community right-to-know provisions are listed at 40 CFR § 372.65. As noted above, hazardous substance reportable quantities are listed at 40 CFR § 302.5. Hazardous substance threshold quantities are determined in accordance with 40 CFR § 372.25. Substances designated as extremely hazardous and the determined threshold and reportable quantities are tabulated at 40 CFR § 355, App. A.

Facility information is generally available to the public on request from local or state emergency planning organizations or the fire department. Information regarding released substances may also be obtained through EPA's Toxic Chemical Release Inventory and Emergency Planning and Community Right-to-Know Hotline.[156] When a facility has been granted trade secret protection for its submissions, information regarding health effects must still be made available.[157] Facilities must provide chemical inventory and identity information, MSDSs, and toxic chemical release information to health professionals when that information is required for emergency medical care, for diagnosis or treatment of non-emergent cases, and for development of preventive measures and treatments by local health professionals.[158] The procedures and limitations on disclosure of trade secrets and confidential business information to health professionals is codified at 40 CFR §§ 350.40(a)–(h).

THE CLEAN AIR ACT

The Clean Air Act[159] sets forth a regulatory scheme designed to preserve air quality and to achieve health-based ambient air quality standards. The major goals of the program are the regulation of primary and hazardous air pollutants, the establishment and attainment of National Ambient Air Quality Standards for primary pollutants, and the prevention of significant deterioration of air quality.[160] New sources of pollution, toxic emissions, motor vehicle emissions, and activities that influence acid rain are important subjects of regulations. The CAA proscribes specific requirements for NAAQS nonattainment areas, imposes tight controls on air toxics, and requires permitting of most sources of significant air emissions.

Prior to its amendment in 1990, CAA hinged air quality regulation on attainment of NAAQS. The 1990 amendments, however, significantly enhanced air quality programs, enlarging the list of regulated toxic pollutants, modifying non-attainment requirements, and imposing individual significant emission source permitting requirements.

National primary ambient air quality standards define levels of air quality necessary, with an adequate margin of safety, to protect the public health.[161] National secondary ambient air quality standards define levels of air quality necessary to protect the public welfare from any known or anticipated adverse effects of a pollutant.[162] The promulgation of NAAQS may not allow significant deterioration of existing air quality in any way[163] and where nonattainment exists, "reasonably available control technologies" must be used.[164] The EPA has, to date, established NAAQS for only a few of the most common pollutants: ozone, carbon monoxide, sulfur dioxide, nitrogen dioxide, particulates, and lead.[165]

The prime vehicle for CAA implementation and achievement of NAAQS is the state implementation plan. SIPs are federally approved, state statutory, and regulatory programs that establish air quality regions where control requirements are imposed to reduce source emissions of pollutants and to achieve or maintain NAAQS.[166] NAAQS are ambient quality standards achieved through regulation of sources identified in SIPs.

Regarding toxic or hazardous air pollutant emissions from specific sources, EPA has promulgated National Emission Standards for Air Pollutants (NESHAPS) that apply directly to the emissions at the source. The EPA has established a list of 189 hazardous air pollutants[167] and a list of other substances for which the EPA has considered the serious health effects, including carcinogenicity, from ambient air exposure to the substance.[168] NESHAPS have been established for radon, beryllium, mercury, vinyl chloride, radionuclides, benzene, asbestos, inorganic arsenic, and for equipment leaks (fugitive emission sources).[169] The EPA has also established NESHAPS for source categories such as dry cleaning facilities, sterilization facilities, gasoline distribution facilities, synthetic organic chemical manufacturers, halogenated solvent cleaning operations, and others.[170] The EPA must promulgate standards of performance for new stationary sources, establishing for each category of sources a standard of emission that reflects the degree of emission limitation achievable through the best technology of continuous emission reduction, the cost of achieving such reduction, energy requirements, and any non-air quality health and environmental impact.[171]

The 1990 amendment also created a regulatory program to address prevention and response to accidental or catastrophic releases.[172] This program requires the determination of threshold quantities of hazardous substances that, upon release, are known to cause, or may be reasonably anticipated to cause death, injury or serious adverse effects to human health or the environment. This program also requires the establishment of a chemical safety board to investigate releases and propose rules minimizing or preventing the consequences of any release.[173] The EPA must also address release detection and control measures, risk management plan development, emergency health care and employee training, and risk-reduction technologies.[174] Chemical accident prevention regulations are codified at 40 CFR § 68 and the list of regulated toxic substances and threshold quantities for accidental release can be found at 40 CFR § 68.130.

The health effects information collected by EPA during enforcement of the CAA is available to health professionals. EPA will ultimately assess and record health effects for all 189 hazardous pollutants regulated under the act. Information and studies on health effects related to NAAQS and other air pollutants are available on request from EPA's Office of Air Planning and Standards.

THE CLEAN WATER ACT

The Clean Water Act of 1972[175] sets forth the basic framework for programs designed to control the discharge of harmful quantities of oil or hazardous substances into the water and adjoining shorelines of the United States. The CWA regulates discharges from both industrial and municipal "point sources" through the National Pollutant Discharge Elimination system (NPDES) permit program.[176] This program requires that every point source be subject to a NPDES permit establishing numerical effluent limitations for water quality conditions and individual substances, and detailed self-monitoring.[177] Point source discharged wastes must be pretreated to meet water quality standards or the most technically feasible standard, whichever is more stringent.[178]

Industries that discharge waste to publicly owned treatment works (POTWs) must apply the best available technology (BAT) economically achievable to pretreat waste, removing toxic pollutants and preventing pass-through of contaminants from the POTW or interference with POTW discharge requirements.[179] For effluent discharges directly to surface waters, industries must apply end-of-the-pipe technology-based standards, specifically, the best practicable control technology (BPT) currently available as defined by the EPA.[180] The EPA defines the BAT and BPT standards for many categories of industrial point source discharges in its effluent limitation guidelines codified at 40 CFR §§ 401–471. Individual discharge limitations are developed for each source in a permit and are subject to compliance monitoring and reporting requirements.[181] The permit will designate allowable concentrations or levels of biologic and chemical constituents, and will specify effluent testing and analysis requirements to assure compliance.[182] Effluent standards for toxic pollutants that pose risk to human health and the environment and for which laboratory toxicity data, epidemiologic studies of human occupational exposures, or human exposure data indicate regulation is appropriate are found at 40 CFR § 129. Toxics criteria for states that have not adopted or revised existing water quality standards for priority toxic pollutants are tabulated at 40 CFR § 131.36.

CWA imposes spill reporting requirements where discharges of hazardous substances above reportable quantities have occurred.[183] The list of substances designated as hazardous under the CWA is tabulated at 40 CFR § 116.4. Reportable quantities for these substances are found at 40 CFR § 117.2. The CWA also regulates discharges due to stormwater runoff to prevent violations of water quality standards or significant contributions of pollutants to waters by direct contact of stormwater with industrial or other facility operations. Permit limit and monitoring requirements may be imposed in this scenario as well.[184]

As the agency designates hazardous and toxic pollutants, water quality standards, and effluent limitations, the EPA conducts research and reviews other scientific studies on the human health effects of various pollutants.[185] Health effects data are available to the public on request from the EPA's Office of Water Regulations and Standards. Individual source discharge information submitted by point source operations in permit applications is also available on request from the EPA's regional office to which the operator's application was submitted.

THE SAFE DRINKING WATER ACT

The Safe Drinking Water Act (SDWA),[186] enacted to protect the quality of drinking water, is designed to ensure that public water supply systems meet minimum national standards. The goals of the act are met by regulating "public water systems"[187] and by prohibiting unpermitted underground injection of fluids to preserve the quality of underground sources of drinking water.[188]

The regulation of public water systems ensures that no contaminant is delivered to any user of a public piped water system in excess of the maximum permissible concentration. Under the SDWA, supplies of water (which can include community water supply as well as private manufacturers or other facilities that provide this their own source of drinking water to employees) cannot exceed health-based maximum contaminant levels (MCLs) for chemicals and other hazardous properties.[189] The EPA has promulgated national primary drinking water regulations that establish maximum contaminant level goals (MCLGs) for substances that are known or anticipated to occur in public water systems and that may have adverse effects on human health.[190] Each MCLG is set at the level at which no known or anticipated adverse effects on human health occur, allowing a recognized margin of safety.[191] National primary drinking water regulations for contaminants for which MCLGs are established then specify an MCL which comes as close to the MCLG as is feasible.[192] Feasibility is determined by the use of the best available technology and treatment techniques and considerations of field performance, efficacy, and cost.[193] The EPA has published primary drinking water MCLs and MCLGs for numerous organic and inorganic chemicals, radioactive substances, radionuclides, and turbidity at 40 CFR § 141. Primary drinking water regulations are enforceable by EPA, but most administrative and enforcement responsibility rests within EPA-authorized state programs.[194]

EPA has promulgated national secondary drinking water regulations establishing secondary MCLs or SMCLs for contaminants that primarily influence aesthetic qualities or public acceptance of drinking water but that also may have health implications at considerably higher concentrations.[195] SMCLs have been set for aluminum, copper, silver, zinc, iron, manganese, sulfate-forming agents, chloride, fluoride, color, corrosivity, odor, total dissolved solids, and pH.[196] Secondary drinking water standards are published at 40 CFR § 143 and are enforced by the state.[197]

SDWA also establishes underground injection control (UIC) restrictions to prevent contamination of underground sources of drinking water.[198] States must designate critical aquifer protection areas subject to SDWA criteria. SDWA prohibits injection that causes the movement of contaminated fluid into underground sources of drinking water.[199] Injection is also prohibited if the presence of that contaminant may result in violation of any primary drinking water regulation or may adversely affect human health.[200] Here, also, primary enforcement responsibility lies within authorized state programs.[201]

Information submitted to EPA or state agencies pursuant to compliance, monitoring, or permitting requirements is available to the public for review and may be obtained on request from the local EPA regional office, the state agency, and in some locales, the local board of health. Information granted confidential status is available where it is required for public health or safety purposes.[202] Information developed in the promulgation of drinking water standards, including advisory board comments[203] and health effects data, is maintained by the EPA at its Criteria Standards Division, Office of Drinking Water. Collectively, the drinking water standards, MCLGs, MCLs, and SMCLs provide bright-line definition of concentrations at which ingestion of listed substances pose risk to human health.

REFERENCES

1. 42 USC § 6901 et seq.
2. H.R. Rep. No. 1491, 94th Cong., 2d Sess. (1976).
3. 42 USC § 6921.
4. 42 USC §§ 6922, 6923.
5. 42 USC §§ 6924, 6925, 6926
6. Pub L. No. 96-482, 94 Stat. 2334 (1980).
7. 42 USC §§ 6912, 6928.
8. 42 USC § 6925.
9. 42 USC § 6925.
10. 42 USC § 6921.
11. 42 USC § 6935.
12. 42 USC §§ 6916, 6991.
13. 42 USC § 6924 (q).
14. 42 USC § 6921.
15. 42 USC § 6924 (d).
16. 42 USC § 6924 (o).
17. 42 USC § 6928.
18. 40 CFR § 262.
19. 40 CFR § 262.20–262.23.
20. 42 USC §§ 6928 (h), 6924 (u), (v); 40 CFR §§ 264, 265.
21. 40 CFR § 261.
22. 40 CFR § 261.10.

23. 40 CFR § 261.11.
24. 40 CFR § 261.30.
25. 40 CFR §§ 261.21–261.24.
26. 40 CFR § 261.3.
27. 40 CFR §§ 261.1–261.3, 262.
28. 40 CFR § 261.2.
29. 42 USC §§ 6925(a)(c).
30. 40 CFR §270.
31. 40 CFR § 270.31.
32. 42 USC § 6939a (a).
33. *Id.*
34. 42 USC § 6339a (b) (1).
35. 42 USC § 6939a (b) (2), sec 42 USC§ 9604 (b) (i).
36. 42 USC §6939a (c).
37. 15 USC §§ 2601–2655.
38. S. Rep. No. 698, 94th Cong., 2d Sess., 5 (1976).
39. 15 USC §§ 2601(a), (b).
40. 15 USC §§ 2603, 2604.
41. 15 USC § 2605.
42. 40 CFR §§ 710.1–710.4.
43. 15 USC §2607.
44. 47 Fed. Reg. 25,767 (June 15, 1982).
45. 40 CFR §§ 704, 710, 720.
46. 40 CFR § 710.1 et seq.
47. 40 CFR §§ 710.5, 712.
48. 40 CFR § 710.33.
49. 15 USC § 2604.
50. 40 CFR § 720.25.
51. See 40 CFR §§ 720.30, 720.36, 720.38.
52. 40 CFR § 720.40.
53. 40 CFR § 720.45.
54. 40 CFR § 720.5.
55. *Id.*
56. See chemical substances listed at 40 CFR §§ 721.225–721.9975.
57. 15 USC § 2611 (b): 40 CFR § 721.20.
58. 40 CFR §§ 721.5, 721.20.
59. 40 CFR §§ 716.5, 716.10.
60. 40 CFR § 716.3.
61. 40 CFR § 716.20.
62. 40 CFR § 716.35.
63. 40 CFR 716.40.
64. 15 USC § 2603 (a).
65. 15 USC § 2603 (b).
66. *Id.*
67. *Id.*
68. 40 CFR § 790.1.
69. 40 CFR §§ 792, 796, 797, 798.
70. 15 USC § 2607 (e).
71. *Id.*
72. 43 Fed. Reg. 11110, 11112, (Mar. 16, 1978).
73. *Id.*
74. See data requirements for adverse reaction recordkeeping discussed infra.
75. 15 USC § 2607 (c).
76. 15 USC § 2607 (c); 40 CFR § 717.1.
77. 40 CFR § 717.3 (i).
78. 40 CFR § 717.12.
79. 40 CFR § 717.10.
80. 29 USC §§ 651–678; See 29 CFR § 1904 for OSHA reporting requirements.
81. 40 CFR § 717.15.
82. 40 CFR § 713.17.
83. 15 USC § 2605; 40 CFR § 750.

84. 40 CFR §§ 720.75 (a) 721.25 (a).
85. 40 CFR § 720.75 (d) 721.25 (a), (d)
86. 40 CFR §§ 720.75 (c) 721.75(a)
87. 15 USC § 2604 (e); See also rulemaking procedures at 40 CFR § 750.
88. 15 USC § 2606.
89. 15 USC § 2608.
90. 15 USC § 2608 (a).
91. 15 USC § 2608 (a), (b).
92. See 40 CFR §§ 747, 749, 761–766.
93. See 15 USC §§ 2613 (b), (c); 40 CFR §§ 716.55, 720.90.
94. FIFRA is codified at 7 USC §§ 136–136y. Prior laws June 25, 1947, C.125, as added Oct. 21, 1972, Pub. L. 92-516 §2, 86 Stat. 975.
95. See June 25, 1947, c.125.
96. 7 USC § 136(b).
97. 7 USC § 136(a); 40 CFR § 152.15.
98. 7 USC § 136(a); for detailed pesticide registration and classification procedures see 40 CFR § 15.
99. 40 CFR § 153.69.
100. 40 CFR § 153.70.
101. 40 CFR § 153.71.
102. 40 CFR § 153.73.
103. 40 CFR § 153.77.
104. 40 CFR § 153.75.
105. 40 CFR § 158.34.
106. 40 CFR § 158.202.
107. 7 USC § 136(a); a listing of pesticides classified for restricted use and the criteria influencing restriction may be found at 40 CFR § 152.175.
108. 7 USC § 136i–1(c).
109. 40 CFR §§ 170.160, 170.260.
110. Id.
111. 42 USC § 9601 et seq.
112. The House Report accompanying the original bill stated:
    (c) Deficiencies in RCRA have left important regulatory gaps.
    (I) [RCRA] is prospective and applies to past sites only to the extent that they are posing an imminent hazard. Even, there, the Act is no help if a financially responsible owner of the site cannot be located. . . . It is the intent of the Committee in [CERCLA] to initiate and establish a comprehensive response and financing mechanism to abate and control the vast problems associated with abandoned and inactive hazardous waste disposal sites. H.R. REP. No. 1016, pt. I, 96th Cong., 2d Sess. 22, reprinted in U.S. Code Cong. & AD News 6119, 6125.
113. *United States v. A&F Materials Co.*, 578 F. Supp. 1249, 1252 (S.D. Ill 1984).
114. *United States v. Reilly Tar & Chemical Corp.*, 546 F. Supp. 1100, 1112 (D. Minn 1982).
115. USC §§ 9604, 9611.
116. 42 USC §§ 9607, 9612.
117. 42 USC § 9606.
118. 42 USC § 9607.
119. See *U.S. v. A&F*, 578 F. Supp at 1256.
120. See *U.S. v. A&F Materials*, 578 F. Supp. at 1256; *United States v. Northeastern Pharm. & Chem. Co.* (NEPACCO), 579 F. Supp. 823, 839 (W.D. Mo. 1984); *United States v. Price*, 577 F. Supp. 1103, 1112–13 (D. N.J. 1983); *U.S. v. Reilly Tar*, 546 F. Supp. at 1113.
121. Pub L. No. 99-499, 100 Stat. 1613 (1986).
122. 42 USC § 9621.
123. See 42 USC § 9603(a).
124. 42 USC § 9604(i).
125. 42 USC § 9621.
126. 42 USC §§ 9621(a), (b)(1).
127. 42 USC § 1412(e).
128. 42 USC §§ 1313, 1314.
129. 42 USC § 9621(d)(2)(A).
130. 42 USC § 9601(14); see also 40 CFR §§ 116.4 and 401.15.
131. 42 USC § 6921(b); 40 CFR § 261.33.
132. 42 USC § 7912; 40 CFR § 61.01.
133. 15 USC § 2606.

134. 42 USC § 9602.
135. 33 USC § 1321(b)(4).
136. 40 CFR § 302.6(a).
137. 42 USC § 9604(i).
138. 42 USC §§ 9604(i)(1)(A-E).
139. 42 USC § 9604(i)(2)(A).
140. 42 USC § 9604 (i)(2)(B).
141. 15 USC § 2603(c).
142. 42 USC §§ 9604(i)(3),(5).
143. 42 USC § 9604(i)(7); 50 CFR § 90.7.
144. 42 USC §§ 9604(i)(8)(9).
145. 42 USC §§ 9604(i)(10)(c),(13); 40 CFR § 90.11.
146. 42 USC § 9604(I)(14).
147. 45 CFR § 5131.
148. 42 USC §§ 11001–11050.
149. 51 Fed. Reg. 41570 (Nov. 17, 1986).
150. 42 USC §§ 11002(b)(1), (c); see Emergency Planning and Notification regulations, 40 CFR §
     355.30.
151. 42 USC § 11021(a); see Community Right to Know Reporting Requirements, 40 CFR §§ 370.20.
152. See OSHA Hazard Communication Standards and MSDS requirements 29 CFR §§ 1910.1200.
153. 42 USC § 11022(1); 40 CFR § 370.40.
154. 42 USC § 11022(d)(2); 40 CFR §§ 370.25(b), 370.41(b).
155. 42 USC § 11004(b)(2); 40 CFR § 355.40(b)(2).
156. For Hotline Information, call (800) 535-0202.
157. 40 CFR § 350.21.
158. 40 CFR § 350.40.
159. 42 USC §§ 7401 *et seq.*
160. 42 USC § 7409.
161. 40 CFR § 50.2(b).
162. *Id.*
163. 40 CFR § 50.2(c).
164. 42 USC § 7502.
165. 40 CFR § 50.
166. 42 USC § 7410; 40 CFR §§ 51–52.
167. 42 USC § 7412(b); 40 CFR § 61.01(a).
168. 40 CFR § 61.01(b).
169. 40 CFR §§ 61.20–61.359.
170. 40 CFR §§ 63.100–63.708.
171. 42 USC § 7411.
172. 42 USC § 7412(r).
173. 42 USC §§ 7412(r)(3–6).
174. 42 USC § 7412(r)(7).
175. 33 USC §§ 1251–1387.
176. 33 USC §§ 1311(a), 1362(14).
177. *Id.*, 40 CFR § 122.
178. 44 USC § 1311(b).
179. 40 CFR §§ 403, 403.5; for specifics regarding POTW secondary treatment regulations. See 40 CFR
     § 133.
180. 33 USC §§ 1311(b)(1)(A), 1314(b).
181. 40 CFR §§ 122.41–122.48.
182. *Id.*
183. 40 CFR §§ 110–117.
184. 40 CFR § 122.26.
185. 33 USC §§ 1254(a),(c).
186. 42 USC §§ 300f–300j - 26.
187. Defined at 42 USC § 300f (4).
188. 42 USC § 300h.
189. See 40 CFR §§ 141, 143.
190. 42 USC § 300g–1.
191. *Id.*
192. 42 USC § 300g–1 (b) (4).

193. 42 USC §§ 300g–l (b) (5), (7).
194. 42 USC § 300g–2.
195. 40 CFR § 143.1.
196. 40 CFR § 143.3.
197. 42 USC § 300g–3 (d).
198. 42 USC § 300h.
199. Defined at 40 CFR § 144.3.
200. 40 CFR § 144.1 (g)
201. 42 USC § 300h–2.
202. 42 USC § 300j–4.
203. See 42 USC § 300g–l (e).

INDEX

Entries in **boldface type** indicate complete chapters.

Abandonment, as liability basis, 125–126
Acquired immunodeficiency syndrome (AIDS),
    confidentiality laws regarding, 141
Acronyms, related to occupational medicine,
    153–172
Administrative law judges, 153
Age, exclusion from Americans with Disabilities
    Act-defined impairments, 7
Age discrimination, bona fide occupational
    qualification defense in, 46–48
Age Discrimination in Employment Act of 1967,
    46, 47, 48
Agency for Toxic Subtances and Disease Registry,
    153–154, 176, 182, 183–184
Aggravation, of work-related injuries, 119, 142,
    150
Agility tests, 11–12, 34, 43
Airborne contaminants exposure, OSHA
    standards for, 64–65
Airline pilots, age-related mandatory retirement
    of, 48
Alberts v. Devine, 18
Alcoholism, exclusion from Americans with
    Disabilities Act-defined disabilities, 8, 95
Alcohol testing, 93, 95
ALJ (administrative law judge), 153
American College of Occupational and Environ-
    mental Medicine, code of ethics, 25–26, 32,
    35
American Medical Association, code of ethics, 35
American National Standards Institute, 153
Americans with Disabilities Act, Title I, **5–16**, 134
    application to drug testing, 22, 25, 88, 94–95
    application to older workers, 48
    conflict with Occupational Safety and Health
        Act, 49–51
    direct threats to health and safety provision of,
        13
    disability definition of, 2, 7
    exemptions under, 2
    exempt employers under, 6
    in federal sector, 142–143
    impairment definition of, 7–8
    impairment provisions of, 8–10
    job descriptions provision of, 10–11
    liability under, 37–38
    medical examination definition of, 14–15
    medical examination provisions of, 3, 13–15,
        33–37, 38
    medical records confidentiality provision of,
        15–16, 22, 25, 26
    in private sector, 142

Americans with Disabilities Act, Title I, *(cont.)*
    qualification standards and selection criteria
        provisions of, 11–12, 35–36
    reasonable accommodation provision of, 10,
        12–13, 36, 48, 49
    undue hardship exemption to, 12–13, 143
ANSI (American National Standards Institute),
    153
Antidiscrimination laws, 41. *See also* specific
    antidiscrimination laws
Armed Forces Institute of Pathology, Department
    of Legal Medicine, 139–140
Arsenic
    medical surveillance program for, 67
    National Emission Standard for, 186
Asbestos
    medical surveillance program for, 67
    National Emission Standard for, 186
Asbestosis, causation analysis of, 117–118
ATSDR (Agency for Toxic Subtances and Disease
    Registry), 153–154
Audiometry, OSHA standards for, 63–64

Battery, as liability basis, 125–126
BEI (biologic exposure index), 154
Benzene, National Emission Standard for, 186
Beryllium, National Emission Standard for, 186
Bill of Rights of Examinees, 38
Biologic exposure index, 154
Biologic hazards, control of, **79–85**
Biologic safety officers, 83
Biologic waste, handling and disposal regulations
    for, 84
Bloodborne Pathogen Standard, 79–80, 84
Board certification, of occupational medicine
    physicians, 107, 125
Bona fide occupational qualifications, 2
Breach of confidence, 125–126
Breach of contract, 125–126
    regarding confidentiality of medical
        records, 17–18
Breach of honor, 17
Breath testing, evidential, 93
Burden of proof, 146
Bush, George, 88

Caisson disease, 118
Caplan's syndrome, 118
Carpal tunnel syndrome, 50, 51, 118
Causation
    criteria for, 149
    dual, 16

193